robert e. dickinson
architect a.i.a.
2004 n. beverly glen
los angeles 24, calif.

STRUCTURE AND FORM IN MODERN ARCHITECTURE

CURT SIEGEL

STRUCTURE AND FORM

IN MODERN ARCHITECTURE

Translated by

Thomas E. Burton

REINHOLD PUBLISHING CORPORATION, NEW YORK

. . . und bemerke, dass es Menschen in unserer Zeit gibt, die Schones geschaffen haben, einzig deshalb schon, weil die Dinge nach der Logik, nach der Vernunft, nach den Prinzipien des vernünftigen Seins der Dinge und nach den genauen, notwendigen und natürlichen Gesetzen des dazu verwandten Materials hergestellt wurden.

HENRY VAN DE VELDE
(in "Kunstgewerbliche Laienpredigten" 1902)

FOREWORD

My real motive in writing this book has been the keen pleasure I take in exploring the meaning of the forms in which everything that is "built" must be clothed. All my life I have been equally moved by the appropriateness of natural forms, the logic of good engineering design and the expressiveness of outstanding works of architecture. As things that are "built" they all seem to me to have a common origin.

This book is an attempt to reconsider, analyze and explain the problems of structural form in modern architecture, from the point of view of the architect yet in the light of our present technical knowledge. In certain quarters it will be dismissed as a misguided effort to raise technology to the exalted level of art. Those who do not share my antipathy to such prejudice, who are unwilling to accept the new building materials and their mechanical laws as valid elements of architecture, who refuse to recognize that the clear intelligence of the impartial engineer, unmuddied by sentiment, is essential to modern technical, and hence *architectural* design, might as well lay down this book at once.

On the other hand, the reader who expects to find recipes for a "calculated" architecture and sees an artistic argument in the slide rule will be equally disappointed. He will inevitably find that in every positive approach to engineering it is occasionally necessary to go beyond conclusions that, rationally, appear inescapable, to arrive at the more important trends and motifs of structural form. My aim has been to clarify such problems of form and they are too complex to be solved by mere computation.

Since I have attempted a graphic presentation of "structural form in modern architecture," which is free of all conventions and clearly founded in technology, my book is simultaneously the expression of a point of view. There may be omissions, since my subject is so broad. There may be contradictions in detail, since the elusive characteristics of form do not exclude different interpretations when examined from different angles. Nevertheless, if my book encourages critical reflection, if it contributes to an awareness of what is unambiguous and demonstrable even in architecture, if it promotes honesty and neatness in design and thereby assists in opposing formalism and effect-mongering with integrity and quality, it will have fulfilled its purpose.

As the discussion is concerned with form, illustration is essential. Since the book represents a point of view, there ought to be criticism of actual buildings. In order to carry the force of my criticism beyond the individual to the typical, I have preferred to illustrate my remarks with anonymous sketches. These have been abstracted to achieve a high degree of general validity.

Before this book could be written, the question of the interrelationship between structure and form had to be very carefully documented. This work received generous financial support from the Association of Friends of the Stuttgart Technical University, to whom I would like to express my sincere thanks.

On numerous occasions I have benefited from the knowledge and experience of expert collaborators. My assistants, Peter Müller, Rolf Schaal and Franz Krauss, together with Mr. Kuff, have stood by me indefatigably with help and criticism. The laborious and tedious work of preparing the sketches was undertaken in a rare spirit of selflessness and understanding by Mrs. Veronika v. Dobrogoiski, aided by a number of senior and junior students. My heartfelt gratitude is due to all these collaborators.

The publishers deserve my thanks for their continuous readiness to indulge, with patience and understanding, all my wishes concerning the form and arrangement of this book. It was a happy partnership.

Stuttgart, Summer 1960   Curt Siegel

6

There can be no architecture without technology to translate architectural concepts into physical reality.

Technology has always influenced building forms and architects of every age have derived inspiration from the technical mastery of materials. The Parthenon and the Gothic cathedral are both essentially ultimate refinements of a particular technique.

The naive affirmation of everything technical that used to characterize all artistic activity has been lost in the wake of mechanization. Art and technology have been banished to opposite poles. Architecture, in which the artistic and the technical have so long been united, is passing increasingly into the hands of the engineer, while the artist is left with the task of applying decoration.

All attempts to reconcile architecture with art will fail, so long as technology remains unrelated to the process of artistic design. In this context, of course, technology is not to be understood as the provision of technical facilities. Environmental control and sanitary installations have nothing to do with the ultimate quality and expressiveness of even modern architecture. Today, however, the structural framing, which, though it has no bearing on comfort, is an essential part of all construction, is emerging as a design factor of critical importance. When we refer to technology, it is these structural aspects that we have in mind.

Modern architecture is characterized by an excess of artistically unassimilated technology. Making technology responsible for this situation is just as wrong as attempting to deny its importance, or, still worse, "humanizing" it by applying decoration. All these responses are futile. There have been many attempts at interpreting the technological phenomenon of our age. Philosophy and religion, art and science have all been dragged into the fray. No one, however, has yet tried to get at the technological origin of individual forms, without pursuing abstract arguments on loftier planes. This is what the author has set out to do. He does not intend to dabble in the theory of architecture. Moreover, he will deliberately avoid the high-flown jargon of the professional art critic. His object will be to trace the technological laws of modern building and explore their influence on modern architectural forms.

It will prove that an objective analysis of structure throws more light on the principles of architectural form than treatises, however profound, on the significance of form itself which, as often happens, completely ignore the technical aspects of the matter.

An understanding of technical form presupposes technical knowledge; mere intuition is not enough. Even architectural forms, if influenced by technology, are not entirely intelligible without some technical initiation. The fact that technical knowledge is required in order to understand the world of architectural forms indicates an intrusion of cold reason into the sphere of esthetics. This must be clearly recognized if one is to explore problems of form in modern architecture with its decided technological orientation.

When technical considerations are made part of a scale of esthetic values, questions of economy acquire enhanced importance. The word "economy" is used here not in the sense of saving money but to denote an intellectual principle, a kind of comprehensive moral law that demands the maximum return (in a spiritual and esthetic as well as in a material sense) for a minimum outlay.

Since modern architecture and modern technology began, the oversimplified question of whether the functional is beautiful has been keenly debated. In his "Kunstgewerbliche Laienpredigten" [1] Van de Velde defined the essence of architectural beauty as *the perfect harmony of means and ends*, while Mies van der Rohe has said: *function is an art* [2].

Deliberately misinterpreted, such dicta have often been made to seem ridiculous. Correctly understood, they express the unity of art and technology that ought to be characteristic of contemporary architecture. Forms born of this union, with features derived from modern techniques of construction, are what we shall call "structural forms." Though "structure" is a cliché which at present is used far too freely in far too many fields, we know of no expression more appropriate to our purpose. In its original sense the word structure suggests the order imposed on everything that is built or assembled.

Structural forms cannot simply be computed; they must be designed. The relationships between structure and form are too complex for the result to be expressible in numbers alone. An element of artistic creation is involved. This provides a further justification for using the term "structural form," which should not be confused with the chance appearance of one particular structure. By structural form we do not wish to imply something accidental and unique, but something typical and enduring. We want it understood as a characteristic, significant form determined by the structure, which, being rooted in an architectural, yet natural order, transcends the particular and acquires a generalized power of expression.

There have always been structural forms in architecture. They constantly recur and outlast individual styles. An elementary example is the stone lintel resting on two pillars (Fig. 1). This motif appears at an early date in prehistoric temples and is re-encountered in refined form in practically every subsequent architectural culture. Depending on the cultural context, different materials and different treatments lead to new variations on the basic form. But the essentials of the form always remain the same, provided the structural principle is respected. In Neoclassical work, in which massive stone lintels are replaced with a stone facing suspended from steel beams, the power of expression of the true form suddenly vanishes, yielding to a craving for monumentality. The structural form is dead.

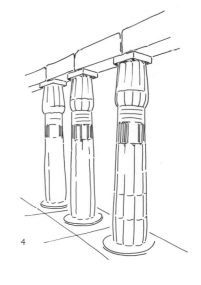

1. The simple stone lintel is a constantly recurring theme:
    1 A prehistoric temple.
    2 The Lion Gate of Mycenae.
    3 An Indian Temple.
    4 Egyptian architecture.
    5 The Parthenon.
    6 In Neoclassical work solid lintels are abandoned in favor of stone facing.

The decay of structural form is not necessarily always accompanied by technical dishonesty. It can also result from frivolous modifications. The simple column symbolizes the ability to support loads. It is found all over the world, wherever the art of building is practiced. Whereas the capital and the base, being points of transition, can be made to suggest the transfer of forces in a hundred different ways, apart from ornamentation the shaft of the column remains a closed, mainly cylindrical or prismatic form, in which the emphasis is laid on the verticals. A pillar consisting of an intertwining cluster of columns is just as unreasonable and degenerate as a single shaft twisted into a helix. In this case the structural content is sacrificed to a theatrical effect (Fig. 2).

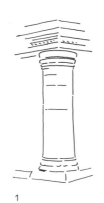

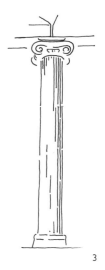

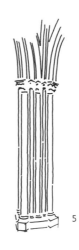

2.   The function of a load-bearing column is best expressed by a simple shaft.
  1 Angkor, Cambodia.
  2 Indian.
  3 Ionic.
  4 Romanesque.
  5 Gothic.
  6 and 7 Neither a twisted bundle of columns nor a single spiral column can express the ability to resist vertical loads.

The prominent vault ribs of the great Gothic cathedrals are not just decorative trimming. They are themselves part of the structure and splendid examples of structural form. The decorative rib patterns of Late Gothic pseudo vaulting no longer reflect the actual distribution of forces. They have no load-bearing function (Fig. 3). They are graphic patterns rather than structural forms.

1

2

3

3.   Vault ribs.
     1 The simple ribs of the great Gothic cathedrals are themselves part of the
       structure.
     2 and 3 The purely decorative rib patterns of the Late Gothic are non-structural.

With the close of the nineteenth century and the emergence of modern technology the rigid order of Western architecture broke down in general confusion. The moribund stylistic concepts of the Late Classical school were challenged by the still uncoordinated forms of the new technology. L'Art Nouveau attempted an artistic and moral revolution but failed to relate itself to contemporary technological achievements. It remains, perhaps for this reason, only half successful.

Fifty years in advance of the times, the Chicago school developed a form of skeleton construction fully consistent with the later ideas of the twentieth century. The impressive skyscrapers of Chicago, which still dominate the architectural pattern of the city, owe their blunt power not least to the impartiality that is a prerequisite for any healthy technical development. It was this alone that made possible, even at so early a date, a really objective understanding of the new functions of large city buildings and, as a logical consequence, the mastery of the technique of erecting them in steel. Even this advance, however, remained no more than an episode. Though a move in the right direction, it had to give way to the spurious taste of the day and was finally halted by a flood of formal and stylistic requirements. Not until the twenties did technical ideas gain broader acceptance as factors that determine form and find corresponding applications in architecture. Remarkably enough, it was not the engineers but architects like Le Corbusier and the men of the Bauhaus who introduced the new technological concept of style into architecture. This was not the result of any special engineering skill on their part; it was rather that they anticipated the new world of technological forms and shaped it by pure intuition. Quite frequently the result was an architectural landmark that was not without influence on later technical developments. However, the time was still not ripe for the final clarification and general recognition of the forms of technological structure. Only in the decades that followed did ideas about building, which continued to remain conventional, undergo a complete transformation and the concepts of technology and modern architecture triumph. At the same time all the restraints that might have ensured a coherent approach to the new architecture dissolved into flux. The situation was characterized not by permanent but by fluctuating values. There was a strong tendency to question all new discoveries and at once plunge further into the still unexplored territory of technology and art.

Technical facility also meant the removal of previous limitations on arbitrariness in design. Everything became technically feasible. Anything, no matter how nonsensical, could be built. The corrective implied by the "technically impossible" was withdrawn. In this ferment the fashionable effect-monger thrived more than ever. His work, enhanced by flattering photography and reproduction and at the same time widely disseminated in popular editions, proved more marketable than more austere forms of true technological worth. The purifying influence of technical logic and its moral force were forgotten and finally the artistic failure was paradoxically laid at the door of technology. This is the point at which we stand today.

In this situation it seems fitting to broach the question of the genuineness of seemingly technological forms in architecture and to attempt a logical and simple answer. The trouble is that the bases of architectural appreciation are never established by purely rational means. They admit a range of standards that is both broad and difficult to define. Logical deductions are easy to challenge "on architectural grounds." On the other hand, whoever questions "artistic" or "architectural" pronouncements and opposes them with equally valid but purely technical arguments immediately runs the risk of being declared a philistine, to whom the doors of art are barred. This is why in discussions about architecture logical arguments carry so little weight compared with reasoning which, however tenuous, champions the "human element" at the expense of the rational. As if reason and logic were not themselves human characteristics!

Since, as we have pointed out, architecture necessarily includes a technological component, it must be possible to encompass at least this side of it within a rational system. In fact, modern architecture, being the architecture of a technological age, cannot afford to forego a clarification of the technical problems that determine form. This is the prerequisite for future processes of purification, which must come, if modern architecture is not to subside into a new formalism. All the symptoms of such a formalism, this time pseudo technical, are already apparent to the alert observer. Since modern architecture rests more heavily on technology than the architectures of the past, it cannot be properly understood without a corresponding knowledge of construction. Or in other words, previously accepted methods of judging architecture solely by esthetic standards are no longer adequate. As a rule, concessions to a "technological world" in the form of purely philosophical considerations completely ignore problems of practical construction and the aims of a well-founded architectural criticism. We are faced with the need to penetrate, far more systematically and extensively than has hitherto been customary or reasonable, into the mechanical, statical and natural (physical) relationships, upon which the development of structural forms is based. Whereas previously building technology was universally intelligible, today we are obliged to seek new ways of speaking and understanding the complicated engineering and scientific language which has become part of architecture. Finally, we must make an effort to grasp the contemporary significance of technology, the importance of which was never questioned in earlier times, together with all the consequences of its pre-eminent position as a form-determining element, and bend them to the service of architecture, uncorrupted and without concessions in the direction of formalism. To accomplish this we must be ready to bring architecture as an art right into the middle of a technological world without creating hostility between the two. We shall then see that technology, the nature of which is rooted in natural laws, will give a powerful impetus to modern architecture. Together they will yield the "structural forms" which constitute the theme of this book.

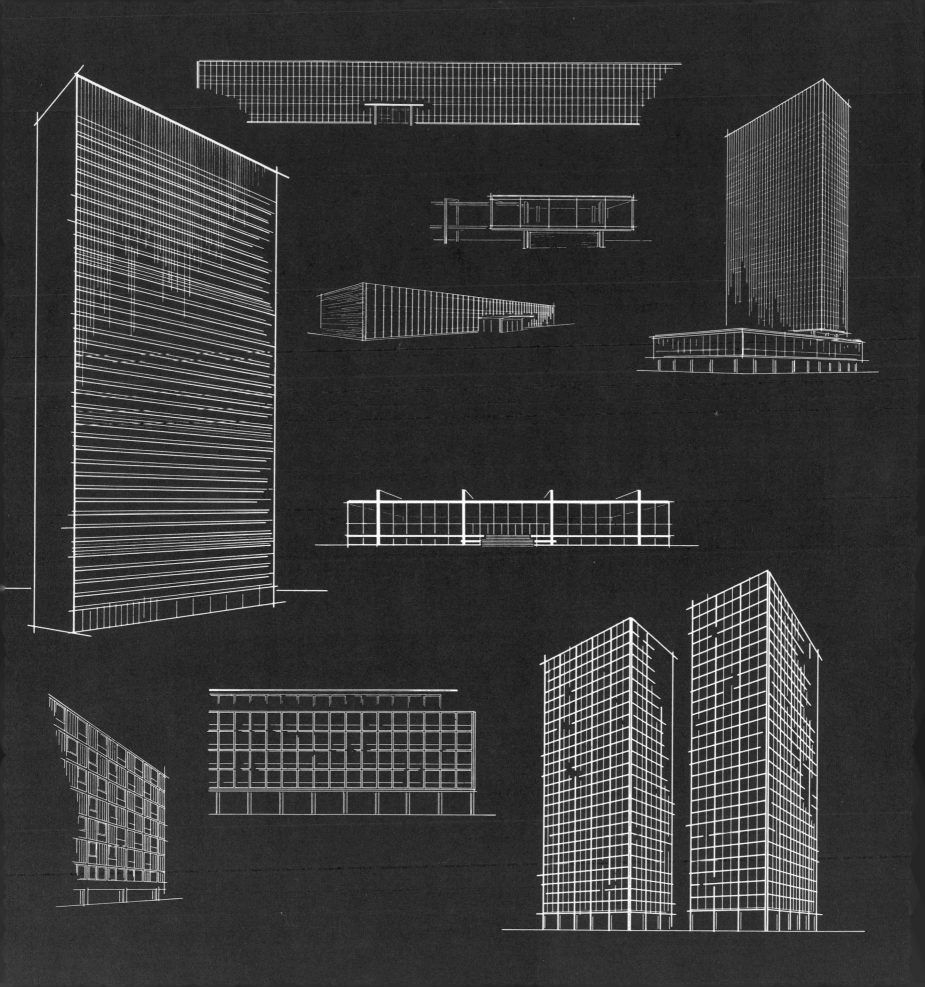

The modern skeleton structure is the result of the rational use of steel and concrete in building. Among its characteristic features are the reduction of all load-carrying members to minimum sizes and a clear division between structural and non-structural elements. The skeleton is composed of rigidly connected beams and columns. It is a particularly suitable form for multistory buildings. The great strength of modern building materials makes it possible to build higher and higher, to meet today's ever-increasing demands. The pattern of our larger cities is being determined by skeleton structures of steel and concrete just as decisively as the pattern of medieval cities was determined by the timber frame. Widespread use has made the modern skeleton structure a central theme of contemporary architecture.

It is hard to give a clear definition of the concept "skeleton construction" in words, although clarity is important where structural forms are concerned. To a large extent, form tends to evade verbal description; it must produce its effect directly. The visual impression received by the observer coincides quite closely with what is meant here by skeleton construction. This impression is captured in the accompanying sketches. Rectangular planes define box-shaped forms; grid-like subdivisions lead the gaze to cellular elements. These alone appear to bear any relation to the human scale. The building is the sum of these individual elements and its internal organization must evidently remain subordinated to the structural function of the skeleton.

The bareness of the facades, the size of the buildings and their severe regularity leave a sense of oppression with anyone who has not yet acquired a feeling for the technological component in modern architecture. The catchphrase "glass and steel," used both in admiration and in contempt, stresses the singular material nature of skeleton construction. The pattern of the facade is determined not by masonry, brick and wood, but by glass, metal and building panels of every kind. These form an outer, space-enclosing skin, which, with no load-carrying function of its own, serves merely to fill out or clad the skeleton frame.

The facades of skeleton structures reveal two opposing tendencies. On the one hand, the structural skeleton may be visible from the outside; on the other, it may remain concealed behind a curtain wall. Naturally, in a discussion of "structural forms" the exposed skeleton is of greater interest. The immediate intelligibility of the design favors a visually received understanding of the structure. Thus, post-war architecture, in which the exposed structural skeleton plays a large part, deserves our particular attention. A number of objections might be made to this on artistic grounds, but our present purpose is not merely to describe model architecture. On the contrary, we are more interested in exceptional clarity, intelligibility and, perhaps, even primitiveness.

The curtain wall clothes the skeleton from the outside, obscuring or even totally concealing the structural principle. The structure thus runs the risk of being reduced to a factor which, if not totally redundant, is at least unimportant in terms of design. If modern architects are searching for a physically and formally perfect entity, they should not treat the structure as a secondary consideration. Even from behind the curtain wall it can act as an important technological component, influencing the design of the whole. It is simply a matter of how the two elements, structural frame and curtain wall, can be embraced in a single, coherent form and cast in a single mold. In the case of the curtain wall, the discussion of the structural problems of skeleton construction is somewhat more complicated than in the case of the exposed frame. It presupposes a study of exposed skeleton structures. Many problems, of course, are common to both forms, though viewed from different angles. Accordingly, we shall begin our discussion with the exposed frame. The curtain wall is treated separately in Section 6 of this chapter.

The following sections deal mainly with the multistory office and commercial buildings characteristic of larger cities. They are almost all skeleton structures. Skyscrapers and buildings designed to resist relatively high horizontal loads (wind and earthquakes) will not be our primary concern since in such cases the horizontal load is critical and overshadows the elementary problem of carrying the vertical loads. In the majority of lower buildings and in those of medium height wind forces present no problem, since they can easily be absorbed by shear walls, stair wells and elevator shafts without much effect on the structural framing as a whole. The skeleton of such buildings is primarily determined not by horizontal but by vertical loads and resisting these is its main structural function. Many framing systems have their origin in this function alone, which thus provides the basis for the general layout of the building. In practice it is impossible to separate skeletons that resist only vertical loads from those which resist horizontal loads as well. A definite boundary does not exist. Thus, limiting the discussion to skeleton structures carrying primarily vertical loads will not prevent us from illustrating and discussing certain details with reference to skyscrapers. The basis of the discussion, however, will be vertical loading, which largely determines the nature of the floor system and the size of beams and columns, though the structural design of buildings accommodating air-conditioning or other bulky equipment will be influenced to a large extent by the needs of the mechanical engineer.

The beginning and essence of the chapter is an analysis of the grid, the basis of the structurally articulated facade. This is followed by an examination of the terminations of the facade that develops out of this grid. The very important lower edge at second-floor level, the corners, the architectural importance of which cannot be exaggerated, and finally the termination at the roof form the subject of further sections. The chapter continues with a discussion of the first-floor setback and curtain wall details and ends with a review of some of the exaggerated forms frequently encountered in skeleton construction.

THE GRID

The word "grid" is readily used by polemicists to characterize third-rate skeleton construction. It conveys the idea of lifeless, inorganic and monotonous subdivision without reference to inner content. Some talk about "grid disease," thus denigrating what in its origins is merely order and only becomes dead formalism on being misapplied and wrongly interpreted.

If we make the effort to free ourselves of these rather meaningless associations, we find that the essence of the grid is a system of intersecting lines. The grid itself is neither good nor bad, it is a way of achieving order, and nothing more. Of course, if it is laid out on a purely formal basis, that is, if it is merely a pretense of order, arbitrarily projected on the facade, it will lack all reference to content, and the result will merely be the rightly despised, barren monotony of so many buildings designed on the grid principle. If, however, the grid has a logical relationship to the architectural problem, itself becomes part of the design and reflects in its proportions the unity of function and form, then it will be necessary to and merge organically with the whole.

For the sake of greater clarity and comprehension, we shall divide the numerous forms of grid into two main groups: the "narrow" grid and the "wide" grid. The distinguishing characteristic is the column spacing. This same characteristic is the source of a number of secondary differences. Since the effect of differences in column spacing on the articulation of the facade does indeed lead to two essentially different systems, this classification into "narrow" and "wide" grids appears to be quite justified.

4.   The grid as an expression of skeleton construction.

14

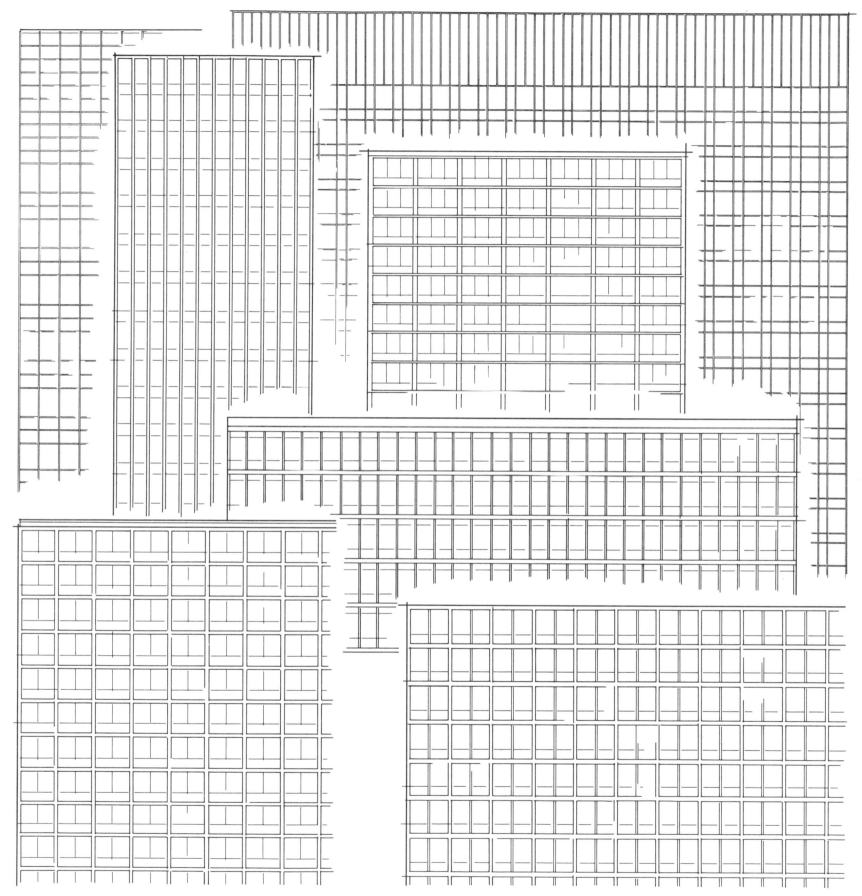

The Narrow Grid

A "narrow" grid is one in which only one window unit lies between each pair of columns. If the columns are more widely spaced and several windows are introduced between them, we speak of a "wide" grid. The difference will be apparent on comparing the typical "narrow" grids of Fig. 5 with the typical "wide" grids of Fig. 11.

The narrow grid has its origin less in the laws of statics than in the function of the plan. An outer wall dissolved into windows, spandrels and columns means that transverse partitions can be located only at the latter. The narrower the column spacing, the greater the number of possible partition locations, the more flexible the plan and the more efficient the use of space. This, of course, always presupposes that partitioned spaces are, in fact, required. Where this is not true, that is, where large open areas are desirable, the above argument does not apply. Where the separate, individual type of office is more suitable, the "narrow" grid, conceived in terms of the divisibility of space, will predominate, but where "open planning" is preferred, as in most large office buildings, the "narrow" grid will seldom be appropriate. In order to understand the following sections, it is essential to have a clear idea of the difference between a "narrow" grid with true close column spacing and a "wide" grid with quasi narrow spacing, which is, in fact, merely suggested by subdivisions of the curtain wall.

Numerous efforts to bring the column spacing of the "narrow" grid into harmony with the plan dimensions of office furniture have given us countless different modules which vary roughly between 90 cm and 3.5 m. All these modules have their advantages and disadvantages. A statistical survey has shown that out of all the more important narrow-grid office buildings erected in Germany during the last ten years roughly 50 per cent have an axial module of about 1.8 to 1.9 m. Obviously, this dimension has been found particularly favorable for German office organization and office furniture and has therefore been given preference. Apart from functional requirements and questions of economy, however, the choice of so important a dimension remains essentially an architectural decision. The narrow grid, in particular, easily leads to a certain uniformity, as the rebuilt cities of Germany with their numerous narrow-grid facades clearly show.

5. In a narrow grid there is only one window unit between each pair of structural columns.

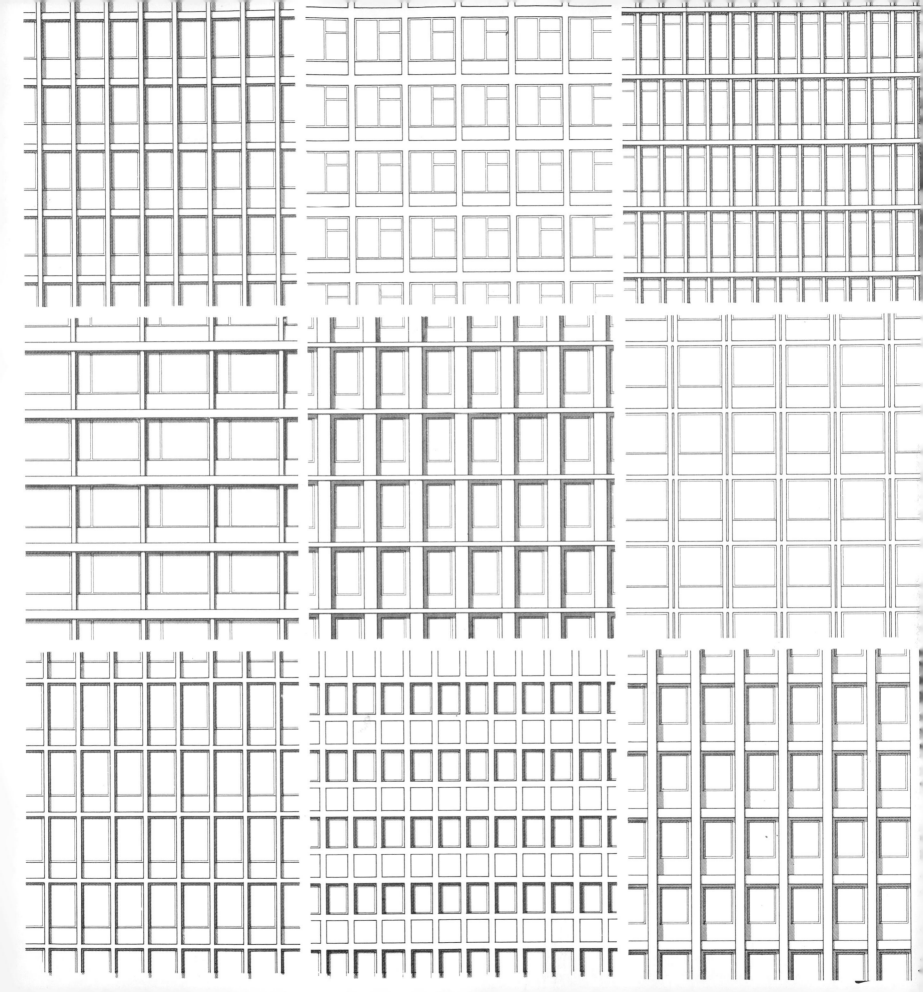

In order to clarify the structural aspects of this form of construction, we shall first examine the normal loads on closely spaced columns and then some of the more important floor systems. From this examination and a consideration of the physical and mechanical problems involved we shall derive the structural form most appropriate to the narrow grid. Fig. 6 illustrates the normal loads and the average column sizes they require in narrow-grid, reinforced-concrete frame buildings of four and twelve stories respectively. In a steel frame building the actual column sizes may initially be smaller, but when fireproofing and thermal insulation have been added, the over-all size is very little different from that of a reinforced concrete column. The column sizes in Fig. 6 are for maximum loads at first-floor level and have been determined purely from structural requirements, without taking any esthetic factors into account. Even in the twelve-story building the narrow spacing means that the columns can be surprisingly slender, the individual column picking up a relatively small load. This is not the picture we are used to. In most narrow-grid buildings the columns have commonly been made much heavier than the loads require. Although a minimum dimension of 20 cm for cast-in-place concrete is generally adequate, and this may even be reduced to 15 cm if prefabricated elements are employed, it is quite usual to see 30 to 50 cm columns, even in relatively low buildings. These are not appropriate dimensions for steel or reinforced concrete. It is possible that they are partly the legacy of old-fashioned masonry design and partly attributable to a certain taste for monumentality, which is still cherished by many architects all over the world but has little to do with the nature of modern skeleton construction.

In a narrow grid the columns are very slender. The relationship between this characteristic and significant form cannot be too heavily stressed. Every unnecessary thickening of the columns, whether it be due to adding pipes, fireproofing, insulation, etc., or to any other cause, detracts from their formal significance.

In narrow-grid skeleton structures with a reinforced concrete frame it is rational to design the floors as concrete joists, spanning at right angles to the longer side of the building and carried on spandrel beams. The spandrel beams span only a very short distance between

20 / 30

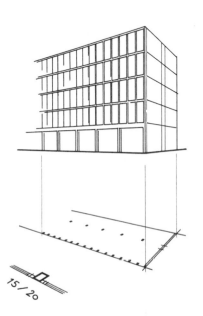

15 / 20

6. Columns laid out in a narrow grid can safely be made very slender, even in tall buildings. The dimensions, given in centimeters, correspond to normal spans and medium-quality concrete.

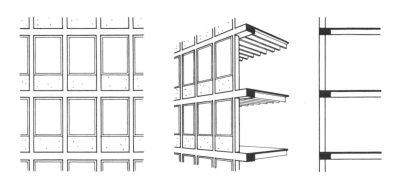

supports (equal to the narrow grid module) and normally do not need to be any deeper than the floor construction itself. For normal spans roughly 25 to 35 cm is enough. The spandrel should be regarded as a thickened edge of the floor with additional reinforcing (Fig. 7.1). Over longer spans the transverse solid slab (Fig. 7.2) will usually be rather heavy and uneconomical. However, it has better soundproofing properties than the joist floor. Its thickness is always less than the depth of the spandrel, which is kept about the same size as in joist construction. Thus, the outward appearance of 7.1 and 7.2 is very much the same. If the solid slab is made to span longitudinally, it must be carried on intermediate transverse beams (7.3). Each of these beams frames into an exterior column and thus is not visible in elevation. Inside the building, however, the beams can be seen projecting below the underside of the slab. The flush ceiling is therefore lost. Because the grid is narrow, the transverse beams lie so close together that the carrying capacity of the slab is rarely fully utilized, especially since, for soundproofing reasons, the slab thickness may not be reduced below a certain minimum. Moreover, it is difficult to dispense with a shallow spandrel beam to carry the outside wall, although this beam has nothing to do with the design of the floor. The layout in 7.3 is a special, theoretical case, requiring no further investigation. As far as the narrow grid is concerned, it is of virtually no importance.

If pipes and ducts for heating, ventilating and air-conditioning have to be accommodated beneath the floor, its total thickness will be increased, but the size of the columns will remain the same. In Europe installations, like air-conditioning systems, that require large construction depths are rare. Accordingly, the floor thicknesses given above correspond roughly with what is visible from the outside. In the U.S., where practically every larger building is air-conditioned, the horizontal bands that represent the floor construction in elevation are often much deeper. However, even without the extra construction depth required for mechanical installations, the narrow grid will always give us slender columns contrasted with substantially broader horizontal floor bands, provided that the pattern is determined by structural considerations alone. Using steel instead of reinforced concrete does not affect the basic principle.

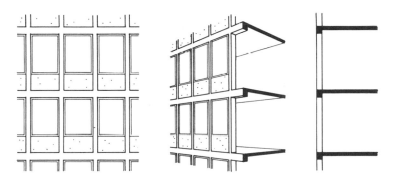

1

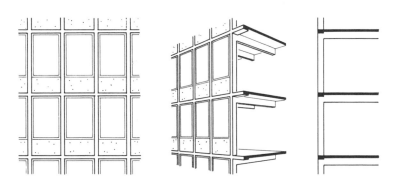

2

3

7. Reinforced concrete floor systems based on a narrow grid:
    1 Joists and
    2 Solid slabs spanning at right-angles to the longitudinal axis are indistinguishable in elevation.
    3 The visible floor band formed by a solid slab spanning parallel to the longitudinal axis is extremely thin and cannot be considered typical.

Facing columns with slabs of natural or artificial stone or other materials and encasing them in thermal insulation makes them wider and obscures the logical proportions referred to above. Naturally, this is not intended to belittle the value of good thermal insulation. The question is merely what method of preventing heat losses does most justice to the structurally pure form.

As far as designs with exposed columns are concerned, there are two extreme cases.

If the facade is flush (Fig. 8.1) and the column lies on the inside, that is, with its mass at the inside temperature, then, even if the climate is cold, it is normally possible to dispense with thermal insulation for reinforced concrete columns. If insulation is provided, it will only be needed on the narrow outside face of the column and will not affect its slenderness.

However, if the columns are completely exposed and no insulation is provided, they will form an undesirable thermal bridge between the interior of the building and the cold air outside. Moreover, sensitive additional stresses due to temperature differences will be superimposed on those due to the normal statical loads. In order to avoid this, fully exposed columns need to be thermally insulated on three sides, with consequent adverse effects on the slenderness of the structural form (Fig. 8.2).

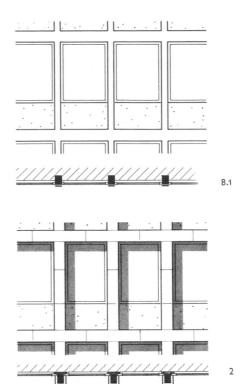

8.1

2

8.   Thermal insulation of exterior columns.
      1 If the elevation is flush, the apparent dimensions of the columns are not
         affected by adding insulation.
      2 If the columns project, adding insulation makes them appear heavier.

9.   Vertical services located inside exterior columns.
      1 The logical division into structural and service columns leads to the wide
         grid.
      2 If the columns are all made the same size, the impression created is that
         of a narrow grid with the dimensions exaggerated.

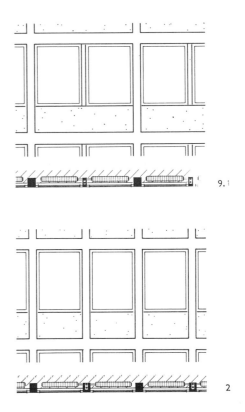

9.1

2

Vertical services may also have an unfortunate effect on column sizes. If they are located in the outside walls, they are best attached to or enclosed within every second column, so as to serve the adjacent lines of windows on each side. This means, however, that different columns perform different functions. While one column carries the loads, its neighbor will be a non-load-bearing service column. The distance between structural columns is doubled. The narrow grid must be abandoned. Because they now carry twice the previous load, the alternate, load-bearing columns must be given a greater cross section. The intervening service columns will be clearly distinguishable. Thus, in the sense of our earlier definition, we have now arrived at a "wide" grid (Fig. 9.1). Unfortunately, it often happens that the service columns are given the same cross section as the load-bearing ones, creating the outward appearance of a series of seemingly equal and over-dimensioned supports (Fig. 9.2). Curiously, giving structural and service columns the same proportions is quite a common practice. A false sense of order prompts many architects to eliminate real differences. What they actually achieve is a monotonous "standardization," while destroying the true structural form and missing an interesting design opportunity.

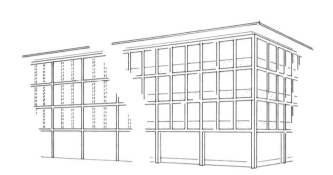

Fig. 10 shows two buildings in which alternating structural and intermediate columns are not differentiated in elevation. The charge of monotony rightly leveled against skeleton structures of this kind has no bearing on the principle of the grid or the technical possibilities of modern architecture; the real offender is a conception of planning which, in misinterpreting the problems of structural form, obliterates the vital elements instead of making them a theme of the design.

The more important characteristics of the "narrow" grid may be summarized as follows:

1. As a rule, exterior columns based on a narrow grid need not be more than 20 cm wide, even in buildings up to twelve stories high. If the column elements are prefabricated, this width may even be reduced. A very slender column is typical of narrow-grid skeleton construction. This is a consequence of the close column spacing and the small loads carried by each column.

2. In elevation the horizontal floor bands reflect the depth of the floor construction. This is determined not by the close column spacing but by the transverse floor span. As a rule the floor bands are broader than the columns.

3. The structural pattern of the grid is based on the relationship between slender columns and heavier horizontal floor bands.

4. This relationship may be robbed of its natural tension as a result of various engineering requirements and, not least, by making arbitrary architectural modifications. However, once its potentialities have been grasped, it can become an eloquent motif in the facade.

Naturally, the above-mentioned dimensions and proportions should not be accepted too uncritically. The uniqueness of every design problem prevents them from being universally applicable. They are only intended as a guide which structural form must follow, if it is to be valid.

10. Failure to differentiate between structural and service columns makes skeleton construction monotonous.

The Wide Grid

In the "wide" grid the structural columns are placed several window units apart. The window units either form a common window strip or are separated by mullions, which do not carry loads or form part of the structural frame, serving only for attaching and separating the windows, housing installations and terminating partitions. The distance between mullions is relatively small, roughly equivalent to the axial module of the narrow grid, which is derived from furniture standards, the dimensions of the individual window and the desire to achieve the greatest possible flexibility in the organization of floor space. However, only the more widely spaced load-bearing columns actually form part of the structure. Together with the horizontal floor bands they form large, horizontal rectangles, as distinct from the small, vertical rectangles of the narrow grid.

11.   A wide grid has more than one window unit between each pair of structural columns. These window units are usually separated by mullions.

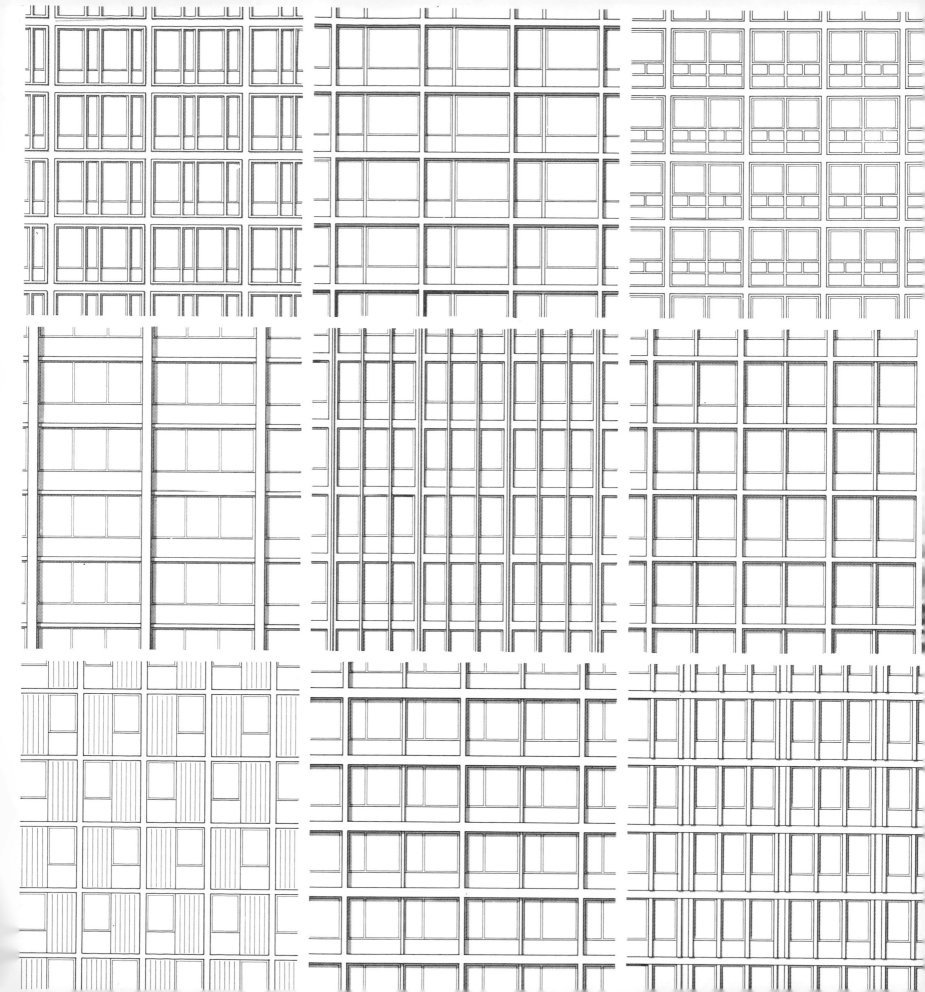

Fig. 12, which is analogous to Fig. 6, shows the loads and minimum column sizes for "wide-grid" structures with four and twelve stories respectively. Since the column spacing is greater than in the case of the narrow grid, the column sizes are correspondingly increased. It remains to determine how great this increase should be. It is immediately clear that if the total vertical load and the structural materials remain the same, the sum of all the column cross sections in each story will be approximately constant, independently of whether many slender or a few heavy columns are employed (wide or narrow grid). The objection that slender columns are more susceptible to buckling than heavier ones and that their sizes will thus be unfavorably affected by additional buckling factors is, in principle, correct. However, the susceptibility of the columns to buckling plays no part in this comparison, since the relatively small effective length (= story height) means that in a narrow grid even the slenderest columns would have no appreciable tendency to buckle. For example, according to the provisions of the German code for reinforced concrete, the buckling factor for the slenderest permissible cast-in-place column with a minimum dimension of 20 cm is 4 per cent, if the story height is 3.5 m. This is a value that has no significance, as far as the order of magnitude of our comparisons is concerned.

In passing from the narrow to the wide grid, the loads on the individual columns, and hence their dimensions, increase in accordance with the increase in column spacing. Doubling the column spacing means doubling the load, and hence doubling the column cross section. Thus, column spacing, column load and column cross section are roughly connected by a linear relationship. However, the column cross section itself is not immediately perceptible as form. To an observer the column width alone is the decisive feature of the elevation. But there is no linear relationship between column width, cross section, load and spacing. The former is a radical function of the cross section. Thus, with increase in column spacing the visible column width increases only as the square root of the increasing cross sectional area. Accordingly, taken together, the few, heavily loaded columns of a wide-grid skeleton present a smaller visible area in elevation than the many, lightly loaded columns of a narrow-grid structure. Or in other words, the sum of all the column widths visible in elevation is always less for a wide grid, that is, the columns always look more slender than in a narrow grid. This rule is true of reinforced concrete columns made of concrete and steel of the same quality and with the same percentage of reinforcement, but it also applies closely enough to fireproofed steel columns, the outer dimensions of which are not very different from those of columns of reinforced concrete.

35 / 60

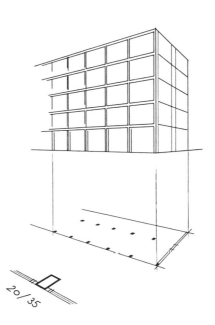

20 / 35

12. In a wide grid the column sections increase linearly with increase in span, but the width of the column, visible in elevation, does *not* increase at the same rate as the span (dimensions in cm).

Now a few words about floor systems. Fig. 13.1 shows a solid reinforced concrete slab spanning longitudinally; this is not a rational system for a narrow grid because the spans are too short (Fig. 7.3). With a wide grid, however, the spans are longer and a beam-and-slab system can be used effectively. Nevertheless, the edge of the slab must be stiffened even more emphatically than in the case of the narrow grid, since the spandrel beam must now carry the exterior wall load over a greater distance. It should be noted that this spandrel beam is not a factor in the slab calculations. From the design point of view it is of no great importance and should therefore be proportioned with appropriate restraint. It should not be stressed more strongly than its modest structural role requires.

The dimensions of the transverse beams framing into the columns are determined by the span and the load. They will usually be made the same width as the columns, while in the vertical direction they will project plainly below the slab. The underside of the ceiling will not be flush. Possible transverse partitions will be of variable height, depending on whether they end in a beam or the slab. This form of construction does not satisfy the requirement for a uniform partition height and a flush ceiling. It is true that a flush finish can be obtained by suspending the ceiling at the level of the underside of the beams, but this solution has other disadvantages. The spandrel beam, which in fact has no real structural significance, will necessarily have to be dropped to ceiling level and thus overemphasized. Headroom will be lost and the valuable light coming through the top of the windows will be cut off; finally, the connection between partitions and suspended ceiling will give a great deal of trouble because of sound transmitted above the ceiling. The advantages of the system shown in Fig. 13.1 consist in the simplicity and clarity of the arrangement of beam and slab. It will serve well wherever exposed beams are acceptable. However, where a flush ceiling is a necessity, both the obscuring of the structure and the technical shortcomings described above will count against it.

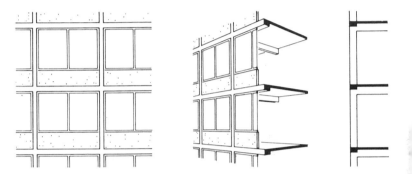

1

13.   Reinforced concrete floor systems based on a wide grid:
       1 Solid slab spanning parallel to the longitudinal axis, transverse beams
       exposed.

If the supports are fairly widely spaced, it will be more convenient to use joists than a solid slab (Fig. 13.2). Long-span joists require greater construction depth. It is then possible to accommodate the transverse beams, which would otherwise project below the slab (system 13.1), as solid bands within the thickness of the floor. The only difficulty is at the point where these bands meet the exterior columns. Only the narrow area of contact offered by the face of the column is available for transferring the forces. If, moreover, openings have to be provided in the beams for the passage of pipes and ducts, insufficient space may be left for the reinforcing steel, not to mention the possibility of exceeding the permissible concrete stresses. These difficulties are reduced, if the joists are made to span transversely as in Fig. 13.3 and if, as in narrow-grid construction (cf. Fig. 7.1), the spandrel beam is designed as a solid band of the same depth as the joists. However, a solid band of this kind has only a limited span. A reasonable limit would be around two-thirds of the distance spanned by the joists. If we assume a room of normal depth, six meters, for example, then the spandrel beam, designed as a solid band, should not span more than $2/3 \times 6 = 4.0$ m. Any further increase in the span of a spandrel beam, accommodated within the depth of the joist floor, results in such a concentration of reinforcement at the columns that concreting becomes difficult and the quality of the concrete may be jeopardized. Moreover, the structure will become too elastic and the material in the narrow zone at the face of the column may be overstressed.

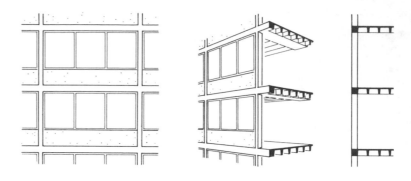

2

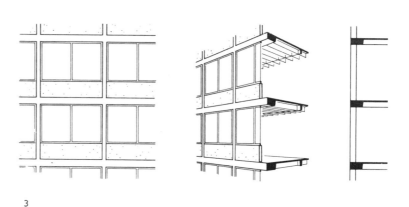

3

13. 2 Joists spanning parallel to the longitudinal axis, flush ceiling.
     3 Joists spanning at right-angles to the longitudinal axis, spandrel beams the same depth as the floor.

If the distance between columns is greater than about two-thirds of the depth of the room, it will be more convenient to employ another form of spandrel beam. The shape shown in Fig. 13.4 is the simplest one to pour, but cuts off a valuable source of light at the window head.

The upstand beam shown in Fig. 13.5 does not have this disadvantage, and, moreover, is capable of spanning eight meters and more with ease; however, it is more difficult to construct. Upstand beams are not suitable for casting in place; concreting has to be interrupted at the top of the slab and this is often the cause of constructional defects.

When we attempt to compare the various floor systems described and to combine them with rational column sizes into a set of rules for the wide grid, we find this a more difficult proposition than in the case of the narrow grid. In discussing the latter, the correct principle of slender columns contrasted with broad floor bands was easily established. As far as the wide grid is concerned, there are several "correct" solutions, which in some respects are widely divergent. The proportions discernible in elevation are not to be understood without the structural concepts that lie behind them. In solution 13.1 floor band and columns are about the same width, though the column may even be wider. In solution 13.5 this situation is reversed. The tall upstand is several times broader than the column.

In the case of the wide grid it is impossible to lay down universally valid rules for the relationship between the width of the columns and that of the floor bands. However, this does not mean disorder and caprice. Structural principles continue to apply. He who conceives the structure, the function of the building and its architectural expression as a single whole will always be able to select the structural form appropriate to a particular skeleton. Many forms and proportions can be structurally right, and just as many wrong and purely formalistic, the "rightness" and "wrongness" varying with the problem to be solved. It is more difficult to make the right choice for a wide grid than for a narrow one. The possible structural variations are more numerous, giving the architect greater freedom in design.

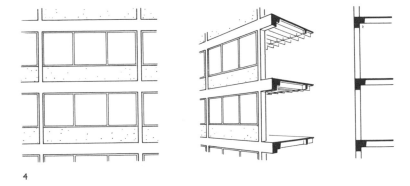

4

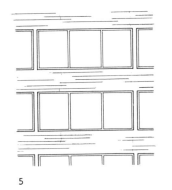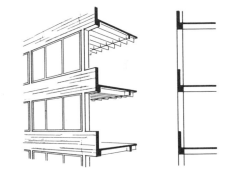

5

13. 4 Joists spanning at right-angles to the longitudinal axis, spandrel beams dropped.
     5 Joists spanning at right-angles to the longitudinal axis, upstand spandrel beam.

The previous section was devoted to a discussion of the grid. In this and the following sections we shall consider the important problem of how to terminate the grid at its various edges. It is true that the proportions of the grid have a decisive influence on the building and that to a large extent the grid gives a skeleton structure its scale, but the grid alone is still not enough to yield a closed architectural form. Ponti [3] writes of "la forma finita," that is, a form with a definite beginning and end. In skeleton construction the beginning and end of a form means virtually the termination of the grid at the edges of the building. These terminations are much more complicated in a skeleton structure than they ever were in masonry construction, in which the closed surface grew smoothly out of the ground, ended laterally in a simple edge formed by a masonry joint and was capped by the roof. The unity of this surface, interrupted only by relatively small, incised openings, was always well preserved. In skeleton construction, however, this closed surface, so easy to terminate, is lacking. In this case the articulated surface is composed in the manner of a relief from the structural parts of the skeleton, concentrated almost into a system of lines, and flat areas of glazing and wall panel. Each part has its own function and structural connections and is separated from adjacent parts by grooves, ridges, joints and sealing strips. The structural and functional interrelationships of these parts form the basis of surface building in skeleton construction, and hence the basis for structurally significant terminations of the facade.

Terminating the Narrow Grid

As a rule the type of skeleton is mainly determined by space requirements in the upper stories. The first floor serves a different purpose. This is necessarily reflected in a break in the structural pattern. Close column spacing is not suitable for show windows, entrance areas and the larger establishments located at street level.

If the frame is based on a narrow grid, a girder must be introduced at second-floor level in order to make possible the transition to wider column spacing. The size of this girder depends on the span, the column spacing in the upper stories, the number of stories, the floor loads and, not least, on the way the girder is designed.

14. The fundamental difference between the old massive type of construction and skeleton construction is clearly expressed in the treatment of the main surfaces and the edges in which they meet.

15. The transition between a narrow grid in the upper floors and more widely spaced columns at street level is achieved by means of a girder at the second floor.

Fig. 16.1 shows clearly how certain columns have to be picked up at second-floor level. In the upper stories the floor band is a normal spandrel beam that simply carries the floor loads to the columns. At second-floor level, however, it seems far too slender to be able to support the accumulated loads of all the upper stories. This is so obvious that it is immediately intelligible even to the layman. Such a facade graphically demonstrates its own internal weakness. One suspects that it is supported by an independent structure which it conceals. The inventive designer can always find a solution, whether it be a steel section buried in the concrete, an unusually broad spandrel beam or an upstand concealed behind the wall panels. It only remains to question his motive. Is the esthetic gain so great? Can a grid that bears so little relation to the actual construction be a meaningful part of the architecture?

Fig. 16.2 shows an L-shaped girder with a cross section of the type that is easiest to pour. Its dimensions are determined by the statical load. The greater the span at second-floor level and the greater the load, the deeper the girder. If this structurally important point is frankly emphasized, the elevation cannot fail to gain in clarity. In this respect the dimensions that will satisfy the computations are by no means rigid. As is well known, they can be adapted to the desires of the architect within relatively wide limits. Flexibility can be achieved by using high-grade steel and concrete, varying the width and depth of the girder or incorporating parts of the slab as compression zones. The girder can be proportioned in many ways and still be statically sound. The designer enjoys a great degree of freedom, provided always that he does not violate a structural principle or practice flagrant deception.

The upstand girder in Fig. 16.3 is a very interesting form of construction. The structural exploitation of the spandrel wall gives it great strength. It is well suited for long spans. However, the cross section is not a simple one. The second floor windows sit directly on the upstand. The pattern of window and wall panel, characteristic of the upper stories, is missing. The effect is so strange and unfamiliar that the architect usually tries to conceal the upstand behind some form of cladding (cf. Fig. 18.4).

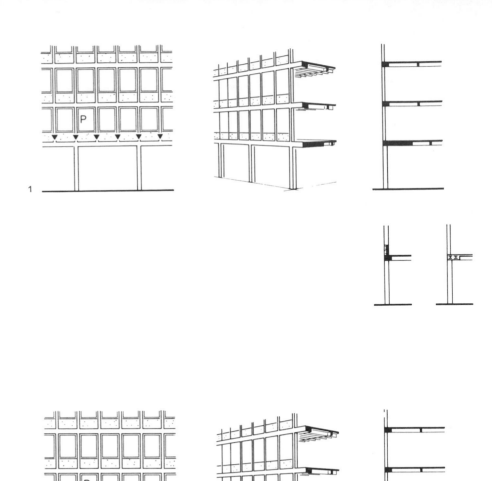

16.   Design of the second-floor girder.
       1 Obvious slenderness is structurally and esthetically unsatisfactory.
       2 A typical girder in its natural position.
       3 Incorporating the spandrel wall gives a very strong upstand beam.

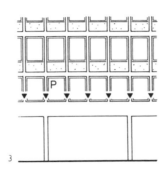

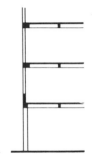

Surprisingly, we have hardly any examples of a skillful and objective treatment of this straightforward structural motif, probably for lack of the courage to accept uncompromising structural forms. This makes it all the more agreeable to come upon the structurally neat, lively and esthetically satisfying solution devised by the Italian architect Luccichenti for an office building in Rome [4] (Fig. 17).

The pitiful lack of interest on the part of architects and engineers in the meaningful design of structural skeletons is revealed in the numerous distorted structures that are continually being built and uncritically accepted. A few typical pseudo structures that crop up repeatedly in various forms receive critical attention in the pages that follow.

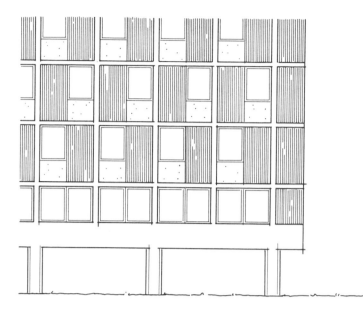

17.   Office building in Rome with a well-designed upstand beam carrying the intermediate columns [4].

Fig. 18.1 shows what seems like a narrow grid. In the upper stories all the columns are the same. One is thus led to suppose that they all carry the same loads and from this it follows that every second column must be picked up at second-floor level. But there is no girder provided for this purpose. The spandrel beam at second-floor level is no deeper than those in the upper stories. Thus, it could not possibly carry the concentrated load from a whole sequence of upper levels. How are we to explain this mystery? The loading diagram and the cross section show that every second column is actually a dummy and carries no load. At every floor the spandrel beams span freely over twice the distance between adjacent columns and also carry the additional dead load of the dummy columns. Thus, the spandrel beam at second-floor level need be no heavier than those in the upper stories, since it carries exactly the same load. A large girder at this point would be superfluous. Nevertheless, its absence is disquieting to the critical observer. The dummy columns are indistinguishable from the real ones. The eye seeks in vain for some ultimate point of support for the loads they appear to transmit. The ambiguity of this design has its origin in the starting point of the train of thought. The first inconsequential step was to make the dummy columns and the load-bearing columns identical. The end result is the deceptive impression that a girder is missing at second-floor level, although, in fact, one is not required. Thus, one structural ambiguity inevitably generates another.

In Fig. 18.2 all the columns carry the same loads and all of them are continued down to the foundations. Thus, there is no need for a girder at the second floor. But, strangely enough, one has been provided. The slight degree of differentiation between the first floor and the upper floors (the column spacing remains the same) suggests that the rooms above and below all have the same function. This makes the heavy girder and its separating action even less comprehensible. Or should the functions of these areas indeed be different? Does the greater story height at first-floor level indicate the presence of larger spaces? In that case the close grouping of the columns does not make sense, and if a heavy girder is already indicated at second-floor level, obviously with the intention of emphasizing the articulation at an important point, why is it not in fact made to pick up the intermediate columns and so reduce the number of columns in the first tier? Or is the girder simply intended to conceal a zone for mechanical installations at second-floor level? This is another possible explanation, but there ought to be other means of achieving this without having to simulate so important a structural element in so prominent a position.

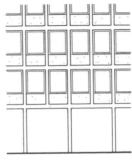
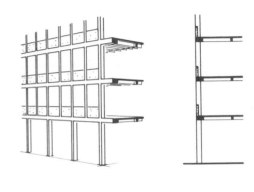

1

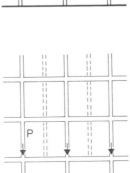
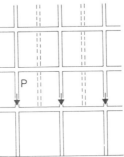

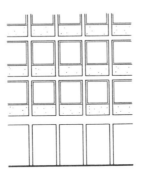

2

18. Insensitive treatment of the second-floor girder.
    1 The fact that all the upper columns are alike suggests that a second-floor girder is missing.
    2 The close spacing of the first-floor columns makes a girder superfluous.

In any case the resulting structural pattern is a false one, however the actual forces are distributed. The clearly recognizable girder in 18.3 apparently picks up every second column at second-floor level. Since the columns in the upper tiers are all the same size, there is no reason to doubt that they all have the same load-bearing function. This impression is reinforced by the slender spandrel beams in the upper stories; beams of this size could scarcely carry over a distance twice the normal column spacing. Obviously, they can only span from column to column. So much for external appearances. They indicate a clear and unambiguous structure. Here again we must turn to the loading diagram and the cross section in order to lay bare the contradiction between external pattern and internal order. The intermediate columns are non-load-bearing service columns. Only alternate columns carry loads, just as in Fig. 18.1. The spandrel beams, that seem to be so shallow, span freely over twice the distance between columns and support the weight of the service columns besides. This they cannot do merely with the construction depth exposed in elevation. They are, in fact, strengthened by means of an upstand, concealed behind the spandrel wall. Since the intermediate columns do not carry loads, the supposed girder at second-floor level has exactly the same function as the spandrel beams in the upper stories. Its pretensions to being an important structural member are false and out of keeping with the simple role of an ordinary spandrel beam. Paradoxically, however, it is the only beam in the entire building whose visible dimensions are really appropriate to its task, namely, spanning over twice the distance between columns. As distinct from the spandrel beams in the upper stories, it does not need any concealed reinforcing. The cycle of confusion is complete.

This example is worth noting because, in spite of the divergence of structure and form, the outward appearance of the building is suggestive of calculated structural clarity. In fact, the facade could easily represent a genuine structural pattern, without altering any of the dimensions of the visible parts, if only the concealed upstand were suppressed. In that case the internal, statical distribution of forces would really have to correspond with appearances. The quasi-structural intermediate service columns would really have to carry loads. The spandrel beams, no deeper than the visible floor bands, would then be able to span from column to column without the aid of a concealed upstand. The girder at the second floor would really pick up the loads from every second column and thus fulfill its apparent function, and harmony between structural pattern and distribution of forces would be achieved.

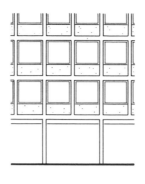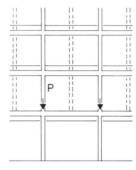

18. 3 The seemingly straightforward proportions of the elevation do not reflect the true distribution of forces.

These are the extremes to which the cleavage between architectural and structural thinking can go. Someone designs a well-proportioned structural frame. As designed, it is structurally sound and no problem to build. But for certain reasons, probably connected with the mechanical services, perhaps to facilitate the installation of risers, the basic structural concept is abandoned. Load-bearing columns are turned into fake columns, though the sizes are left the same. The span of the spandrel beams is doubled, but their visible dimensions are retained and a concealed upstand is added. The girder at second-floor level, however, does not need any disguised reinforcing. Its original dimensions are more than adequate to carry the load from just one floor. In the first instance it was designed to pick up much heavier loads. The engineer is satisfied because he has not had to make any changes in the architect's design. The architect accepts his solution because he is largely unaffected by what goes on under the surface, in a structural sense.

Outwardly, Fig. 18.4 closely resembles 18.1. Again it is a question of a narrow grid. All the columns are the same and they all appear to be load-bearing. The absence of a girder at second-floor level, however, is felt even more painfully than in Fig. 18.1. The distance between the first-floor columns is so great that it is quite incredible that the slender floor band should bridge it. One is reluctant even to believe it capable of carrying a single floor over this span. How could it possibly pick up the loads from several floors concentrated at two points! So long as the observer retains the least shred of natural structural awareness, he will find the sight of such a frame disquieting. He must sense the absence of a girder to pick up the column loads at the second floor. Without hidden support the structure ought to collapse. Thus, the visible portion of this frame cannot express the true inner distribution of forces. The load diagram and the cross section reveal how this distorted picture has come into being. In order to keep the dimensions of the grid outwardly the same, a deep girder has been concealed behind the wall panels. The effective natural contrast between slender spandrel beams in the upper stories and a heavy girder at second-floor level has thus been thrown away. All that remains is the customary monotony of such skeleton frame buildings. Note carefully that this result is not determined by technical considerations but is quite arbitrary and inconsequential and without practical logic. It is to a large extent the consequence of that questionable "artistic freedom," which, in the wrong hands, soon becomes caprice and overthrows true design. This manner of thinking is fatal to the development of genuine structural forms.

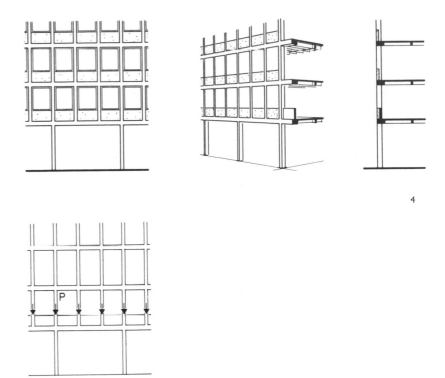

4

18.   4 Concealing the upstand gives the structure an alarming air of instability.

Figs. 19.1 and 19.2 are characterized by a girder at second-floor level, the dimensions of which are obviously determined by the function of carrying a single floor, not column loads from the upper stories. The door opening, however, calls for a girder capable of carrying the concentrated loads from intermediate columns. For the sake of a rigid order, that has nothing to do with the structure, this girder is concealed behind the spandrel wall. Anyone with the slightest appreciation of materials and statics gets the feeling that a girder must be tucked away somewhere.

Figs. 19.3 and 19.4 show girders at second-floor level that have no real function. All the columns are carried down to the foundations. The girders are superfluous.

The building in Fig. 19.5 is a typical expression of the petit bourgeois desire to "have a skeleton frame of our own." The unreality of the faked facade is immediately obvious from the fact that one of the supposed main columns ends in the middle of a door opening. If the differentiation of the columns in the upper stories were interpreted as a wide grid technique, the girder at second-floor level would be superfluous. Its only function would be to carry the main column over the entrance to the store. However, the obviously faked position of the columns (the real columns are indicated in the sketch) casts doubt on the validity of the design as a whole. Whether the girder is really justified or not, the general impression left by this frame is one of total structural confusion. Unfortunately, this is not just a horrid example, concocted for the purposes of the present discussion. Countless buildings of this type actually "adorn" our newer suburbs. As a matter of fact, specimens of the order of 19.5 are not worth mentioning, even critically. However, a lack of understanding of modern architecture and presumptuousness in aping it are also typical of much more pretentious contemporary building. The same lack of understanding and the same presumptuousness can be found in the head offices of insurance companies, banks and other businesses, among the marble, bronze and Persian carpets. The same spirit produces the "modern skeleton frame" of our smaller towns, with its steep-pitched roof and vernacular overtones, and the "modern office building" of the larger cities with its neoclassical monumentality. Neither have any connection with the spirit of the times or modern architecture.

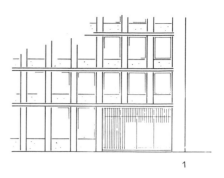

1

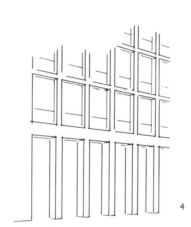

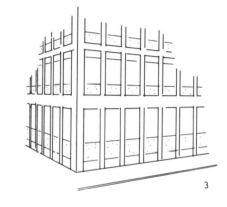

2

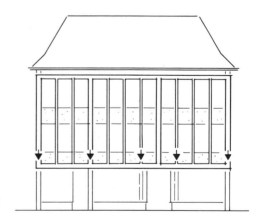

3

4

19.   Some examples of the improper use of second-floor girders:
       1 and 2 The concealed girder.
       3 and 4 The superfluous girder.
       5 Utter structural confusion.

5

Terminating the Wide Grid at Second-Floor Level

Since in a wide-grid design the intermediate columns are non-load-bearing (cf. the definition of a wide grid on page), no girder is required at the second floor. At this level the horizontal floor band carries exactly the same load as those in the upper stories. Structurally there is no distinction to be drawn between them. The termination of the grid at the second floor does not call for any special measures. From the outset the wide-grid module is in harmony with the layout of the first-floor columns. Accordingly, it is usually unnecessary to adopt a column spacing different from that characteristic of the upper levels. The more simply and naturally the pattern of the upper stories is repeated at the second floor, the more gracefully the visible structure will reflect the true distribution of forces. This direct and honest form suggests itself quite spontaneously. If a zone has to be set aside for mechanical services underneath the second floor, it should be so designed that it cannot be mistakenly attributed a structural function.

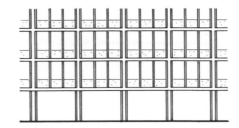

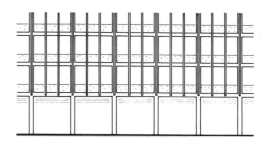

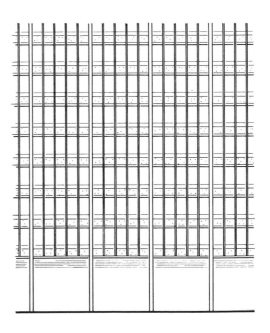

20.   Treatment of the bottom edge of a wide grid.

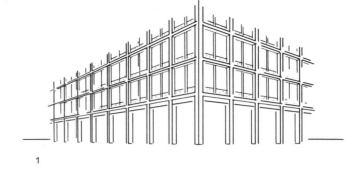

1

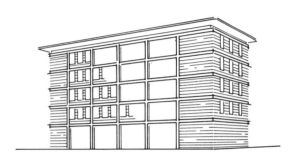

2

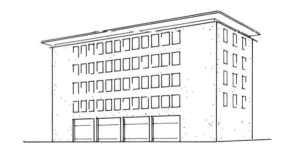

3

The wide grid suffers relatively few distortions, in fact only two are at all common. Fig. 21.1 shows a frame based on a true wide grid. The load-bearing columns have the same spacing in the upper stories as at the second floor. The intermediate verticals do not have any load-bearing function. The structure of the building expresses this clearly. Nevertheless, we can discern a girder at second-floor level. It has to carry exactly the same load as the spandrel beams in the upper stories. The emphasis placed upon it, in spite of its typicality, suggests some confusion with the structural pattern of a narrow grid. Possibly the designer has also been influenced by recollections of a certain monumentality, associated with facades composed of podium, main floor, mezzanine, etc. and still prevalent in some quarters.

Fig. 21.2 shows a building in a hybrid style. The lines of the structural frame are clearly discernible. In the finished structure the latter is filled out partly with load-bearing and partly with non-load-bearing masonry and then stuccoed. The abuse of materials and structural illogic involved are, of course, equally applicable to narrow-grid and wide-grid designs. The larger spans of the wide grid, however, show up the structural frame even more clearly and the confusion with the masonry work becomes even more disagreeably obvious. That is why the hybrid style is being discussed in conjunction with the wide grid. The finished, stuccoed facade has nothing at all to do with skeleton construction. Only with the passage of time, when the building has settled and repeated temperature changes have had their full effect, will the pattern of the frame again be revealed in a series of inevitable cracks. These cracks will be the outward expression of an abuse of the nature of the materials and structural principles. The hybrid style is not redeemed by replacing the stucco with a skin of mosaic or other non-structural ornamentation. It is an abortion of non-structural thinking and is mentioned here only as an example of which to beware.

21.   Non-structural variations on the wide grid.
    1 The superfluous girder.
    2 and 3 Composite construction.

TERMINATING THE SKELETON AT THE CORNERS

Corners are the important junctions formed by the intersection of adjacent wall planes. The corner is where the latter begin and end. The simple continuity of the masonry wall compels a valid solution at these points. The outer surfaces of skeleton frame buildings, however, are multiply articulated. The beams and columns interpenetrate and are staggered in depth both with respect to each other and with respect to the windows and spandrel walls. It is rare for all the parts to lie flush in a single plane. The result is generally some kind of high or low relief. This multiple articulation makes the design of the corners of the skeleton frame building a real structural problem.

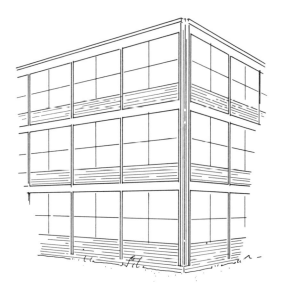

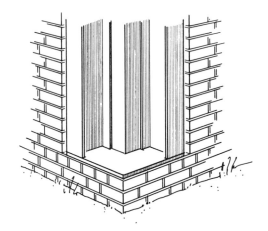

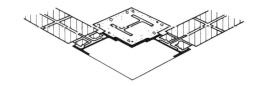

22.   Some corner details.

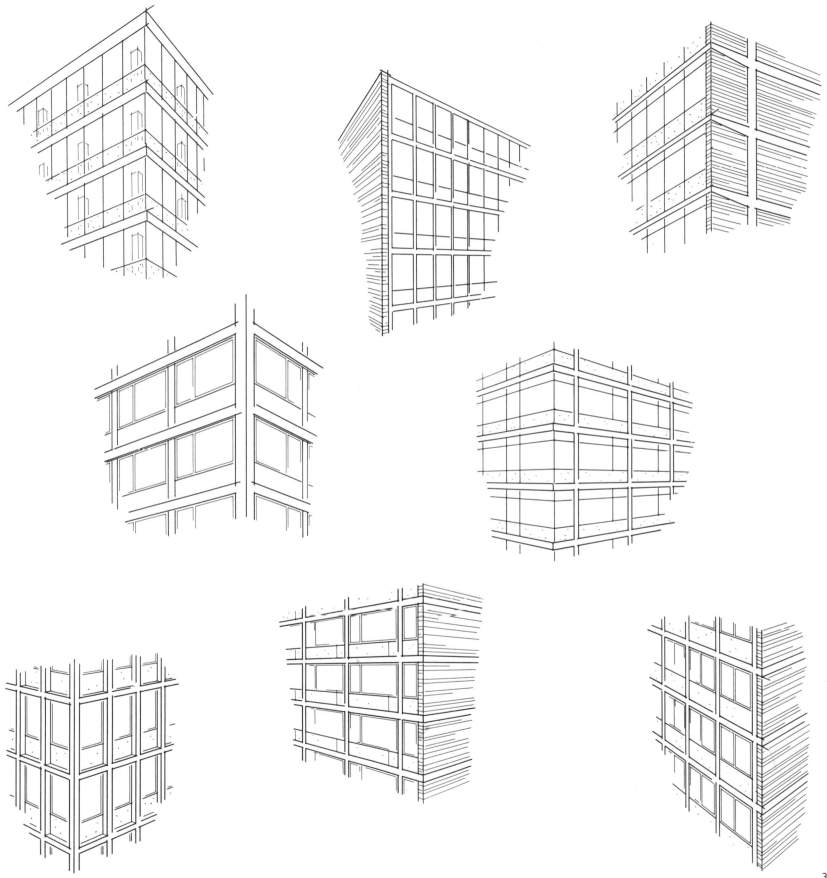

Load-bearing Corner Columns

Nothing seems simpler than to lay out identical columns at regular intervals, making the last one a corner column, and repeating the same arrangement once the corner has been turned. This is the familiar pattern of the skeleton building with identical elevations on all four sides.

The corner columns are given the same dimensions as the regular columns, unless they are made even heavier for reasons still to be discussed. How little such an arrangement accords with the true stress pattern is obvious from the load distribution diagram. Fig. 23 shows a narrow-grid frame with the floors spanning in the short direction. The columns down the long side of the building are all the same. Their cross sections are unambiguously determined by equal portions of the floor load. Let us call this portion the typical load and take it as representing 100 per cent. The load on the corner columns is substantially less. Since the contributing area is reduced by half, it amounts to 50 per cent of the typical load, and the column is relieved still further by the continuity of the spandrel beams at the intermediate supports. Along the short side of the building the center column is the one most heavily loaded. It carries one end of the girder that runs down the middle of the building and, receiving 300 per cent of the typical load, it is the most severely taxed of all the exterior columns. The remaining columns along the short side of the building carry virtually no load at all. In theory they are superfluous. In practice, however, they make a certain contribution and further relieve the already only lightly loaded corner columns. Because the actual distribution of the loads is uncertain, it is hard to estimate just how much the corner column carries, but very probably it finally transmits no more than 10-20 per cent of the typical load to the foundations. Thus, the corner column has little structural significance, carrying hardly any load.

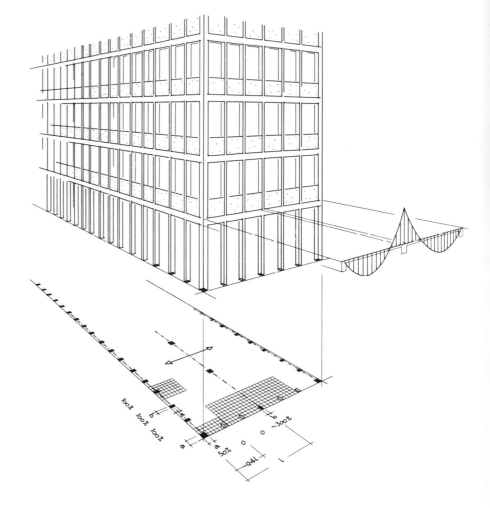

23.   Load distribution diagram for a building frame with load-bearing corner columns and equal column spacing on all sides. The corner columns carry the least load.

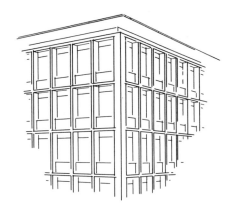

The unimaginative designer, through lack of technical comprehension and for so-called "esthetic reasons," "standardizes" unlike elements into lifeless uniformity. Thus, the structure is deprived of that lively differentiation it might have acquired naturally, from its own inner logic. This ought to be made clear to those who see the reason for a certain formal impoverishment in modern skeleton construction in an overemphasis on technological aspects. They would do better to seek a connection between these shortcomings and the too frequent neglect of technical consequences. Technical illogic, as, for example, the equating of unequal columns, illustrated in relation to the corner column, is much more often the cause of poverty of form than over-valuation of the structure. The antithesis between art and technology that has, regrettably, been injected into the contemporary discussion of architecture quite often contributes to a complete reversal of the facts. As it is easy to see, this antithesis is the product of a world of abstractions essentially hostile to everything technical and lacking any comprehension of the beauty and logic of technical relationships. This is why so many architects feel themselves above such simple, mechanical processes as working out the correct distribution of loads, and this is why "experts" demand the liberation of architecture from the shackles of technology. Accordingly, we should not be surprised, if structureless grids, designed "from a purely artistic point of view," merely simulate a building frame, without having the slightest relationship to its inner logic; nor should we be surprised, if a world of such lifeless forms should produce an impression of monotony.

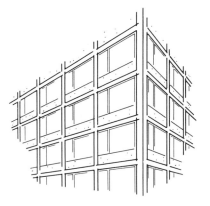

A few examples of exaggeratedly heavy corner columns are shown in Fig. 24. In spite of their size the load they carry is demonstrably the smallest. Their appearance clearly contradicts their statical function, and yet today this corner solution is one in common use. What is the reason for this?

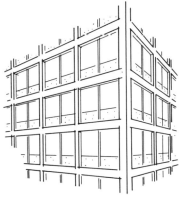

24.   The structural illogicality of a heavy corner column.

If the detail at the junction between wall panel and corner column is the same as that between wall panel and typical column, then the corner column must have the same depth as a typical column on both sides of the corner (see Figs. 25.1 and 25.2). If the typical column is rectangular, i.e. deep and narrow, the corner column must be square, and as broad on all sides as the typical column is deep. This is the main reason why the corner column is often made even more massive than the typical column.

To this must be added the perspective effect. The eye does not register the corner column frontally as the dimension a, but, from the great majority of positions, as the projected dimension c. The latter is always greater than the projection c' of a typical column. Every rectangular chair or table leg produces the same effect when viewed at an angle, appearing broader than in a front elevation. This law of perspective is of fatal significance for the design of corner columns, for although it occurs, as it were, "by itself" (one is tempted to say "naturally"), the phenomenon is nevertheless antagonistic to structural form.

Even attempts to break up the column by introducing narrow ribs set at right angles (Fig. 25.3) do not lead visually to the desired result. Neither does Mies van der Rohe's corner solution (Fig. 22, bottom right), though rightly praised and much publicized, and certainly one of the most refined modern corner details in steel [5]. Although a feeling of grace and lightness is vividly conveyed by the modeling (the solution is a complete one for the sense of touch alone), visually the individual parts of the design flow together and, at a certain distance, produce the effect of a single, very compact mass. It is also regrettable that the component parts of this corner column do not all belong to the supporting skeleton. They are to some extent merely a kind of incorporation of the masonry cladding, which is carried in front of the structural columns. Even though it provides a solution applicable in principle to a special case, Mies' column cannot be regarded as "the" solution to the problem of "the corner in skeleton construction."

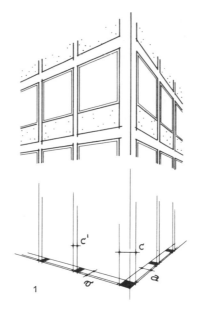

1

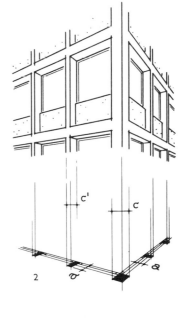

2

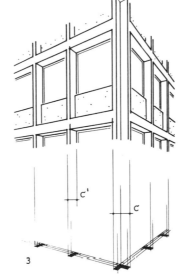

3

25.   The detailing and perspective effect of corner columns.
        1 and 2 In perspective a square corner column gives the effect of the dimension "c", always appearing heavier than the typical rectangular column.
        3 An L-shaped corner column looks less massive than a square one, but the dimension "c" still remains greater than "c'."

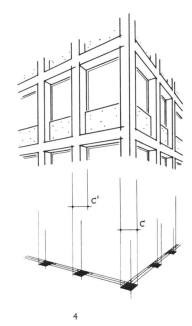

A corner column that gives a relatively slender impression is shown in Fig. 25.4. If the window element is set back deep into the frame and the typical column is made square, the corner column will appear relatively slim, at least no thicker than the typical column. However, an even more slender effect, one accurately reflecting the true distribution of forces, cannot be achieved by these means. Moreover, this solution has technical disadvantages connected with the recessed window detail.

Another possibility is deliberately to broaden the typical column. This measure may have certain advantages in relation to flexibility, e.g. it will provide surfaces against which to place furniture and variable connections for transverse partitions and at the same time reduce the area of glazing which is often excessive (Fig. 25.5). Then, the corner column will always appear slender compared with the typical columns. However, the unwieldy mass of the latter does not fit in with the general conception of skeleton construction. The column loses its character and assumes that of a strip of wall. This solution may be justified in prefabricated construction, but as far as skeleton construction is concerned it is unsatisfactory.

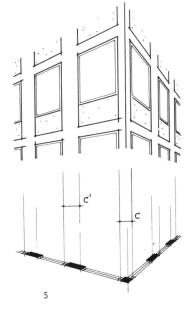

25.   4 If the outside wall is set back and the typical column made square, the
         dimension "c" approaches "c'."
       5 Widening the typical column to achieve the effect of a slender corner
         column is to contradict the nature of skeleton construction.

For the reasons given above, it is practically impossible to get a corner column that, in keeping with its reduced load, appears more slender than the typical column. The question therefore arises whether the demand for a very slender corner column is not perhaps exaggerated and of only theoretical importance. It is interesting to note, however, that this structural requirement largely coincides with an emotional distaste for fat corner columns. Whoever is at all familiar with the esthetic scales of value of modern architecture will clearly sense the discord such columns introduce. This coincidence of rational and emotional judgements indicates a common cause with its basis in the logical beauty of a structural form that functions perfectly, a structural form that gives new substance to the old laws of proportion. If, as we have seen, the slender corner column is an almost impossible achievement, nevertheless the recognition of its structural significance has provided a starting point for some quite definite trends in design. These trends are clearly perceptible in the following photographs and are frequently to be observed in the best examples of modern architecture.

In modern skeleton structures overdimensioned corner columns lack both elegance and logic. Nevertheless, relatively few conscious efforts are being made to improve the corner design. It seems as if the problem has not been generally understood. All the variations on the load-bearing corner column discussed so far have had shortcomings. There appears to be a likelihood that a happy solution, with no residual problems, is not to be found. This negative result is confirmed by experience. Not one of the known solutions yields a perfectly satisfactory structural form.

Interestingly, the same problem reappears in connection with the window detail. Where two bands of windows meet at a corner, the posts and mullions repeat the same pattern as the columns in the skeleton frame. Inevitably, for constructional reasons, the corner post is the heaviest, although for esthetic and structural reasons it ought to be the most slender.

Volkswagen repair shop [6]
Arch: Friedrich Wilhelm Kraemer. ▶

Corners Cantilevered on One Side

As the preceding section has shown, all attempts to terminate a skeleton frame with a load-bearing corner column have failed to produce a structurally satisfactory solution.

Statics suggests another alternative. It is typical of skeleton construction, and easily understood with reference to Fig. 23, that the corner column should be the one to carry the least load. Statically it is as good as meaningless. It would be most in harmony with the nature of skeleton construction to dispense with it altogether. The light loads at the corners can easily be picked up by means of a freely cantilevered floor structure and transferred to the typical columns. Fig. 26 shows the load distribution in a wide-grid frame in which the floors are cantilevered out along the short side of the building (corner cantilevered on one side). Logically, all the columns along the short side of the building, including the corner columns, are rendered superfluous, while the columns down the long side of the building remain in the facade. With the same dimensions and almost the same load, they integrate the long side of the building in terms of the supporting function of the frame. They form a contrast with the columnless articulation of the short side of the building. Here the pattern is determined by the cantilever. The one-sided cantilever, to which this section is devoted, thus not only contributes to a corner solution but also enriches the architectural composition as a result of the necessary differentiation between the various elevations.

The train of thought began with a law of statics. It arrived by way of a clear distribution of the loads at a lucid structural system, demonstrating that a meaningful structural form imparts directionality to a building, i.e. differentiates between the longitudinal and the transverse structure. Thus, the one-sided cantilever is intimately connected with a reorganization of the elevations on the long and short sides of the building. The open-minded architect, with a feeling for structural design, will be grateful not only for the elimination of the embarrassing corner column but also for a revitalizing of the facades more intense than any achievable with merely decorative additions. Structural reasoning again proves itself to be a valid means of dispelling the monotony of thoughtlessly standardized formal elements. The stimulus is inherent in the technology itself. An understanding of the loading diagram leads to the omission of the corner column and the logical consequence is the cantilevering of the floor.

In this case the cantilever has nothing to do with a preconceived notion of form, but in skeleton construction it is a fruitful device in many ways and especially typical as far as the solution of the corner problem is concerned. The rational application of cantilever construction calls for an understanding of its structural principles and its relationship to the supporting frame. A freely cantilevered beam is not in itself an eloquent structural form. What is important is how it is loaded, where it cantilevers, how it is restrained and the relationship between the cantilever span and the supporting structure.

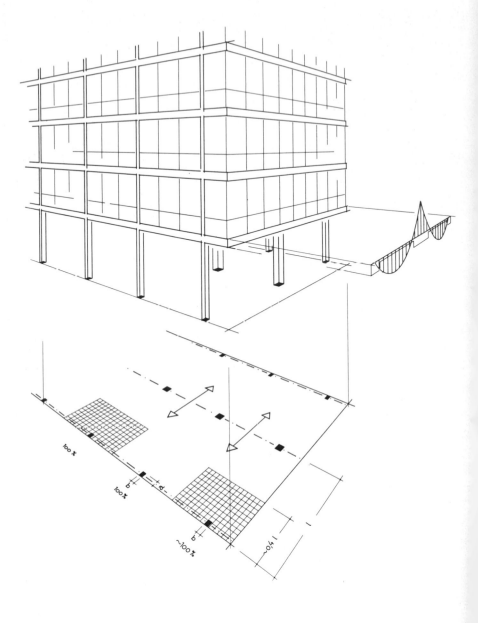

26. Load distribution diagram for a wide-grid skeleton cantilevered on one side, corner column omitted.

Lever Building, New York [7]
Arch: Skidmore, Owings and Merrill

Cantilevered beams should be organically related to the frame as a whole. If the cantilever has the right proportions, it will have evolved naturally from the dimensions of the floor construction. The cantilever and the main frame should fuse into one. Fig. 27 shows a frame with fixed column spacing and a variable cantilever together with the corresponding bending moments. The cantilever moments at the support should bear a quite definite relation to the bending moments in the other spandrel beams. If the cantilever moment is too high, the capacity of the typical spandrel beam with its limited construction depth will soon be exhausted. For example, in Fig. 27.3 the beam needs to be strengthened locally at the first support, where the cantilever joins the main frame, in order to withstand the high bending moment; in certain circumstances the whole series of spandrel beams might have to be increased in size. In either case the cantilever construction, which, in relation to the general conception, is only a neat termination and not a central motif, would be overemphasized. The obvious order of the structure would be disturbed without good reason.

If the overhang is pushed to the extreme, while preserving the depth of the typical spandrel beam at the support, the cantilever will be overstressed and a convincing design will be turned into a forced one. The weakness of the joint will clearly point to an abuse of materials and an overelastic frame. The trained observer will inevitably experience a general sense of disquietude. If the overhang is extremely small, it will usually lose in expressiveness, although no structural snags need be involved. Of course, in certain special cases the very small cantilever convinces purely by its functional logic. In Fig. 28.1, for example, the overhang is determined entirely by the thickness of the wall.

It is certain that there is always such a thing as the "right proportions" for a cantilever. What these should be, however, cannot be formulated in a general rule. The deciding factor is always the relationship between the span of the spandrel beam, the length of the cantilever and

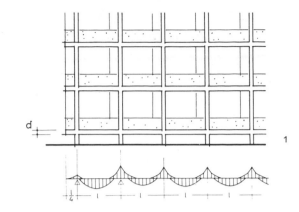

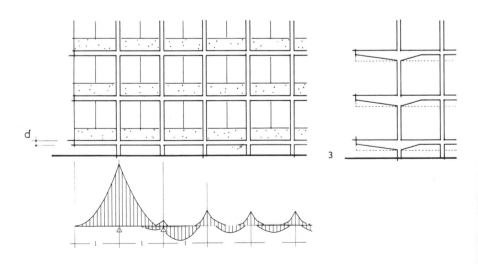

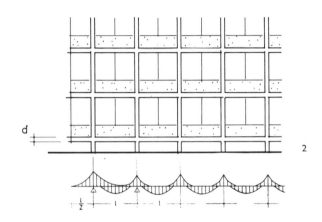

27. The "right" proportions for a cantilever:
1 Cantilever understressed.
2 Cantilever fully stressed.
3 Cantilever overstressed and needing reinforcement.

the magnitude of the load. If, for example, a massive end wall, which may also introduce wind forces, rests on the end of the cantilever, the capacity of even the heaviest spandrel will soon be exhausted. In such circumstances the right length for the overhang is unusually small. It cannot be found merely from a study of esthetic proportions. The proposed dimensions need to be mathematically checked and the results may require revision of the original design.

Only by repeatedly balancing the design against the computations is it possible to arrive at good structural form, even in unusual circumstances.

In narrow-grid construction it is difficult to express the cantilever clearly. Even so lucid a solution as Fig. 28.1 lacks the lightness characteristic of cantilever design. In wide-grid structures, on the other hand, the cantilever can be expressed strongly and eloquently. The clear distinction between load-bearing and intermediate columns then works in favor of the cantilever form. The delicate, obviously non-structural mullions are repeated at the corner and along the cantilever. In contrast to the load-bearing columns down the long side of the building, their presence is a distinct contribution to the design. From this point of view the wide grid seems to be especially suitable for cantilevered corner solutions. Surprisingly, however, one-sided cantilever designs of the type described are relatively rare in skeleton construction. Nevertheless, the few buildings conceived along these lines include some of the best and most famous examples of modern architecture. Only in the work of the average architect is the one-sided cantilever apparently neglected, in spite of the simplicity and clarity of the conception. Simplicity and clarity are qualitative concepts with a rarity value. It is obviously more difficult for a designer to master them than for him to turn out dressed-up versions of everyday solutions. For 25 years the prototypes of Mies van der Rohe have stood alone, in spite of the fact that they are so cleanly designed and really solve the corner problem. Only in the last few years has this group of buildings been joined by a number of equally significant structures.

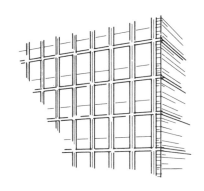

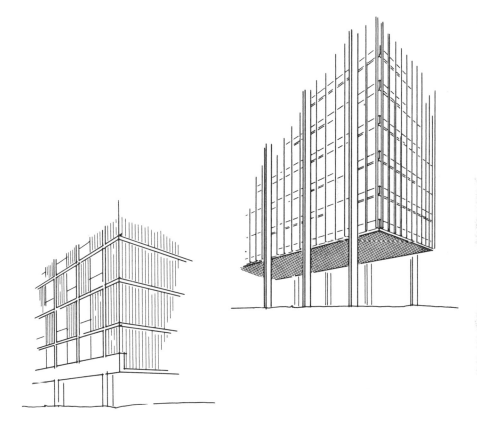

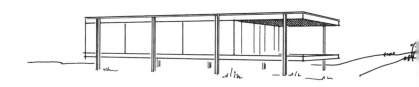

28.   Examples of building frames cantilevered on one side.

Corners Cantilevered on Both Sides

The one-sided cantilever without an end column was a decisive advance towards a solution of the corner problem in skeleton construction. It is also feasible to cantilever the floor on both sides. It remains for us to examine what consequences this may have as far as significant structural form is concerned.

Fig. 29 shows how in a wide-grid skeleton the loads are distributed almost uniformly over all the columns, if the floors are cantilevered in both directions. The transverse overhang means that the outside columns now carry virtually the same load as the inside ones. This is the ideal case where all the columns are equal in size and almost equally loaded. This solution presupposes a wide grid. Cantilevering on both sides is not really suitable for a narrow-grid skeleton, because the column spacing in the long direction is too close to satisfy internal space requirements. In wide-grid construction there are fewer columns in the long direction and these can be more easily integrated into the floor plan as a whole. If not, a one-sided cantilever is to be preferred. This will always be the case where a large number of flexible partition walls must be provided. Only if the rooms are large and free of subdivisions will a long row of setback columns be acceptable. Where conditions permit, the two-sided cantilever with set back columns is an excellent solution of great structural clarity.

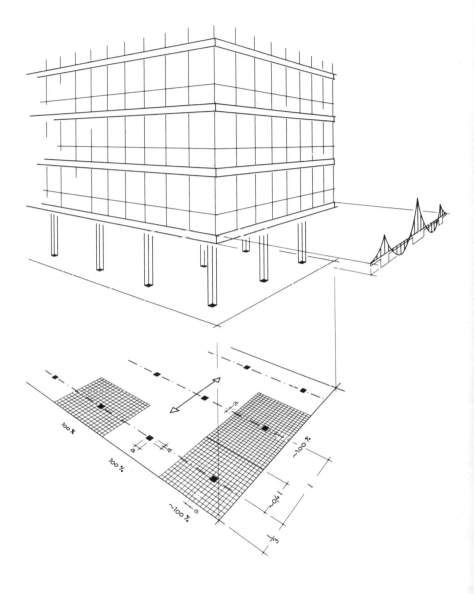

German Pavilion at the 1958 Brussels Exhibition [8] , Arch: Egon Eiermann, Sep Ruf

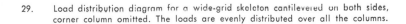

29.   Load distribution diagram for a wide-grid skeleton cantilevered on both sides, corner column omitted. The loads are evenly distributed over all the columns.

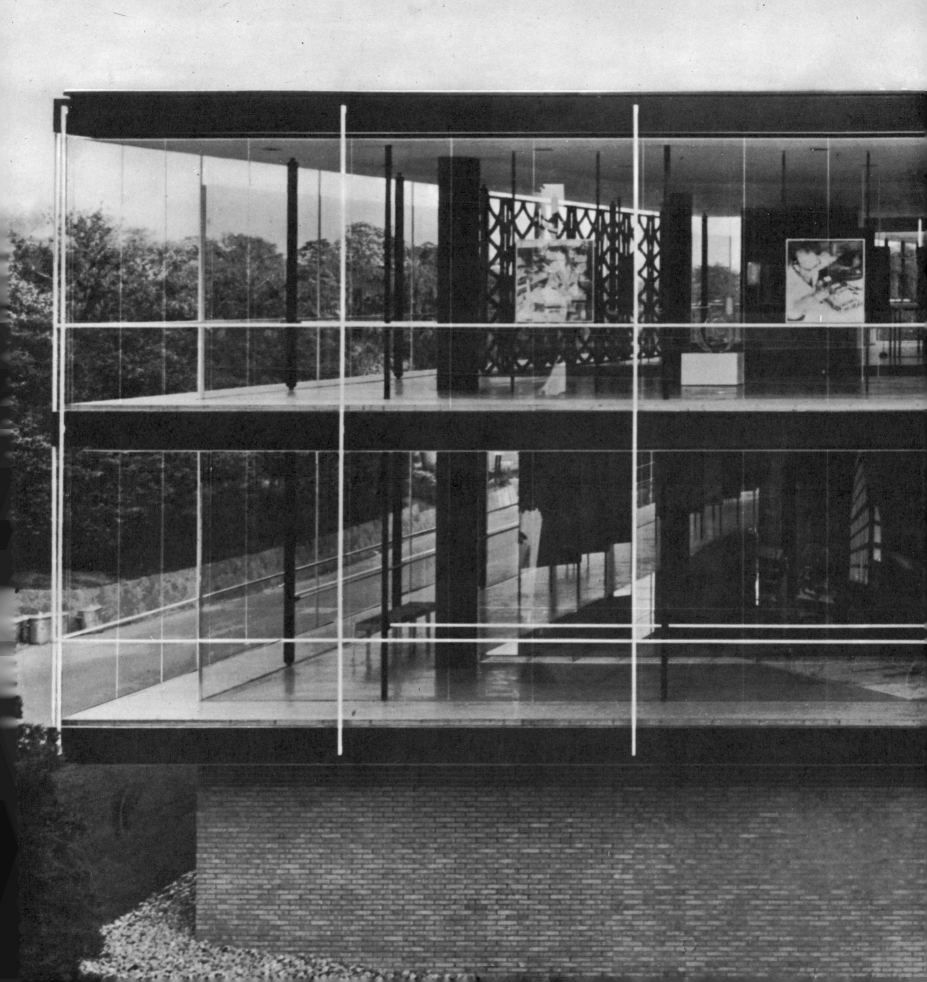

Fig. 30 shows a few buildings with cantilevers on both sides. The structural frame has retreated from all the elevations and is only distinguishable from outside thanks to the transparency of the window areas. Everything that lends expressiveness to the elevations is derived from the geometry of the curtain wall, in designing which the architect now has perfect freedom. This freedom is an advantage when it comes to designing the columnless corner. However, it may equally well be a disadvantage, as far as the articulation of the elevations is concerned. Whatever the quality of the detail, a curtain wall assembled from industrially prefabricated parts does not guarantee significant structural form, still less good architecture, if it is simply hung haphazardly from the frame. In these circumstances everything depends on preserving a valid relationship between the outer skin and the supporting skeleton. If freedom turns into caprice under the touch of an unskilled hand, the bond between structure and facade will certainly be severed, and the unity of inside and outside dissolved. The inner frame and the outer cladding will then have nothing more in common. The two-sided cantilever offers the same chance of solving the corner problem as the one-sided. As far as the design of the elevations and structure of a homogeneous building is concerned, a one-sided cantilever will generally be less ambiguous.

30.   Corners and elevations of building frames cantilevered on both sides.

Corner Solution with Gable Wall

All the corner solutions that we have discussed so far have presupposed that the corner is formed by the intersection of two sides of a skeleton frame. Under these conditions the corner column is virtually free of load. A light, possibly columnless corner then becomes a leading feature of the design.

The situation is different when only one side is formed by a skeleton frame, the other being a solid wall. The reader should not confuse this treatment with the superfluous "flesh," arbitrarily inserted between the corner and the structural frame, which is critically examined in a later section of this book. A wall that closes off the whole of one side of a building and forms a corner with a skeleton frame running the length of another may perform a perfectly valid function. Equivalent spaces, open to the light on one side and closed at either end by solid walls, when repeated, give a building type with the long (skeleton) side largely glazed and massive gable walls. This kind of construction is appropriate for certain school and office buildings. Normally the end walls have no structural function but are merely intended to enclose space and keep out noise, heat and cold. If they are specifically designed to carry loads as well, a task for which a solid masonry or concrete wall is very well equipped, the statical functions of wall and skeleton frame must be merged. However, the two have such different characteristics that they do not blend directly into an harmonious structure. The skeleton frame is reduced to highly stressed, minimum cross sections, whereas, because of its space-enclosing function, the wall is overdimensioned. Moreover, the two types of construction have different degrees of deformation, settlement and shrinkage. Everything suggests a positive separation.

The laboratory and administration buildings of the General Motors Research Center in Detroit [9] are model examples of an end wall clearly separated from a skeleton frame (Fig. 31.1). The narrow face of the masonry wall is almost flush with the frame and tight up against the last column. Frame and wall are integrated in a common structure, yet neatly separated from each other. The end column is the same width as the typical column. It fits naturally into the pattern of the long facade. The unfortunate perspective effect that makes the corner column look so heavy is avoided, because the column is screened by the gable wall. The wall is self-supporting and only attached to the skeleton frame to provide lateral stability.

In multistory buildings this very simple and hence highly convincing solution runs into certain difficulties. Over greater heights the differential settlement of the frame and the "self-supporting" wall adversely affects the integration of the two elements. At the same time, a gable wall extending to the foundations might interfere with the special functions associated with the freer layout of the first floor. In such circumstances it is better for the end wall to be carried by the skeleton frame, from floor to floor. An example of this kind of construction is shown in Fig. 31.2. In this case the absence of a wall at first-floor level is quite compatible with the general design.

1

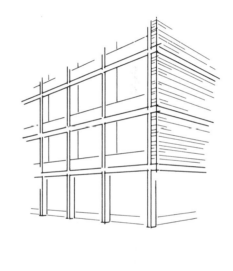

2

31.   Corner solutions employing a gable wall.
      1 Non-load-bearing masonry wall closing off the structural frame.
      2 In multistory buildings the gable wall is supported at each floor.

Finally, it remains to mention the kind of gable wall that is formed when the voids in the structural frame are filled in with masonry (Fig. 31.3). The wall and the frame then lie in the same plane and can only be distinguished by differences in texture. At the corner we are again faced with the old difficulty. A dumpy-looking corner column cannot be avoided. However, the idea of filling in the voids in the frame is quite consistent with skeleton construction.

There are many good examples of filled-in frames to bear witness to the validity of this technique, which, naturally, cannot be judged solely on the basis of the corner effect.

The above-mentioned solutions (Figs. 31.1-31.3) presuppose that the wall is made of stone, brick or some other material easily distinguishable from the frame. A concrete wall is not always appropriate, especially if it is poured in place together with the reinforced concrete skeleton frame. If the distinction between wall and frame is to be preserved—and this is normally essential to the achievement of a clear-cut structural form—then the design of a concrete wall must be given special attention. One possible solution is to carry the wall clear of the frame and support it on the end of a cantilever (Fig. 31.4). In view of the weight of a massive concrete wall the overhang will have to be kept small. Only then will its structural efficiency be credible (cf. Fig. 27).

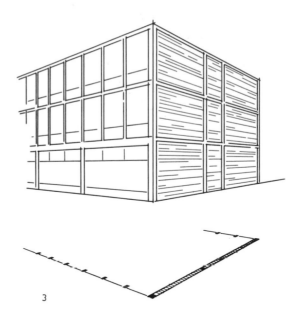

3

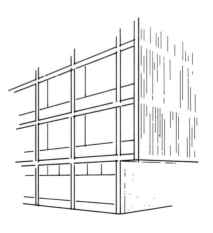

4

31.   3 Masonry infilling flush with the structural frame leaves the corner column looking heavy, as explained in connection with Fig. 25.
       4 Though they do not carry vertical loads concrete walls supported on short cantilevers can resist wind forces.

General Motors Technical Center, Detroit [9] Arch: Eero Saarinen ▶

If the wall is separated from the frame, it ceases to carry vertical loads. At the same time it continues to act as a stiffening diaphragm resisting horizontal wind forces. To pursue this function further would be to carry us outside the scope of the present chapter. Our discussion must be restricted to the skeleton frame and, in particular, to the vertical loads by which its structural form is primarily determined. These few examples can only serve to outline the general principles affecting the design of a corner with a wall on one side. Doubtless, there are other ways of joining a solid wall and a skeleton frame. However, wall and frame must always be clearly distinguished. They must come in contact along this important junction without blurring the design or forfeiting their native characteristics. Otherwise the result will be forms as distorted and artificial as those illustrated in Fig. 32. These are intelligible neither in relation to the organization of space nor in relation to the structure of frame or wall. Their questionable esthetic pretensions are those of a fashionable cliché.

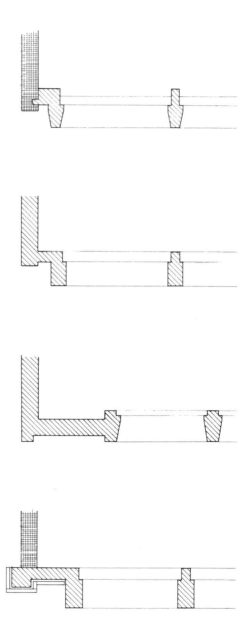

32.   Examples of poor detailing where skeleton and gable wall meet.

The terminations of the grid at its corners and lower edge are largely governed by statical considerations. At these points the members and their cross sections are determined by the loads. The combination of these members determines the form. At roof level the loads are comparatively light, and the form is mainly the result of other factors. When most buildings had massive walls and steeply pitched roofs, the situation was different. The eaves line of the old, wooden carpenter's roof is a region of high stress, where the not inconsiderable loads from a tiled roof are transferred to the massive substructure. Here the most important dimensions are determined by the dead load and by the weatherproofing action of the eaves, form being primarily a compromise between materials and function. The more pretentious cornices on city buildings are almost without exception merely refinements of the primitive forerunner referred to above. Whatever the complication of the final form, the basic configuration will be a utilitarian one.

The gently pitched Alpine roof is the prototype of the cross-ventilated flat roof, which today is again in favor as the most satisfactory engineering solution. The low pitch and the ventilation of the underside of the roof ensure that in winter the snow will stay where it falls. If the pitch were made steeper, the risk of snow sliding off the roof would increase, and if the underside of the roof were heated, the snow would melt, forming pools that might result in water damage. The wide overhang is another functional form. It provides protection from the weather and distinctly relieves the roof structure, which has to withstand some very heavy snow loads. The roof as a whole is structurally and formally a mature solution.

The completely different statical principle of the medieval German timber roof yields a completely different but equally logical form. The steeply inclined rafters lean against each other and develop thrusts similar to those developed in a trestle. Their feet must have a firm bearing on the tie beams, the distance from the point of support to the end of the tie being determined by the horizontal thrust and the shear strength of the timber. The overhang of the tie beam is part of the structure just as much as the tilting fillet, typical of this type of construction, which smoothes out the angle between the rafter and the tie beam. Other functional requirements, other climates and other building techniques give different, but equally finished structural forms.

1

2

33. In old wooden buildings the design of the eaves was originally determined by strictly functional requirements and the limitations imposed by the materials.
  1 The traditional gently pitched Alpine roof is the prototype of the modern cross-ventilated flat roof. The wide overhang both provides protection from the weather and relieves the stresses in the rafters. If the space beneath the roof is heated, incorporating an overhang may lead to water damage.
  2 The shape of this steep roof is determined by the distribution of the forces and the mechanical properties of timber.

The forms generated by the modern flat roof have nothing like the same clarity. Roof loads are so light that they present no problems for normal reinforced concrete construction. There is no eaves design so irrational that it cannot be built in reinforced concrete. A few of the many ways commonly used to terminate a flat roof are illustrated in Fig. 34. Hardly any of them show signs of a structural origin.

34.   Many of the cornices used today have no structural significance.

If we take into account our physical and engineering knowledge about insulation in winter and protection from the heat in summer, if we take adequate precautions against condensation and the cracking of exposed parts, and if, finally, we try to reduce the structure to the bare essentials, we are left with the simplest cubic forms (Figs. 35.1 and 35.2). An overhang of the type shown in Fig. 35.3 is no longer strictly necessary. In tall buildings it is quite illusory to imagine that a projecting cornice will provide protection for the facade.

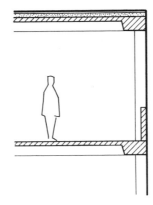

1

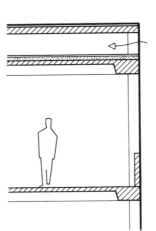

2

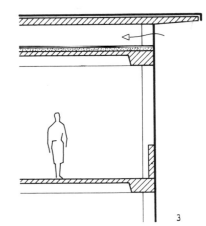

3

35. Flat roofs and their function in skeleton construction:
   1 The unventilated roof. The structure and thermal insulation are carried to the outside face of the building.
   2 The cross-ventilated roof. The structure and the thermal insulation are again carried through to the outside face of the building. The waterproofing ends at the same point.
   3 There is no point in cantilevering the roof slab. As far as tall buildings are concerned the idea that this protects the elevation is quite illusory.

The unadorned cubic form appears to be taking hold. At any rate, hardly any of the more important buildings erected in the last ten years have prominent cornices (Fig. 36).

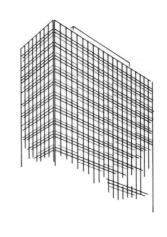

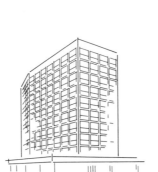

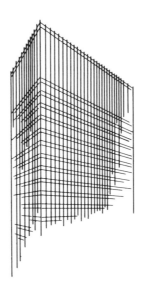

36.   A simple flat roof is in keeping with the nature of skeleton construction.

The special functions of the topmost stories, cross ventilation of the roof space, accommodation of open roof terraces, mechanical installations, penthouse structures, etc., are often taken as a reason for terminating the building with a flourish. However justifiable such efforts may be in principle, there is no excuse for the many misunderstood "motifs" of purely compositional origin, which often enough bear no relation to function or structure, but merely "embellish." A favorite theme is a top story of exaggerated height or the last two stories grouped in a single, monumental "super-story." The decorative grille in front of the spandrel wall, the stilted, atypical window form and the dormer-pierced attic persistently recur in modern skeleton construction, like other clichés of the neoclassical style. All these efforts indicate that outmoded forms, borrowed from long obsolete stylistic concepts, still enjoy great popularity. They are very remote from what we mean by structural form.

It is extremely difficult to define the idea of what is structurally "right" for the upper termination of a skeleton frame. This makes it all the more important to consider what actually are the functional and structural attributes of the roof in skeleton construction. The art of reducing things to their essentials and stripping them of all unnecessary frills will be of greater service in designing this exposed and important section of the skeleton frame than any skill in decorative trimming. Wherever we are concerned with the purification of the language of form the same principles apply.

37.   "Architectural motifs" are not structural forms.

The idea of setting back the first floor of a multistory building originates in a desire to make a strong contrast between the substructure and the upper floors.

If we offset the first-floor outside columns, we create a structural problem described later in Chapter 2 of this book (see page 116). The vertical continuity of the columns is then interrupted and special measures are needed to redistribute the forces. The tapered column discussed in Chapter 2 is one of these. Fig. 82 in Chapter 2 illustrates the relationship between the permissible offset and the magnitude of the load. The higher a building and the more acutely the loads are concentrated in the columns, the less rational it is to offset the first-floor columns, where, of course, the loads are greatest. It is more in harmony with the character of skeleton construction, with its well-defined horizontals and verticals, if such heavily loaded columns are not offset at all but carried straight down to the foundations.

There are two ways of providing a first-floor setback without offsetting the columns.

All the cantilever designs, already described in connection with the corner problem, result automatically in the "offsetting" of the exterior columns with respect to the area under the cantilever. Fig. 38.1 shows the effect that can be achieved without actually breaking the continuity of the columns. The only disadvantage of this solution, if it can be considered such, is the displacement of the columns into the interior of the building. This may cause problems in the upper stories.

Where the upper floors are not cantilevered, a modest setback can be achieved by making the outer wall flush with the outside face of the columns at the upper levels and flush with the inside face of the columns at first-floor level. This setback is exactly equal to the depth of the columns. If the columns are slender, the overhang will be comparatively small. In tall buildings, however, where the loads and hence the column sections are large, the setback is more pronounced (Fig. 38.2). It has the advantage of great structural clarity.

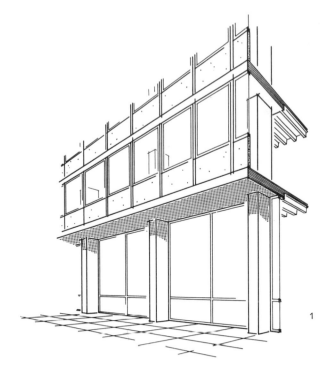

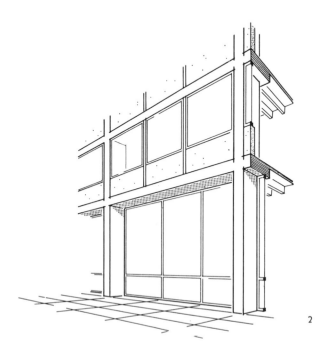

38.   Setbacks at the first floor.
　　　1 The setback effect is the result of cantilevering the upper floors.
　　　2 Setback effect based on the contrast between a flush elevation in the upper
　　　　stories and a first floor terminating at the inside face of the columns.

Unfortunately, many first-floor setbacks lack this clarity. The preconceived idea of a first floor that must be set back at all costs may lead to a violation of structural logic. Everywhere this occurs, the first-floor setback becomes a fashionable concession to a passing whim.

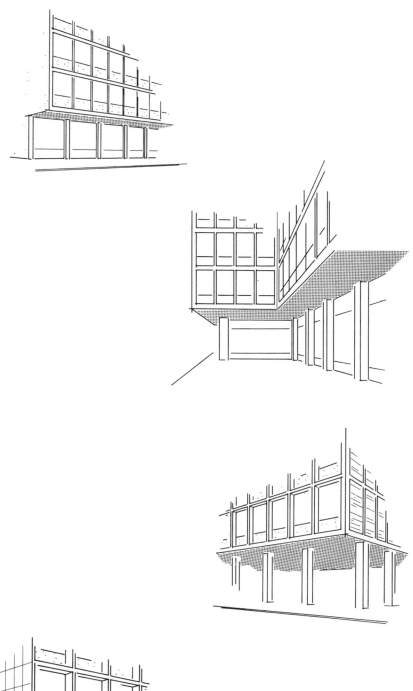

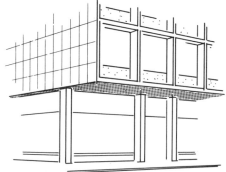

39.   Arbitrary setbacks unrelated to the structure.

As its name implies, the curtain wall hangs like a curtain in front of the structure. It is the outcome of separating the structural frame from the space-enclosing walls. The curtain wall itself has no load-bearing function. It merely screens the interior of the building from the outside. The aim of the curtain wall designer is to provide the building with a light skin with mainly physical functions. If a curtain wall will ensure adequate illumination and good ventilation plus reasonable protection against rain, heat and cold, and if, moreover, it is light in weight, durable and easy to erect, it will meet all the demands likely to be made on it.

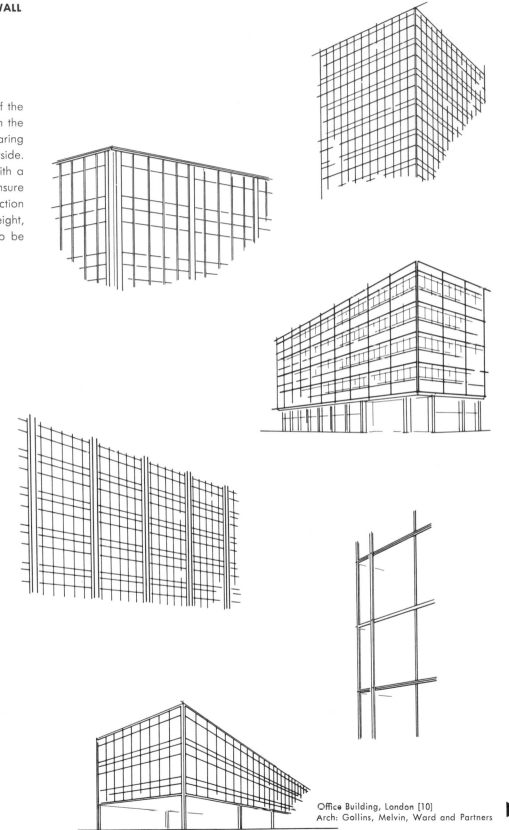

Office Building, London [10]
Arch: Gollins, Melvin, Ward and Partners

40.   The curtain wall.

Statically, the curtain wall only has to carry its own weight over the height of a single story and transmit wind forces to its points of attachment. In skeleton construction the horizontal floor bands provide the best anchorage for a curtain wall. The vertical unit is then clearly fixed by the story height. Further vertical subdivisions are determined by the depth of the floor band, the size of the windows and the height of the spandrel wall. The vertical pattern of a curtain wall is unaffected by constructional details, by whether it is built up of mullions and panels in situ, or composed of large sheet metal elements or prefabricated into even larger units, assembled from individual parts before erection. For practical reasons the subdivisions of the grid will always be closely related to the story height. Here is an important link with the skeleton frame. The designer may recognize and exploit it, or he may ignore it to the detriment of the structural form.

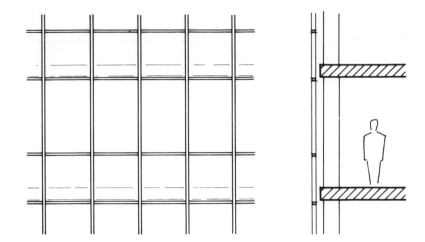

41.   In the vertical direction the divisions of a curtain wall are directly related to the story height.

In the horizontal direction there is no obvious natural unit. The only guiding principles are that the individual element should not become too heavy and unwieldy and that it should harmonize with the column spacing. It is true that in some buildings the subdivision of the curtain wall is arbitrary and unrelated to the column spacing, but this is the precise opposite of what we should look for in the marriage of curtain wall and structural frame. The usual horizontal module lies somewhere between 1.25 and 2.00 meters. There are at present relatively few examples of the use of wider units. Hence, the outward pattern always suggests a narrow grid, although the function of the curtain wall is actually completely different. If curtain wall elements of uniform size are repeated indefinitely across the elevation, the result is a very indifferent pattern (Fig. 42.1) bearing no apparent relation to the structure. Inside the building dead spaces are left between columns and windows. The columns get in the light and fail to make a purposeful impression. The element of conscious design is lacking. As far as the corner detail is concerned, the same principles apply to the curtain wall as applied to the structural frame. The heavy corner column may either be exposed even more emphatically than before (42.2) or be completely glazed in (Fig. 42.3). In the first case, it is the only column visible in elevation, thus making an acute contrast with the slender mullions of the curtain wall. In the second case, the dead space left between glazing and corner column is not very felicitous, when viewed from inside the building. The solution shown in Fig. 42.4 conceals the corner column completely, since the columns are well set back behind the curtain wall. This also avoids the unfortunate impression that the columns are blocking the light. On the other hand, any positive expression of a relationship between inside and outside again tends to be lost.

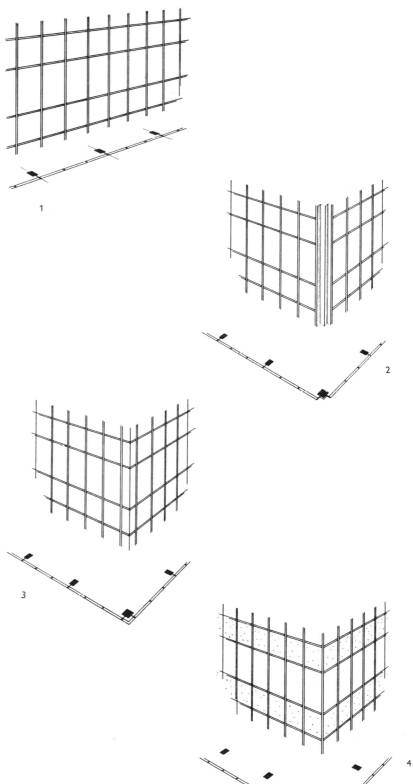

42. Curtain walls horizontally unrelated to the structural frame:
     1 The monotonous appearance of uniform mullions.
     2 The clumsy corner column.
     3 The glass-encased corner column.
     4 The corner cantilevered on both sides.

The elevation may also be a combination of curtain wall and structural columns. Fig. 43.1 shows a flush facade, in which the columns stand directly behind a special panel, exactly the same width as the columns themselves. The aforementioned dead space between curtain wall and column then disappears. The structure is visibly expressed in elevation. Moreover, the horizontal subdivisions of the curtain wall are now related to the structural skeleton. This solution, however, has one shortcoming: the grid, on which the floor plan is based, necessarily includes a break of column width at every column. This irregularity in the grid inevitably complicates the design of uniform wall elements for interior partitions. Consistent champions of regular floor grids will raise objections.

On the other hand, it would not do to underestimate the opportunities afforded by breaks in the grid for the articulation of the elevations and the organization of internal space. A grid with breaks of column width is especially appropriate when the columns are placed on the outside (Fig. 43.2). In fact, when the columns are on the outside and there is no break in the grid, the clear distance between columns will not be a simple multiple of the curtain wall module. Certain windows will be partially masked by the columns and thus lose their raison d'être. In order to avoid this and at the same time retain a regular grid, a number of important buildings have been designed with the curtain wall divided irregularly between columns (Fig. 43.3). Each of the curtain wall elements immediately adjacent to a column is made half a column width smaller than the typical curtain wall element. The result is a broken rhythm, which, however, is based on the dimensional order of the structure and therefore avoids any arbitrary or disquieting effect. The elevations of the Inland-Steel Building in Chicago [11] (see photo) provide an example of this principle of subdivision. It is clear that the curtain wall, too, can be related to the structural order and does not necessarily imply a dreary facade.

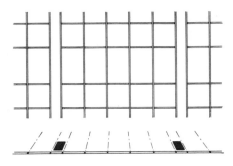

1

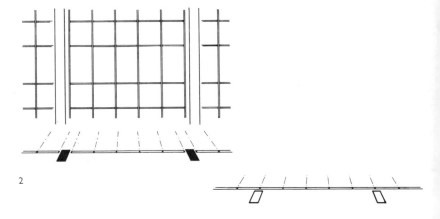

2

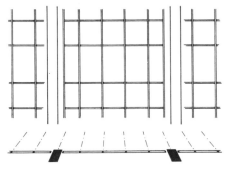

3

43. Curtain wall and structural frame horizontally related:
     1 Flush elevation with columns enclosed but clearly expressed.
     2 Facade elements uniformly spaced between projecting columns.
     3 Facade elements irregularly spaced between projecting columns.

Inland Steel Building, Chicago [11] ▶
Arch: Skidmore, Owings and Merrill

So far we have confined our discussion to mullioned walls. However, our account of the curtain wall would be incomplete without a reference to the various panel wall systems. Like mullioned walls, the panel wall raises certain problems in relation to the structure, namely, the dimensional characteristics of the wall elements, the masking or accentuation of the structural frame, the clumsiness of the corner and the integration or non-integration of the dimensions of the wall elements with the plan module (Fig. 44).

1

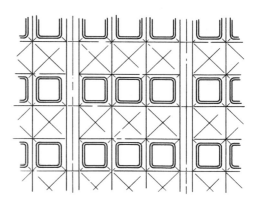

2

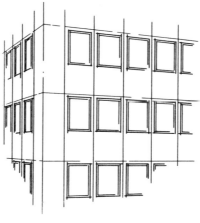

3

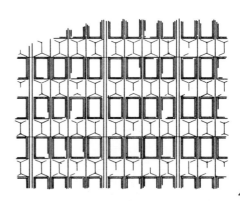

4

44. Panel walls:
    1 The monotonous appearance of a regular arrangement of panel units.
    2 The clearly expressed structure of the Alcoa Building in Pittsburgh. The rounded corners of the windows are consistent with panel wall construction.
    3 The disproportionately heavy corner column.
    4 Elevation enlivened by expressing the frame and using rigid, pressed-metal panel units with a three-dimensional motif.

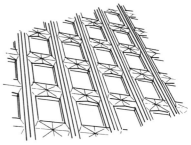

The curtain wall, too, has its share of non-structural solutions. Panel walls, in particular, seem to invite a frightening amount of primitive ornamentation.

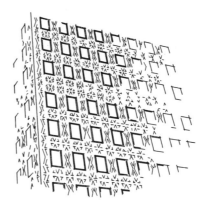

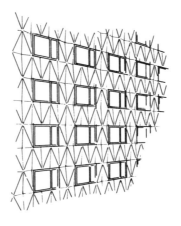

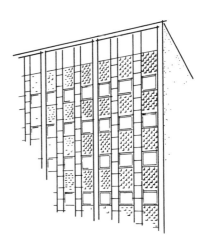

45.   Curtain walls with non-structural ornamentation.

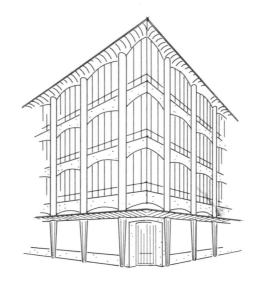

SOME CURIOSITIES

This section is devoted to a number of singular, degenerate forms that are encountered frequently enough to make them appear typical. They have nothing in common with true structural forms and result from a misunderstanding of structural principles.

Beautification

The "enlivening" of skeleton structures by means of "fancy details, costly materials, lighting effects, decorative grilles and ornamental metalwork" involves a face-lifting operation with no bearing on the problem of structural form. Yet buildings like those illustrated in Fig. 46 always attract flocks of admirers. Their formal language is not derived from genuine and deep-rooted relationships. The field is dominated to an appalling degree by false Romanticism, Neoeclecticism (which uses engineering forms in the wrong places), a taste for primitive ornamentation and a respect for monumentality, associated with newly acquired wealth. But no grid and no skeleton frame, however heavily accented, can deceive the expert eye.

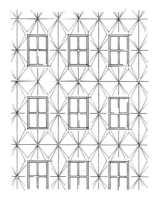

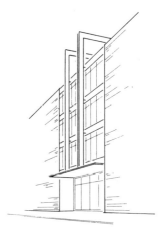

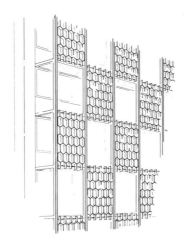

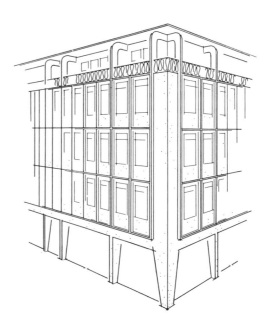

46.   "Dressed up" facades have nothing to do with structural form.

"Fleshy" Corners

It has proven difficult to design a skeleton frame with a slender corner column. Stopping the frame short of the corner must be interpreted as an attempt to escape from this dilemma. The result is a "fleshy" corner (Fig. 47). In masonry construction there is a good reason for such fleshiness (cf. Chapter 2, Fig. 54.2). Arched window heads develop horizontal thrusts, which, at the corners of the building, can only be withstood by the dead weight of a corresponding mass of masonry. Thus, the corner detail is of decisive importance for the stability of a masonry structure. This is not true of skeleton construction, since such horizontal thrusts are not developed. Only vertical forces are transferred to the corner columns and there is no structural justification for a "fleshy" corner. Nevertheless, arbitrarily introduced wall surfaces do make it possible to stop the frame short of the corner and thus evade the difficulty of finding a corner solution. But this means that the structure is seriously diluted. It gives way to a "composition," in which the grid forms a graphic pattern "contrasted" with an arbitrarily created wall surface. This surface, however, represents an alien idea, borrowed from masonry construction.

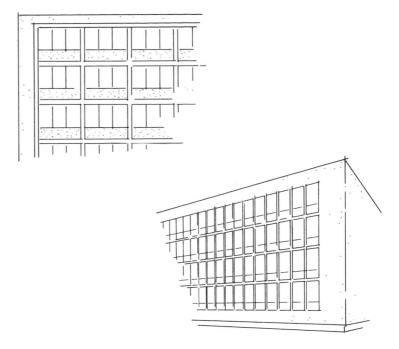

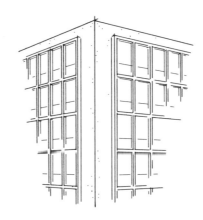

47.   The "fleshy" corner is a makeshift solution.

The Grid in Passe-partout

In skeleton construction the most difficult problems of structural form are boundary problems. These are the origin of some very dubious solutions. Obviously, it is much more convenient to stop the frame short of the corner than to go to the trouble of finding a structurally neat corner solution. Embarrassment can be avoided in similar fashion at the upper and lower edges of the grid. The skeleton frame then appears to be embedded in "flesh" on all four sides. It floats on a surface, the dimensions of which are determined solely by a "sure feeling for true proportions." Hart [12] makes a telling point when he refers to such designs as "architecture in passe partout." The last link with the structure is abandoned. The visible portion of the frame, symbol of the structural, hovers unsteadily over an arbitrarily dimensioned surface. It appears as if projected on a structureless picture plane. The elevation becomes a framed exercise in graphic design. Not infrequently these "grids" prove to be applied stucco or artificial stone. This is not surprising, since it accords perfectly with their non-structural character.

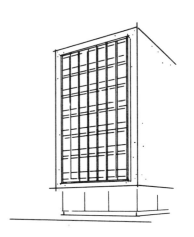

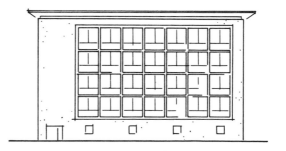

48.   The grid in passe partout. Frames, which in fact are not truly structural, floating in the middle of a wall surface.

The Cabinet Frame

The "cabinet frame" has similar antecedents to the frame in passe partout. Again the edges of the structure lack clarity. The elevation is bordered by a frame to which it bears only a pseudo-organic relationship. This too is a solution designed to avoid embarrassment. It relieves the architect of the trouble of working out honest peripheral details. The cabinet frame arbitrarily confines the grid within a bland and monotonous surround. Structural logic is ignored.

The "cabinet frame" is a pictorial concept intended to attract attention (Fig. 49), but unable to define. It suggests a box-like enclosure and thus, at the same time, calls to our notice a significant error in scale. Cabinets and picture frames are household objects, not elements of architecture. The buildings in Fig. 49 are painfully reminiscent of chests of drawers and TV sets. Like much of what is deprecated in this book, the "cabinet frame" is the result of imposing a spiritless sameness on dissimilar structural elements, without regard for their essential differences. A surround that looks exactly the same, top, bottom and sides, is no real structural form. The front of a building is not just a graphic design that can be framed. Its life is more than skin-deep. Such difficult details as those at the corners and the eaves cannot be forced into identical molds. All this has just as little to do with correct scale as with structural form.

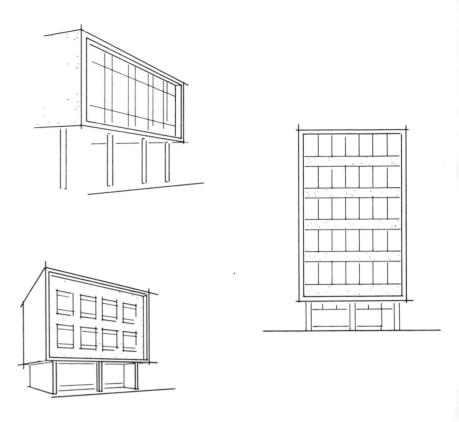

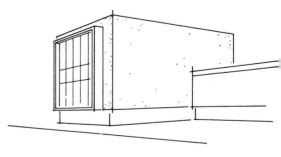

49.   "Cabinet frame" is an expression borrowed from furniture-making to draw attention to the false scale of certain non-structural framed facades.

This brings us to a brief digression on the subject of scale. Architects talk freely about "the right scale" and often use the idea to bolster their arguments. But just what kind of scale do they mean? The sources from which the arguments supporting this concept are drawn are all of a purely emotional nature. Very few are aware that "the right scale," one might even say "the right proportions," for buildings that obey mechanical laws is, within certain limits, actually definable, and even mathematically demonstrable. However, the limitation to "buildings that obey mechanical laws" is of critical importance. This implies a bond with materials and mechanical principles, without which building is unthinkable. In architecture this bond is indispensable. Without it architecture is impossible, or, at the most, a mere exercise on paper. This contrasts strongly with a painting which always remains a model and has no significance as far as its material substance is concerned. Now let us consider furniture, which we have just compared with buildings incorporating a "cabinet" type of frame. A shelf 20 mm thick and 100 cm long (Fig. 50) will satisfy all normal requirements. Everyone will feel that this is an appropriate form. The shelf's own weight produces hardly any deflection and it will carry an additional load of books and other objects, several times its own weight, without appreciable deformation. It is just as easy to prove this by calculation

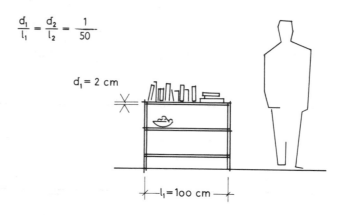

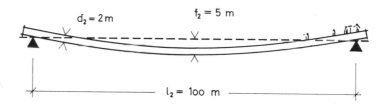

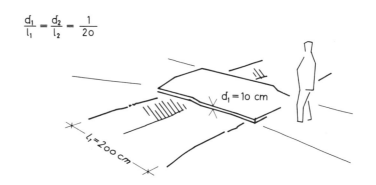

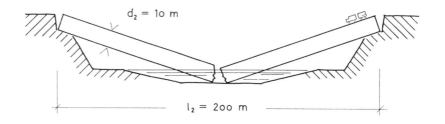

50. In any given instance the "right" structural form depends on the absolute scale of the structure.
1 Two wooden planks of identical proportions do not behave in the same way if their absolute dimensions are different. On a small scale deflection can be neglected, but on a large scale it can render a structure useless.
2 If two stone slabs have the same proportions but are sufficiently different in absolute size, the smaller will withstand its own weight plus an additional live load, while the larger will break under its own weight alone.

as by experiment. If we consider a similar shelf made of the same wood but one hundred times as large, that is, 2 m thick and 100 m long, the deflection at mid-span due to its own weight alone will be about 5 m. This represents five per cent of the span. In terms of the bookcase five per cent would be 5 cm, an impossible deflection. Moreover, if the giant shelf is loaded with no more than twice its own weight, it will collapse, whereas a shelf of normal size will easily support its own weight many times over.

Another example: in areas where slate is found, the local inhabitants naturally discover many practical uses for slate slabs. Solid slabs about 10 cm thick and 2 m long are often suitable for bridging ditches and small streams. These slabs are very strong and even when subjected to a live load roughly equal to their own weight are rarely stressed beyond a tenth of their capacity. If, instead, we think in terms of a slab 100 times larger (10 m thick and 200 m long), its own weight alone will produce bending stresses three times greater than the ultimate strength of the material. Hence the slab will collapse.

Thus, the "right form" or "the right scale" for elements stressed in bending is not always the same but depends on their absolute size and is clearly definable in terms of this dependence.

How can we explain these observations?

1. The bending stresses in the structures just described depend not only on their proportions (depth to span ratio) but also on their absolute size. The stresses in the material increase linearly with absolute size, even though the form remains the same. Thus, there is an upper limit to the span, beyond which a structural element of given proportions cannot be employed.

2. Even when the proportions (depth to span ratio) remain the same, the deflection is a function of the *square* of the absolute size; thus, the deflection varies with the absolute size even more sharply than the stresses.

What are we to conclude from all this?

For a given absolute size and a given material, every structure that acts in bending has a quite definite "proper" form. Or in other words, the depth to span ratio, i.e. the proper form, is *not* contstant. It is not the same for a short span as for a long one. Of course, it is assumed that the economical utilization of material is a decisive factor in the design. Conversely, in bending a given depth to span ratio is only "right" for a particular absolute size and a particular material. The ratio is not directly applicable to other materials or other gravitational fields. This, however, is precisely the assumption so often made by the formulators of supposedly universal laws of proportion, moduli and "Golden Sections." The laws thus established are then readily invested with a secret magic and circulated as architectural recipes. As far as structural form is concerned, this is a highly questionable and, indeed, as we have shown, even an essentially misleading enterprise.

Where genuine building is practiced, hence where real architecture with more than the pictorial significance of a graphic design is brought into material being, structurally derived laws of proportion and form, which cannot be abstracted, will also apply. As already explained, such laws are demonstrably dependent on the properties of materials, mechanical principles and the gravitational field in which they operate, and hence on absolute size.

The effect of absolute size on structural forms is also discernible in many of the works of Nature. Short grasses are slender and elastic and made of relatively soft material. Tall trees rely on their tough wood and innate strength to withstand the force of gales. The smallest animals make the best jumpers. It would be imposssible to create a leaping species of elephantine proportions, even if Nature were so perverse as to attempt it. The tiger, the largest leaping animal known, can spring only two or three times the length of its own body, the flea more than 100 times. Insects and tiny birds (humming birds) beat their wings at tremendous speeds, the bigger birds much more slowly. No doubt it could be proved that for the largest "birds" we know, man-made flying machines, a flapping motion is not only very difficult to realize but fundamentally wrong. In view of this clear, obvious and all-pervasive dependence of form on absolute size, we should beware of applying abstract studies of proportion to actual buildings. The not infrequent attempts somehow to reconcile a Mondrian composition with an architectural design are fundamentally aberrant and indicate a quite superficial awareness of the essential principles of building.

Whatever they may be, the forms eventually adopted for space structures (or should we boldly say "space architecture") outside the Earth's gravitational field will undoubtedly be quite different from those to which we are accustomed. These new forms and proportions and the new scale of esthetic values they generate will only be discovered and appreciated through an awareness of what is structurally "right," along the lines suggested above. What other esthetic criteria may be applicable is not relevant to the present discussion. It is insisted only that the criteria mentioned *also* apply and in any circumstances must apply to real structures. They are the foundation for everything that follows. The mathematically demonstrable validity of this proposition extends only to the proportions, and hence to the form of material structures. However, architecture itself always implies a material structure. It is therefore improbable that good architectural form is at variance with good structual form. It is more likely that the two are related, supplementary and mutually beneficial.

In concrete terms this means that the Eiffel Tower would lose all value as a design, if it were reduced to a replica one one-hundredth life size. Its proportions would no longer be the "right" ones; it would lose all distinction and become a mere knickknack.

Similarly, if the Parthenon were enlarged x times or transferred from the gravitational field of the Earth to that of Jupiter which is x times as great, in either case its proportions would cease to be the "right" ones, even though the geometrical relations of the parts were scrupulously preserved. The scale of the building would no longer be in keeping with the mechanics of the loads or the properties of the material. The marble lintels, which have now stood for 2,000 years, would collapse. Leaving aside the question of the loads, such a Parthenon would be valueless as architecture. The structural unity would disappear and with it all esthetic value.

This digression was prompted by the scale of the "cabinet frame," borrowed from the furniture designer. Such a scale is inapplicable to architecture. However, the sketches in Fig. 51 show that the same theme, namely the peripheral termination of a skeleton facade, can undoubtedly be handled with a fine sense of scale. Here the border is composed of different elements, each of which seems "right" and unforced in relation to its specific function. A deliberate effort is made to avoid the monotony of four identical edges.

To summarize: forcing essentially dissimilar elements into an identical mold destroys the scale and impoverishes the design, while the accentuation of genuine differences enlivens it. The differentiation of parts, in accordance with their particular significance, imparts the "right" scale to the whole. In skeleton construction more than anywhere else true differentiation is derived from structural principles. Achieving it gives significant structural form.

1

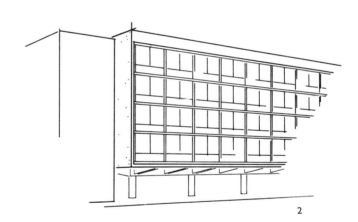

2

51.   In contrast to the "cabinet frame" (Fig. 49), the structural surround of these
      elevations develops organically from the different conditions prevailing at top,
      bottom and sides.
      1 Olivetti office building in Milan [13].
      2 Technical school in Berne, Switzerland [14].

The sketches on the opposite page will give the reader an idea of what the author means by a V-shaped support. This is a term he applies to any supporting member with the tapered shape of a letter V. The concept can be extended to include the inverted V of the ancient buttress, which broadens towards the base. However, the more recent form, the V-support that tapers downwards, is of more immediate interest. This chapter is inspired both by the seeming contradictoriness of these two forms and by the increasing popularity of the modern V-support.

81

Since the days of antiquity men have been familiar with the idea that a structure should start from a broad base and only taper upwards. This idea is expressed in every retaining wall and every sloping buttress. The Gothic pier, which is increasingly reinforced as it descends, is equivalent to scientific evidence of the rightness of this form. For centuries no one would concede beauty to any other. At the same time the upward taper was appreciated as an expression of studied equilibrium (Fig. 52).

Early structural forms are characterized by the ponderous bulk of broad-based masonry. They are simple, heavy and pose few problems. The structural organization of material keeps pace with refinements in thematic differentiation. The architectonic expression of the controlled play of loads and forces is a feature of technically oriented Western architecture that cannot be lightly dismissed. In the Gothic Age it achieved a previously unknown degree of structural differentiation, producing in the buttress a form closely related to the support under discussion, though in this case the V-shape is inverted.

52.   The ancient buttress is an inverted V-support.

In medieval churches the cross sections of the vault-bearing piers increase steadily downwards. An excellent early example is provided by the choir buttresses of the Late Romanesque abbey church of Heisterbach [15]. With an astonishing understanding of statics the master builder opposed the lateral spread of the vault thrusts with sloping counterforts. Though ignorant of structural calculations, with a shrewd eye for the equilibrium of forces he set up a ring of massive piers around the vaulted choir. The abbey at Heisterbach is a work of art and at the same time an example of medieval engineering genius. The necessity of controlling a definite system of forces by structural means yielded a form in which both art and technology are successfully united.

53. Inverted V-supports form part of the choir of the abbey church at Heisterbach, Germany [15].

Similar solutions were repeated throughout the Gothic Age in ever more refined form. The design was determined by the forces and the manner in which they were carried to the ground. Bit by bit superfluous material was pruned away, until finally only the essentials remained. The structure thus acquired a previously unknown importance. Compared with the Gothic, vault construction in ancient Rome was only a rough and ready affair. Never before the Gothic had a building technique been so refined and perfected, or stimulated design on such a scale. In Gothic architecture the technical component contributed decisively to the development of ideas. Without the vault technique and the extension of its influence to every detail, the Gothic spirit would never have found such powerful architectural expression.

Because it resists the thrusts from the vaults, the pier forms an indispensable part of every elevated vaulted structure. Inevitably it is given the form of an inverted V, broadening out towards the base. This is what the play of forces demands and, indeed, in masonry is the only solution technically possible. Though familiar to us in connection with medieval churches, the typical buttress form is also found in secular buildings. For example, the townscape of Berne is clearly characterized by this motif.

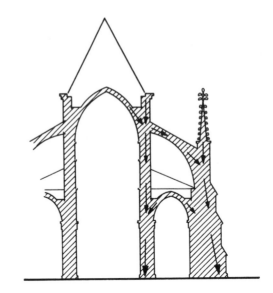

1

2

54. 1 In Gothic architecture the inverted V-support is a logical result of the structural principle.
2 As a purely utilitarian form the buttress is a characteristic feature of the ancient city of Berne with its vaulted arcades.

All our historical examples relate to uprights subjected to lateral loads at the top. The same description also applies to posts strutted to resist the pull of wires. Familiar examples are farm fences and telegraph poles. The resemblance to a tree is also unmistakable. The stem of the tree grows in a manner organically adapted to the increase in wind moments towards its base.

All these related forms, whether natural or architectural, are alike in obeying the following laws:

1. Any member restrained at the bottom and horizontally loaded at the top is stressed in bending.
2. The bending moments increase downwards.
3. The maximum bending moment occurs at the base.
4. A form that grows broader towards the base is the one best adapted to this distribution of bending moments.

Our discussion so far has served to demonstrate the statical correctness and esthetic obviousness of the familiar buttress forms of masonry construction and related forms in nature. Anchorage at the base requires a form solidly rooted in the ground. Tapering is acceptable only if directed upwards.

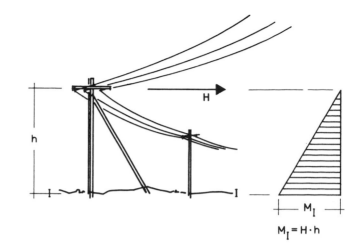

$$M_I = H \cdot h$$

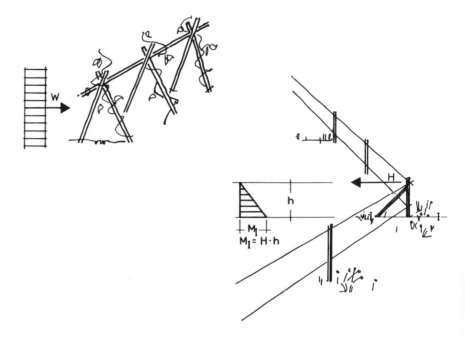

$$M_I = H \cdot h$$

$$M_I = W \cdot h$$

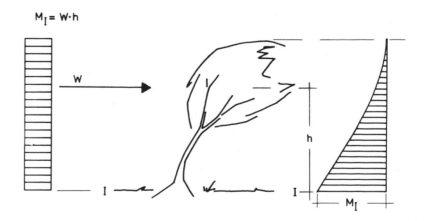

55. The strutted post is a primitive form of V-support. The tree is perfectly adapted to resist wind loading.

Thus, the modern V-support, which tapers downwards, appears to defy the laws of statics. There is hardly a trace of it in the architecture of older civilizations. Yet in a few decades it has suddenly achieved widespread acceptance. By the turn of the century only a handful of engineers had perceived the statical significance of the new form and ventured to put it to practical use. Today it is a well-established part of the repertoires of rather too many architects. Not all of them have correctly interpreted the new form and some merely take advantage of its outward characteristics to give their buildings a semblance of modernity. Undoubtedly, anyone not versed in statics will at first have a negative reaction to this rejection of an historically familiar and clearly intelligible order.

Nowadays the modern V-support appears in many different guises. It is employed both in furniture design and bridge-building. It appears as a decorative feature in window displays and as an uncompromising expression of a principle of statics in architecture. The V-support is a form that recurs in every branch of structural design. Formulas like "point bearing" and "hovering effect" long ago found their way into newspaper reports and the technical press. But these are mere phrases that fail to do justice to the deeper significance of this structural form. A superficial appraisal of the outward characteristics of the V-support leads only too easily to the confounding of cause and effect. A thorough analysis of the structural behavior of this type of support is absolutely imperative. It will reveal much that is unexpected and remarkable. Every tapered support, and this applies both to the inverted V of the Gothic buttress and to the V-leg of the modern rigid frame, is, in the first place, a product of its technical function. Its form is adapted to a bending moment that varies from zero to some maximum, and this is how it should primarily be interpreted. The technical function and structural relationships of a V-support in steel or reinforced concrete are somewhat more complicated than those of a Gothic buttress or a castle wall. They cannot be understood at a glance or by sheer instinct. Only a grasp of a particular line of engineering reasoning and an impartial analysis of the structural facts will lead to a true understanding of the genesis of these new structural forms. And only thus is it possible to detect the sterile pseudo form that simulates a technical function but is, in fact, a hollow sham. Such deceptions retard the development of an architectural language of form based on technology. They help only to blur valid forms and compromise structural honesty. One of the aims of this book is to expose and eradicate them.

At first, the idea of a V-shaped support appears so primitive a design concept that any profound treatment of it would be misplaced. Compared, for example, with the Greek capital, which has remained full of fruitful potentialities for two thousand years, the simple cone appears a poor and barren thing. Indeed, the difference is a fundamental one. A beautiful capital appeals directly to the esthetic sense. If, in addition to this, it achieves structural significance, at least symbolically, by marking the point at which the load from the roof is transferred to the column, this significance is irrelevant to its immediate appeal, which rests entirely on the beauty of the form. This is not true of a member like a V-support. The V-shape alone means nothing. It leaves the observer unmoved. It has not even any symbolic content. However, the V-support is an elementary structure and does make a statement of a structural kind. This and this alone is its significance. It symbolizes nothing; it simply "is." Those who desire to develop a feeling for modern structural form and experience its esthetic charm must learn to appreciate this essential difference. An esthetic response to structural form is impossible without recognition of its structural content, that is, of its "being"; hence the references to the "rightness" of modern structural forms as a prerequisite to any esthetic claims. As a piece of geometry, a V-shaped support is no more beautiful than two parallel lines or a pyramid. Its proportions, attitude and position can only make an esthetic statement in relation to its function as part of a greater whole.

Here is one reason more for distrusting formalism in modern architecture. Whereas a handsome detail, like a classical capital, will always have a certain value in its own right, there is no justification for a structural form deprived of its functional relationships. In such circumstances it loses all esthetic content and becomes completely sterile. Conversely, if a structural form both fulfills and is molded by its function, then it will live, and have a claim to consideration as a work of art.

Although there are virtually no early examples of the architectural use of the V-support, it has long had a place in furniture-making. The legs of tables and chairs are also stressed in bending by lateral forces, which, however, act not at the top but at the bottom. Thus, the bending moments increase upwards. They are greatest at the point where the leg is attached to the frame and diminish gradually to zero at its tip. The furniture-maker, therefore, was quick to give chair and table legs a taper in the direction of the floor.

Why were the legs of tables, chairs and benches not given the form of an upright cone, like the full-grown tree and the buttress? A table top can also be supported on trestles which owe their stability to their broad base, just like the buttress and the tree. If such a table were fixed in position and the trestles anchored to the ground, the analogy with the buttress form would be obvious. However, since furniture is made to be moved about, it is better to design it with the legs rigidly connected to the frame at one end and free to slide at the other. The result is a downward taper.

The modern rigid frame is based on the same principle as the chair. The horizontal member of the frame corresponds to the seat of the chair and the verticals to the legs. The rigid joint at the intersection of the horizontal and vertical members leads logically to what we have termed a V-support. Even though large rigid frames do not need to be transportable, we have an unconscious sympathy for all that is mobile, light and rests freely on the ground. The floating effect of a structure resting on V-supports is more to our taste than the heavily buttressed vaults of the Middle Ages.

The possibilities offered by modern building materials, then, are in harmony with our changing esthetic preferences. The rigid frame forms the starting point for a new, perfectly definite world of forms. It leads to the modern V-support, the subject of our second chapter.

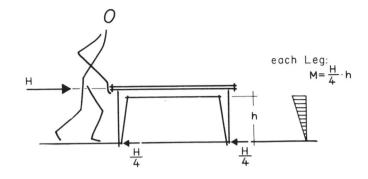

each Leg:
$$M = \frac{H}{4} \cdot h$$

1

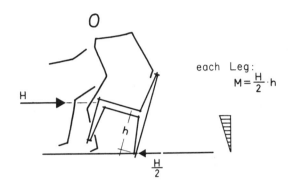

each Leg:
$$M = \frac{H}{2} \cdot h$$

2

56.　1 The V-shape of the legs of tables and chairs is a direct consequence of the way in which they are stressed. The broadest part is at the top.
2 Tables with legs that broaden out towards the bottom are difficult to move.

The V-support that tapers towards the base owes its origin to the development of the modern rigid frame. The two-hinged frame is the prototype of this kind of construction. Comparison with a chair will make its structural action plain (Fig. 57). If a fairly flexible chair is placed on a smooth floor and heavily loaded, the legs will tend to spread. If this spreading is prevented, the legs, owing to their flexural stiffness, will produce a counter-rotation at the joints and thus reduce the stresses in the seat. The degree to which the stresses are relieved can be measured in terms of the reduction in deflection.

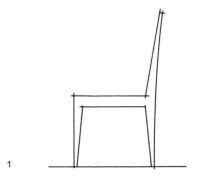

1

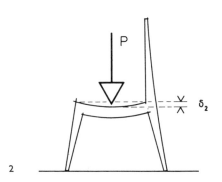

2

$$\delta_2 > \delta_3$$

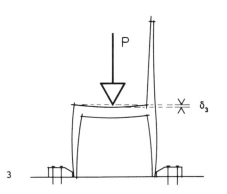

3

57. The chair considered as a rigid frame:
  1 Free of load.
  2 Under load the legs tend to spread.
  3 Preventing the legs from spreading relieves the stresses in the seat. The deflection is less than in case 2.

Fig. 58 shows the elastic line and the corresponding bending moments for a two-hinged frame subjected to a uniformly distributed vertical load. The bending moments characterize the degree of bending induced in the frame at any section. In the diagram they are plotted on the side of the frame where tensile stresses are developed. The points at which the diagram crosses from one side of the frame to the other are points of zero moment, that is, neutral points free of bending stresses. They are also "points of inflexion of the elastic line," that is, points where the direction of curvature of the deformed frame changes.

If such a frame is to work, the material must resist bending, the joints must be rigid and the feet must be hinged and prevented from moving sideways.

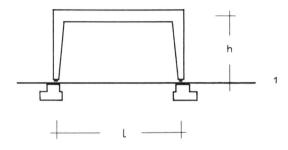

1

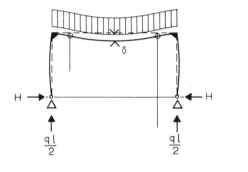

2

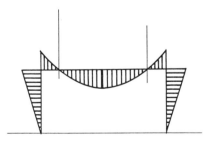

3

58. The two-hinged frame:
  1 The two-hinged frame is comparable with a chair with legs prevented from spreading sideways.
  2 Under vertical loads the frame deflects in the same way as the chair in Fig. 57.3.
  3 The bending moment diagram shows the magnitude of the bending stresses. The points of zero bending coincide with points of inflection of the elastic line (58.2).

Masonry has no tensile strength along the mortar joints; it is therefore unsuitable for frame construction. Although strong in tension and compression, wood is not an easy material in which to form a rigid joint. The mortise and tenon joint does good service in furniture-making but is of little value to the structural engineer. Rigid frames can be made of wood but only by using steel connections or glued laminated techniques. This kind of construction is relatively rare. Thus, the rigid frame is a purely modern phenomenon simply because it can only be built in reinforced concrete and steel, materials of quite recent invention. These materials have considerable strength in bending; they can be used to form rigid corner joints and effective hinges (Fig. 59).

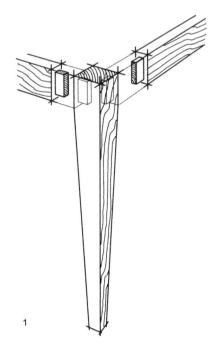

1

59.   Rigid corner construction:
        1 Mortise and tenon joint in furniture-making.
        2 Timber frame with steel connections.
        3 Glued laminated timber frame.
        4 Steel frame.
        5 Reinforced concrete frame.

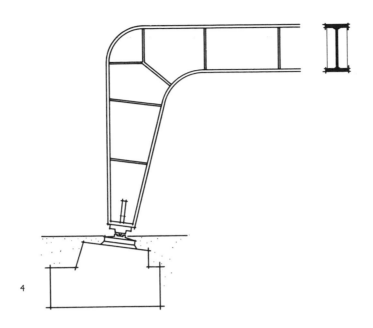

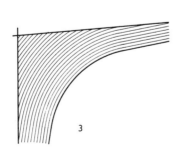

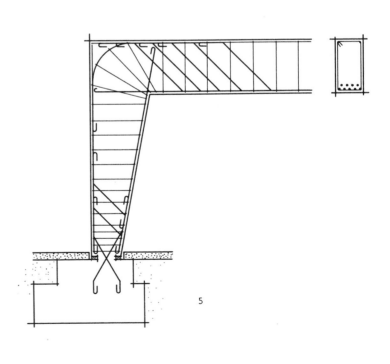

The structural logic of the two-hinged frame will be clear from the series of diagrams in Fig. 60. In the first column we have a simple beam on two supports together with diagrams showing the elastic deformation and the bending moments for a uniformly distributed load (Fig. 60.1). In the next column we have the same beam but this time with the addition of two cantilevers, each carrying a concentrated load at the free end (Fig. 60.2). The magnitude of these concentrated loads is such that the ends of the cantilevers are brought back to the level of the axis of the undeformed beam. Thus, the beam undergoes a counter-rotation at the supports, while the stresses at the center of the span are relieved. At the support the tangent to the deformed axis of the beam forms an angle of rotation τ_2 with the horizontal, less than the corresponding angle τ_1 for the beam without cantilevers. Likewise, the deflection δ_2 at mid-span is less than δ_1, and the maximum bending moment is only half that for the simple beam. The loaded cantilevers relieve the main span.

The legs of the frame (Fig. 60.3) are exactly the same length as the cantilevers in 60.2. Their feet correspond to the ends of the cantilevers. Just as the latter were held vertically in their original position by applying a load P, the former are prevented from moving horizontally by the rigidity of the foundations. The resistance offered by the foundations to the tendency of the frame to deform horizontally is characterized by the horizontal force H. H is equal to the load P applied to the cantilevers in 60.2. The mid-span deflection of the frame δ_3 and the angle of rotation at the joints τ_3 are the same as for the beam with overhangs. Similarly, the bending moment in the horizontal member of the frame is the same as that in the beam in 60.2. At the same time it is half the bending moment in the beam without cantilevers (Fig. 60.1).

Since the legs of the frame also act as columns, the two-hinged frame proves to be an economical and rational form of construction. At this point we are interested in the V-shape of these legs. This form is determined primarily by the bending moments, which are greatest at the corners of the frame and zero at its feet. The V-shaped legs of the two-hinged frame thus reflect the distribution of bending moments in the structure.

Loading and deflection. ▶

Bending moments. ▶

Basic shape. ▶

60. The relationship between beams and frames:
1 Deflection and bending moments in a simply supported beam.
2 Loading the cantilevers relieves the stresses at mid-span.
3 Preventing the legs of the frame from spreading relieves the horizontal member in the same way as loading the cantilevers in 60.2.

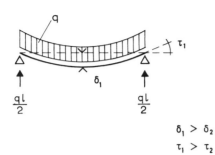

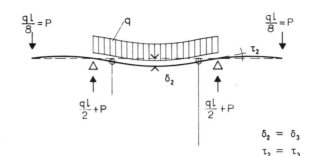

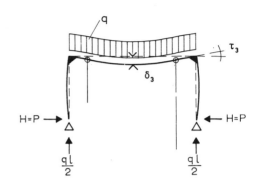

$$\delta_1 > \delta_2$$
$$\tau_1 > \tau_2$$

$$\delta_2 = \delta_3$$
$$\tau_2 = \tau_3$$

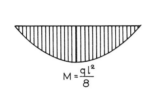

$$M = \frac{ql^2}{8}$$

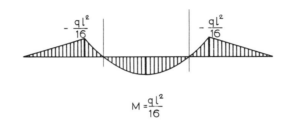

$$M = \frac{ql^2}{16}$$

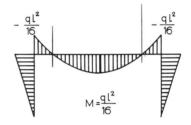

$$M = \frac{ql^2}{16}$$

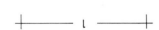

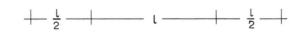

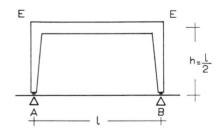

$$h = \frac{l}{2}$$

1   Simply supported beam.   2   Beam with cantilevers.   3   Two-hinged frame.

It is worth noting that the structural form of the frame leg is not merely a result of computation; on the contrary, the computation is equally a result of the form. One is dependent on the other. Fig. 61 shows two possible extremes. In one instance the heavily tapered verticals are very stiff compared with the horizontal member; in the other, they are slim and flexible. The two frames develop different bending moments under the same load. These moments are concentrated at the sections where the members are stiffest and offer the most resistance to bending. The stiffer and less flexible the verticals, the more bending moment they attract and the more they prevent the rotation of the corners. The more inflexibly the corners resist rotation, the more they relieve the horizontal member (Fig. 61.1). Conversely, the more supple the verticals, the less marked the frame action and the closer the bending moments in the horizontal member to those in a simple beam. The frame then loses its significance as a continuous structure and is resolved into a beam and columns with virtually independent action (61.2).

The "rightness" of the form makes itself felt in two ways. Those who judge only by their feelings will immediately recognize the esthetic superiority of a frame of the type shown in 61.1 and the comparative insignificance of that shown in 61.2. The structural designer, who is less swayed by esthetic considerations, arrives at the same conclusion by another route. Before beginning his calculations, he must estimate sizes. Only at the end of his investigation does he discover whether the estimated sizes are compatible with the calculated stresses or whether he must start again from the beginning. It is interesting to note that a rigid-legged frame is less sensitive to wrong estimates and construction errors than a slender-legged one. Thus, to improve the accuracy of his estimates, shorten his calculations and make his design less sensitive to errors in construction, the designer will give preference to frames with stiff legs. Evidently this form is the "right" one both for the experienced engineer and for those whose judgments are purely esthetic.

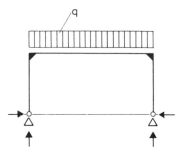
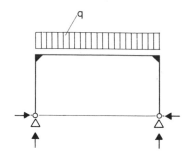

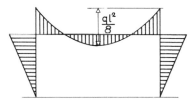
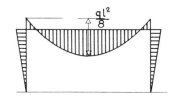

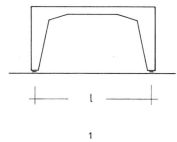
1

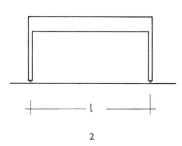
2

61. Relative stiffness of the members in two-hinged frames:
   1 Stiff legs prevent rotation of the corners and relieve the stresses in the horizontal member.
   2 Slender legs do little to prevent rotation of the corners. The stresses in the horizontal member approach those in the equivalent simply supported beam. In these circumstances the frame loses its significance.

In addition to ordinary dead and live loads, horizontal wind loads play a big part in the design of buildings. Their effect on a two-hinged frame is illustrated in Fig. 62. Here, too, the bending moments in the legs vanish at the hinged feet; here, too, they are in harmony with a V-shaped support.

The final design of a two-hinged frame is determined by its behavior under simultaneous vertical and horizontal wind loading. Both types of loading result in a triangular distribution of bending moments in the legs of the frame. Hence, in both cases the V-shape is correct.

Loading and deflection.

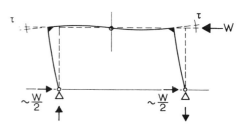

Bending moments.

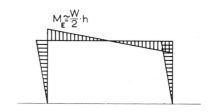

Basic shape.

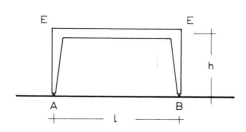

62.   The two-hinged frame under wind loading. The tapering of the legs reflects the distribution of bending moments.

95

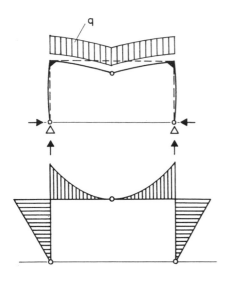
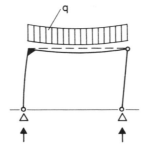
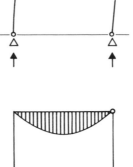

Vertical loading and deflection.

Bending moments due to vertical loads.

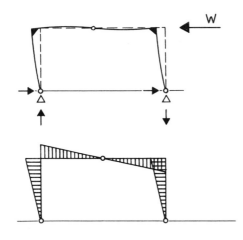
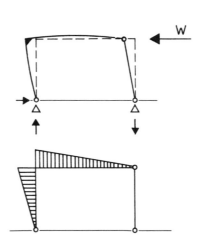

Wind loading and deflection.

Bending moments due to wind.

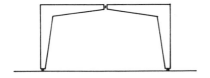
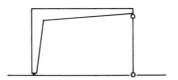

Basic shape.

63.

The V-shape is also appropriate for the legs of both the three-hinged frame (Fig. 63.1) and the half-frame (Fig. 63.2). Whenever the legs of a frame are rigidly connected to the horizontal member at the top and hinged at the bottom, ordinary loading conditions will always produce a triangular distribution of bending moment, diminishing from a maximum at the corners of the frame to zero at its feet. In such circumstances the appropriateness of a V-shaped support is self-evident. The situation is completely different, if the feet of the frame are fixed, so that they cannot rotate. In this case significant bending moments and bending stresses are developed at the base of the legs, requiring cross sections of the same order of magnitude as those at the corners of the frame. Fig. 64 shows the changed form of the bending moment diagrams and the corresponding elastic deformation of the frame for this case. Under these conditions a V-support would not make sense.

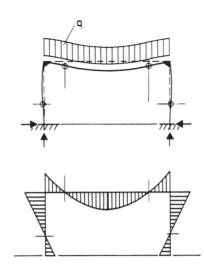

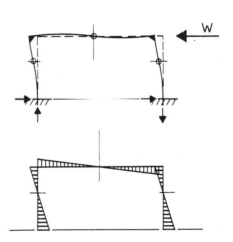

63.   The bending moment diagrams for three-hinged and half-frames are also triangular for the principal types of loading.

64.   There is no justification for tapering the legs when the feet of the frame are fixed.

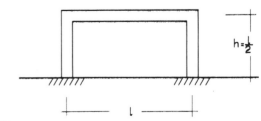

64.

Fig. 65 shows some typical applications of the two-hinged frame. The bridge in Fig. 65.1 spans clear across the river with maximum economy of materials. The shallower the deck, the greater the vertical clearance and the less the dead weight of the structure. The lightness of the deck system is largely due to the rigidity of the corners of the frame and the massiveness of the short, squat abutments, its legs. Without the frame action the bridge girders would be subjected to a much higher bending moment at the center of the span and would have to be made correspondingly deeper. Even though the massive supports are partly obscured by the embankment, the observer is keenly aware of the strength inherent in the rigid connection between them and the girders. In the Pilgrims' Church at Lourdes [16] the legs of the frames are resolved into tension and compression members (Fig. 65.3). Their joint action is equivalent to that of a tapered leg. Fig. 65.2 shows a section through a railroad underpass in Duisburg [17]. Here, too, the V-supports are clearly derived from the frame action. The other two examples are light building frames. Because the loads are smaller and the spans shorter, the dimensions of these frames are less than those of a bridge, but here too the tapering of the legs is clearly recognizable and perfectly intelligible in the light of their function. Frames of this kind have many applications in engineering and architecture. Wherever it is a question of long spans and column-free spaces or of giving a tall building obvious transverse stability, rigid frame construction will suggest itself. And if the feet of the frame are hinged, the legs should logically be tapered.

65. Some typical two-hinged frames:
     1 A reinforced concrete bridge.
     2 A pedestrian underpass [17].
     3 The Pilgrims' Church at Lourdes [16].
     4 An exhibition hall.
     5 A gymnasium.

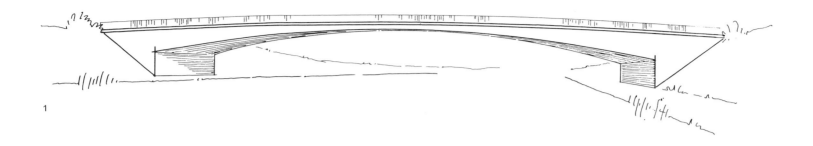

1

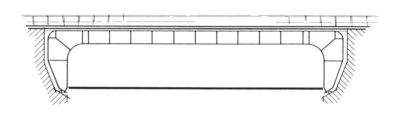

2

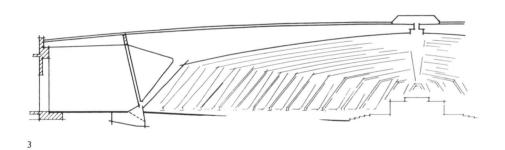

3

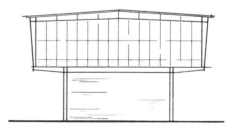

4

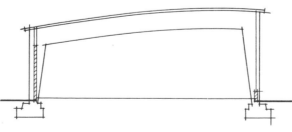

5

Rigid frames make good platforms on which to erect multistory buildings. The upper stories, all having the same function, form a closed, cube-shaped unit. The first floor, on the other hand, communicates with the outside. The rigid frame is a form that opens up the building and at the same time concentrates the vertical and wind loads at its base in a structurally impressive way. A number of notable modern buildings are carried on rigid frames with strikingly tapered legs. One of the most interesting solutions of this kind (Fig. 66) is the Unesco Building in Paris [18]. The splaying of the legs of the frame and their pronounced taper emphasize the special function of the first floor and at the same time speak the unambiguous language of modern structural engineering. The structure was designed by Nervi. The upper stories are carried on just two rows of interior columns, which bring down all the loads exactly on the corners of the two-hinged frames at the base of the building. These loads are mostly transmitted as axial forces and produce very little bending. The vertical loads on the horizontal member of the frame come entirely from the second floor and are the same as the floor loads in the upper stories. They are not critical as far as the design of the frame is concerned. The form and function of the first-floor frame are determined by the wind forces and the transverse stability of the building. This is only true, if, as mentioned above, the vertical column loads are brought down precisely on the corners of the frame. Another important function of the legs of the frames is to stiffen the building against wind forces acting in the longitudinal direction. This point is discussed in greater detail on page 168 in a later section of this book.

Figs. 66.1 and 2 show a section through the building and the bending moments in the first-floor frame due to wind. These moments are faithfully reflected in the shape of the legs. Nervi says that all his designs emerge spontaneously from a knowledge of the distribution of the forces and a search for forms that express, simply and economically, the way they interact. This is very much to the point. Such forms are not "computed," they are designed. Computations are simply means of checking whether the form is compatible with the stresses. Other forms might also be proposed and found capable of withstanding the loads. However, only one form is the best, or, as Nervi says, structurally "right," and this is the form in which the principle of economy is most clearly expressed. Searching for it and finding it is a creative act, which fundamentally has nothing to do with "computations." By the "principle of economy" we mean more than simply "economical" in price. It is a complex idea that permeates the entire design process. The greatest effects, even esthetic effects, are achieved with the most sparing means; this is a principle that applies to every area of creative activity, both technological and artistic, and even to Nature.

That there is no connotation of "cheapness" here is vividly illustrated by a bon mot attributed to Mies van der Rohe: "Make it as simple as possible, however much it costs!"

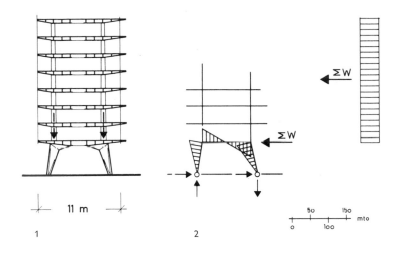

66. The Unesco Building in Paris [18].
     1 Section showing two-hinged frame with tapered legs at first-floor level.
     2 Bending moments due to wind.
     3 Perspective.

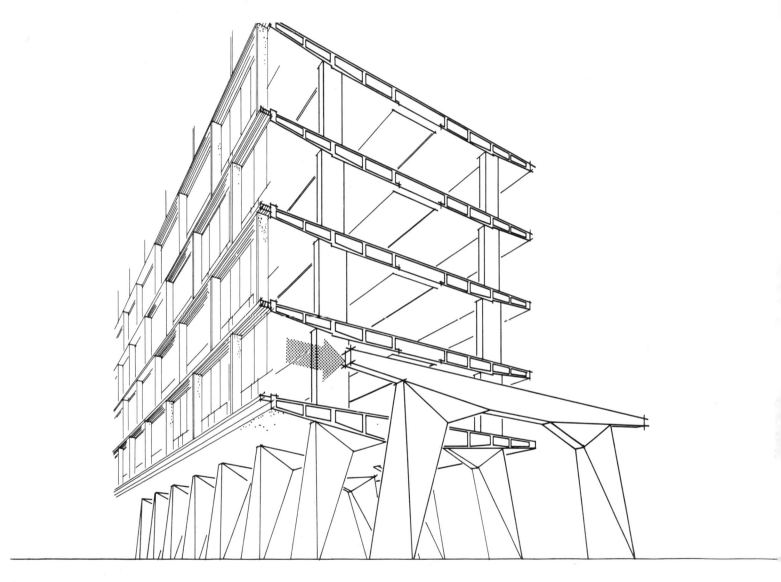

3

Another notable building supported on rigid frames with tapered legs is Corbusier's Unité d'Habitation in Marseilles [19]. It is true that, at first glance, the function of the V-supports is not as obvious as in the Unesco Building; nevertheless, the structural design is based on the same principle.

Since this is an apartment building, the mechanical installations are much more complex. The relatively close spacing of the cross walls means that every second wall has to be picked up at second-floor level. Above the first floor an entire story is set aside for horizontal services and the legs of the frames are given a special hollow cross section to accommodate vertical pipes and ducts.

The mechanical organization of the building is best understood with reference to the perspective in Fig. 67.4. The same figure illustrates the form of the supporting frames with equal clarity. Again we find the vertical loads concentrated over the legs of the frame, part of the load being transferred to them directly and part indirectly by means of longitudinal girders. Again the function of the frame is determined by the wind forces and the transverse stability of the structure. The wind moment diagram and the V-shape of the legs once more betray a common origin.

Since the loads from such buildings are very heavy, it is difficult to design frames with true hinges at the base. In reinforced concrete construction loads of this magnitude are carried more easily by frames with fixed feet. Even if reduced to a minimum, the legs are so wide at the base that a certain amount of fixation is inevitable (Fig. 67.2).

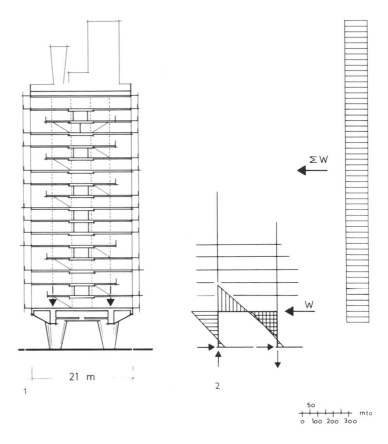

1

21 m

2

50
o loo 2oo 3oo
mto

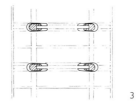

3

67.   High-rise apartment house in Marseilles designed by Le Corbusier [19].
       1 Section showing rigid frame with tapered legs at first-floor level.
       2 Bending moments due to wind.
       3 Plan.
       4 Perspective showing service installations.

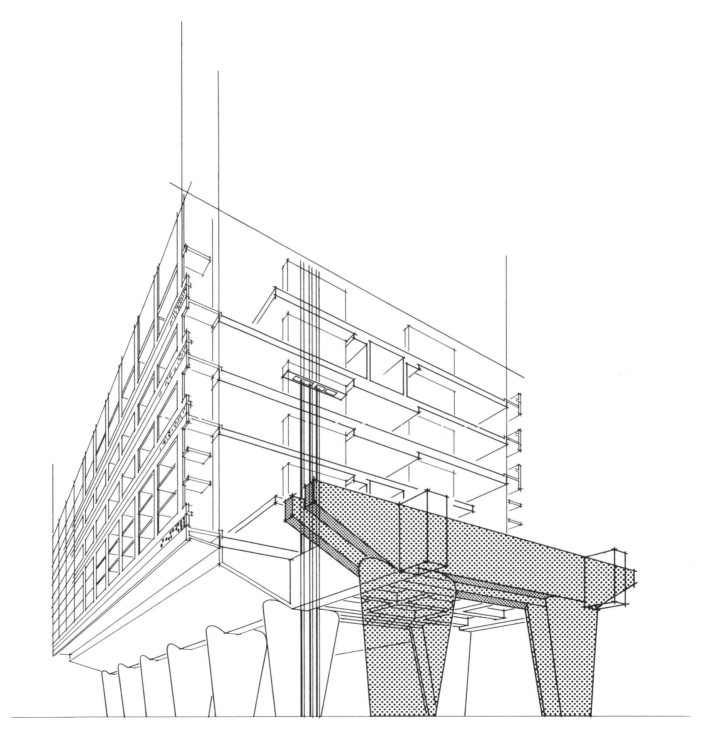

4

These two examples, Unesco and the Unité in Marseilles, show how in tall buildings the design of the first-floor frame is determined by wind forces. With a two-hinged frame it is natural to taper the legs. The taller the building, the more pronounced the taper as a visible expression of transverse stability.

At the same time there are other ways of giving lateral stability to a structure. An engineer will gladly use massive walls, elevator shafts and stair wells for this purpose. These solutions, too, express clear-cut structural principles, the application of which leads to sound structural forms. However, these have nothing to do with rigid frames and V-supports. Nevertheless, many architects insist on introducing V-supports for the sake of their attractive appearance, even though, with the best will in the world, no structural justification can be found for them. In this case the shape is no longer generated by the laws of statics and the result is rarely more than the shadow of a form, the real nature of which has been misunderstood. Fig. 68 shows a fairly common example of this kind of error. There is absolutely no structural justification for tapering the first-floor columns. The building is adequately stiffened by the stair walls and the elevator shaft, to which the whole building is firmly tied by the massive floor slabs. No horizontal wind forces are ever transmitted to the "frame." There are no bending moments to justify the V-shape of the columns, which carry only vertical loads. The simplest parallel form would be perfectly appropriate. Moreover, if this were a genuine frame, the legs would be far too spindly for the lateral wind forces acting on the building. The duct openings that pierce the horizontal member along the whole of its length are convincing evidence that this "frame" is nothing more than a fake. The V-supports are there simply to create a plastic effect and bear no intrinsic relation to the horizontal member, the stiffness of which has been destroyed; thus the suggestion of frame action is quite illusory. The conjecture that perhaps the supports broaden upwards in order to make a clean transition to columns of corresponding breadth in the upper stories is also erroneous. Immediately above the "frame" the column section is sharply reduced and half the V-leg supports thin air. The suspended ceiling, behind which the horizontal member is completely concealed, underscores the emptiness of the general conception and the unrelatedness of the V-shape of the supports. Compared with the powerful structural forms of the Unesco Building in Paris and the Unité d'Habitation in Marseilles, which clearly express their statical function, this design is false and pallid and owes its existence solely to a misunderstanding of structural principles and a hankering for a touch of modernity.

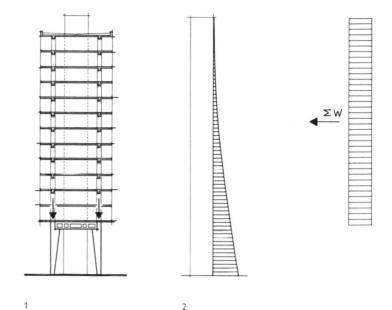

1   2

68.   Tall building with ornamental tapered legs.
       1 The perforations in the horizontal member prove that this is not a true frame.
       2 The wind moments are absorbed by the elevator shafts and stair tower.

In Fig. 68 the structural inconsequence that leads to a weak and meaningless form is easy to recognize. This is not always so. A dishonest structure may also lie concealed behind a seemingly powerful form. Sophisticated design is no guarantee of structural integrity. The first impression made by the frame in Fig. 69 is that of a strong, incisive structural form. No one would dream that it had anything other than a statical origin. The configuration suggests a sturdy wind bent, designed to ensure the transverse stability of the building at first-floor level and at the same time carry all the loads from the upper floors. This first impression is reinforced by the statically credible proportions, which point to an understanding of structural design. The disappointment is all the more intense, when one discovers that the wind forces are not transferred to the frame at all but are entirely absorbed by a massive service core at the center of the building. This alone is enough to shatter many illusions. But it is not all. The inclined legs of the frame lead the eye to the geometrical points, at which the loads from the upper floors might be expected to descend (cf. the Unesco Building, Fig. 66, and the Unité d'Habitation, Fig 67). In fact, the loads from the upper floors do not descend here, but are delivered by means of a line of columns in the exterior wall and a heavy, longitudinal girder to the tip of the cantilever, while at the other end they are transferred to the bearing walls of the core. The corner of the frame, though the obvious point at which to terminate a line of columns, receives no direct vertical loads at all. Neither the V-shape of the supports, nor the inclination of their axis nor their powerful dimensions nor, in short, the pretentious form of the frame as a whole have any real justification. They simulate a function, which, in fact, they do not perform. The engineer is left with the dubious task of getting the concentrated loads from the upper floors away from the tips of the cantilevers and down to the foundations by whatever route he can. The tortured nature of his solution is obvious from a glance at the real statical system employed and the corresponding bending moment diagram (Fig. 69.3). This system has nothing to do with a true frame. The maximum moment occurs in the cantilever, which is rather stunted, while the giant legs of the frame are grossly overdimensioned. Though there appears to be a horizontal member, in fact there is none.

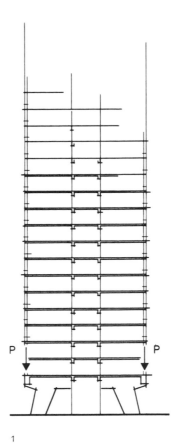

1

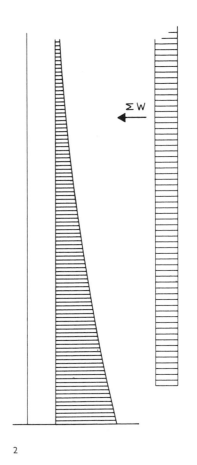

2

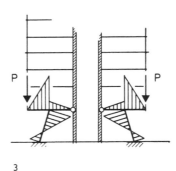

3

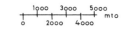

69. A tall building with a pseudo wind-frame.
     1 The vertical loads are not transferred directly to the most logical points, the tops of the inclined legs, but are carried on the ends of the cantilevers.
     2 The wind moments are absorbed by the elevator shafts.
     3 The structural and bending moment diagrams show that in this case there is no justification for a V-legged frame.

The occurrence of false frames with tapered legs is not confined to large buildings only. More modest structures have their share. In fact, in the latter the purely formalistic V-support predominates. Concern for the principle prompts us to offer a few typical examples. We have established the supreme importance of having a rigid joint between the vertical and horizontal members of a frame. This continuity is essential to true frame action. Without it tapering the verticals is senseless. However, when the horizontal member has nothing like the same stiffness as the verticals or is not designed as a horizontal member at all (Fig. 70.1), frame action will never be developed, no matter how tapered the verticals may be. The V-shape of the verticals in 70.1 implies a true frame with hinged feet. This impression is deceptive. The columns are actually fixed at the base and it is here that the highest moments develop. The fixity of the columns alone guarantees the stability of the structure. The relatively thin roof slab is in no position to act as the horizontal member of a frame. Here form and function are mutually contradictory.

The form of the balcony supports in Fig. 70.2 is just as misleading. All the rigidity is in the main structure. There is practically no structural continuity between the supports and the balcony slab, because the slab is too flexible to attract bending from the very much stiffer columns. Moreover, there would be no room for heavy reinforcement in so thin a slab. The V-shape of the supports has no structural significance. It is quite false and can only be interpreted as fashionable confusion.

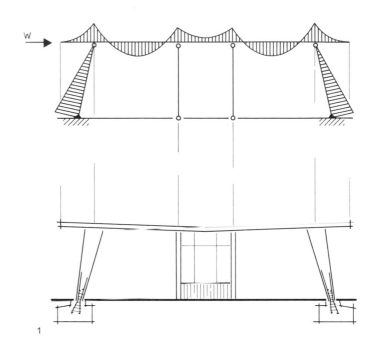

1

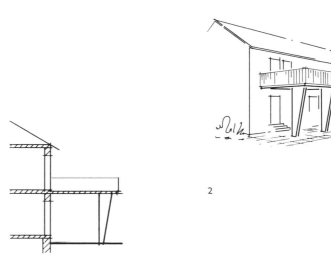

2

70. False V-supports.
   1 It is impossible to develop a rigid connection at the junction of a tapered column and a thin roof slab. The feet of the columns are fixed, their form contradicts their function.
   2 A V-support carrying a thin balcony slab is mere technical formalism.

The hall in Fig. 71.1 has a series of tapered columns that appear to be the legs of rigid frames. That these are true frames is very doubtful, since, if they were, it would be illogical to make them span the building in both directions. Tapered columns down the long side of the building would be enough; the other side could be left free of columns altogether. V-supports down both sides of a building betray a purely formal intention. An architect who did not appreciate the significance of frame construction might easily use V-supports as decorative elements evenly divided among all the elevations.

Just as tapered columns can be used indiscriminately to adorn both the long and short sides of a building, without performing any corresponding structural function, they can also be found decorating corners (Fig. 71.2). The mere idea of a diagonal frame, which is all a corner can suggest, is itself absurd, at any rate if other frames appear to span the building at right angles. A tapered corner column is a decorative effect in technological disguise, a device which can only result in confusing an otherwise lucid structural form. Fig. 71.3 shows a facade pretentiously crowned with tapered fins. This is an idiom inadvisedly borrowed from the language of the V-support. Here it merely serves to convey a sense of false and oppressive monumentality. The modest, two-story building shown in Fig. 71.4 is not made more impressive by decorating the elevations with tapered columns. The absurdity of this technically oriented formalism is revealed particularly clearly in cross section. The roof projects over the broad tops of the columns, which support the humble cornice with bombastic extravagance.

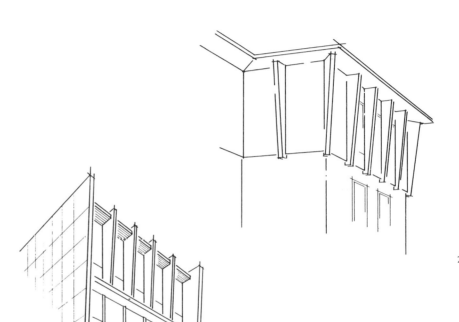

1

2

3

71. The ornamental V-support.
    1 True frame construction calls for V-supports on the long sides of the building. The short sides should be free of columns.
    2 A genuine V-support at the corner would indicate a frame spanning diagonally, an absurd situation if the other V-supports indicate frames spanning at right-angles to the outside walls.
    3 The V-form used to create a spurious impression of monumentality.
    4 Superfluous V-support.

4

The previous section dealt with V-supports, the shape of which was attributable to their function as the legs of frames or pseudo frames. The point bearing of a modern V-support is an expression of the absence of moment at hinged feet. If there is no frame action, the stability of an isolated column depends on a firm anchorage at the base. Only a massive foundation will make it stand. Lateral forces, like those due to wind, produce bending moments which reach their maximum at the foundations. It is therefore natural to make a free-standing column broadest at the bottom. Masts, towers, pylons and chimneys (Fig. 72) are all equivalent to a free-standing column. Nature has found a perfect solution to this "structural problem" in the growth of a tree. The engineer can only hope to do as well. The Eiffel Tower and the Stuttgart TV Tower [20] are some of his more outstanding achievements. The structural principle becomes evident on comparing the form with the wind moment diagram. A section through the Pirelli Building in Milan [21] reveals how the entire structure is inspired by the same idea. Thus, wherever frame action is absent, the inverted V-form makes good sense. Broad-based and firmly rooted, it at once recalls the ancient buttress (cf. Figs. 52 to 54).

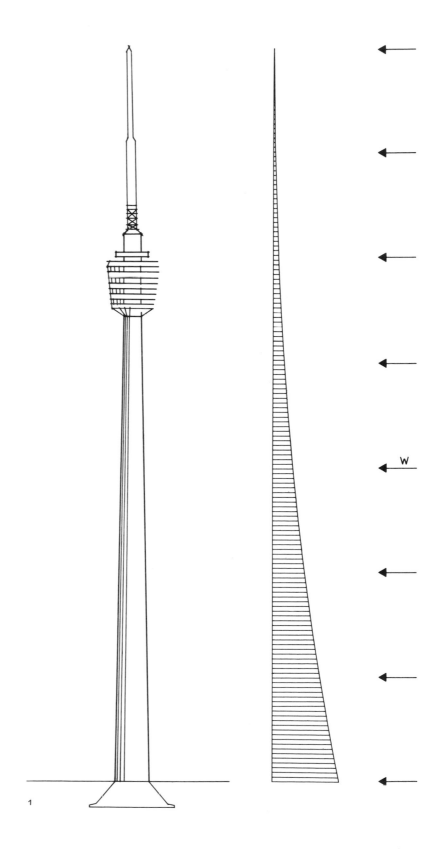

72. The inverted V-shape is appropriate for free-standing towers and masts, since a broad base provides effective anchorage.
1 Television tower, Stuttgart, Germany [20].
2 The Eiffel Tower, Paris.
3 Cross section through the Pirelli Building, Milan, Italy [21].

2

3

W

This would exhaust the simple theme of the free-standing support, were these considerations not so frequently disregarded in actual practice.

Canopies over platforms and filling stations often rest on supports that taper towards the base, even though they clearly act as free-standing columns. If a series of isolated supports happen to be placed one next to the other, this should not be confused with rigid frame construction. It is obvious from Fig. 73 that there is no frame action in the plane of the V and that the supports function independently. Even if a frame effect is achieved in the longitudinal direction, that is, at right angles to the plane of the paper, this contributes nothing to the lateral stability of the structure. In the transverse direction, that is, in the plane in which the V-shape acts, the stability is entirely determined by the fixity of the feet. The V-supports in Figs. 73.2 and 3 act in isolation. If there were true hinges at their feet, they would not be stable. Hence, if, in actual fact, such structures do not topple over, it is only because the feet are not really hinged. On the contrary, the reduced sections at the base of the columns are points of maximum stress. In practice these sections are given the necessary stiffness, and the structure as a whole its stability, by providing additional reinforcement. Nevertheless, the outward form contradicts the statical function. It is not a genuine structural form.

73. Free-standing V-supports:
   1 The bending moments in a free-standing column fixed at the base diminish towards the top.
   2, 3 and 4 Various free-standing columns of inappropriate shape with pseudo hinges at the base.

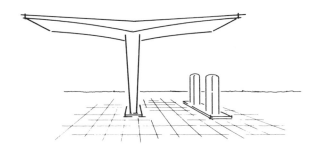

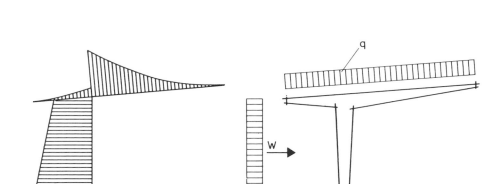

1

M_{max}

q

W

2

3

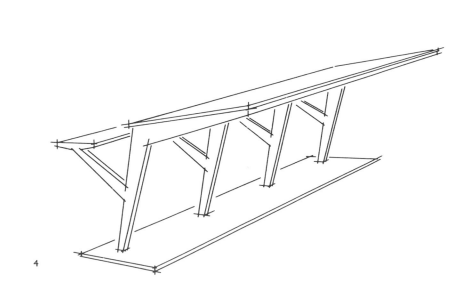

4

This contention is illustrated by the series of sketches in Fig. 74. The typical two-hinged or three-hinged frame is stable. A pair of T-frames can be made into a three-hinged frame by means of a hinged connection. A single T-frame, however, needs additional support. It can be made stable by propping it on one side or by tying it back on the other. If it receives no additional support, being hinged at the bottom, it will overturn.

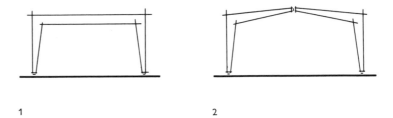

1   2

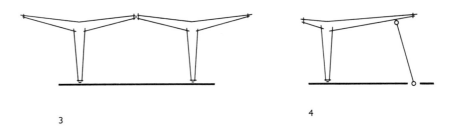

3   4

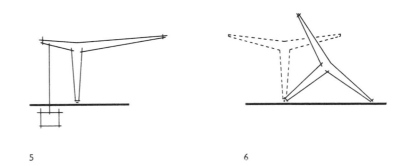

74.   Various ways of providing stability:
       1 and 2 Two-hinged and three-hinged frames are always stable.
       3 A pair of T-frames can be made stable by inserting a hinged connection.
       4 A single T-frame needs to be propped up or
       5 tied back.
       6 If the joint at its base is a genuine hinge, an unsupported T-frame will
          overturn.

5   6

The structure shown in Fig. 75.1, in which a row of T-frames is used to support a long roof, will also be unstable, unless the roof is designed as a rigid horizontal slab spanning between massive walls, or other elements of equal stiffness, in such a way that all lateral movement is prevented. In these circumstances, however, it is no longer a question of an isolated support, dependent for its stability on its own rigidity alone, but rather of a three-dimensional system in which the T-frame with its tapered leg and hinged base plays a perfectly legitimate part. In the absence of transverse stiffening elements the stability of the design depends entirely on the degree of fixity at the foot of each frame and the adequacy of the section at this point.

Surely this is a wrong-headed approach, to make the most heavily stressed point in a frame look like a hinge? Why do we so rarely encounter solutions like that in Fig. 75.3, in which the play of forces is truly reflected? Are they too obvious and crude? Certainly, the canopies that shelter so many modern filling stations, with their apparently unstable V-supports, do not represent good structural form. Nevertheless, they appear to please. Then what is the reason for all the fuss? Objections of this kind are familiar to everyone who has had anything to do with structural design. It is useless to argue. No one will be deterred from doing what he "pleases" merely out of respect for a structural principle. On the other hand, a structural principle will never be overthrown by the mere existence of a non-structural form, however pleasing it may be.

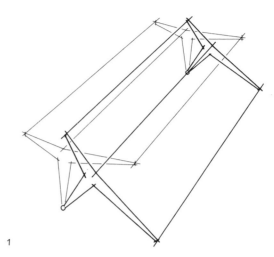

1

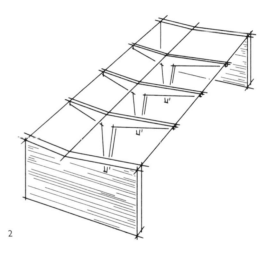

2

3

75.   Hinged T-frames in series:
       1 Unless additional support is provided, the structure will overturn like a
         single T-frame.
       2 The structure can be stabilized by tying the roof slab to end walls or
       3 by anchoring the T-frames to the foundations.

The same scale cannot be applied to everything indiscriminately. What may be all right for a filling station canopy is not necessarily suitable for a skyscraper. When a larger structure is balanced on a tapering support, the precariousness of the situation becomes more obvious. If, for example, a single-story building is imagined perched on a row of one-legged frames, in the manner of Fig. 76, the entire problem of the downward tapered V-support becomes strikingly clear. Let us assume that, in the present case, raising the building on stilts is a functional and convenient device and concern ourselves solely with the hinged T-type substructure. The downward taper of the isolated supports suggests hinged feet. This, however, is impossible; otherwise the building would overturn. The frames must be solidly and rigidly anchored to the foundations. The bending moment diagram shows that the maximum moment occurs at the base of the upright. Section 1-1 is stressed to the limit and heavily reinforced. At section 2-2 the stresses are somewhat lower. The column is broader at the top, not because the moments there are greater but because the cantilever must be reduced to a minimum. The broader the head of the column, the shorter the cantilever and the less the cantilever moment at 3-3. It is very important to reduce the stresses at section 3-3, because it too is stressed to the limit. This is the real reason for the upward broadening of the support. In this design sections 2-2 and 4-4 are stressed much less heavily than sections 1-1 and 3-3. They are decidedly overdimensioned. If the strength of these sections were fully utilized, we would get a frame of quite a different shape (Fig. 76.3), a shape of which Nature, an economical designer, would be more likely to approve. Now there can be no misgivings about possible hinged feet. Every dimension is in harmony with the inner play of forces. The design as a whole has the dynamic vigor appropriate to its task, and yet it breathes stability. It reflects the logic of the structure. Here, where the downward tapered V-support would be so unreasonable, is it such an esthetic loss to do without it?

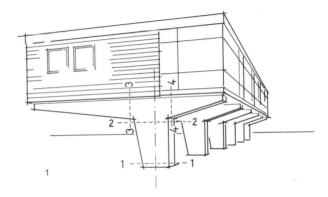

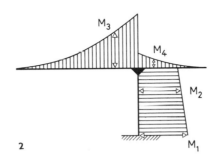

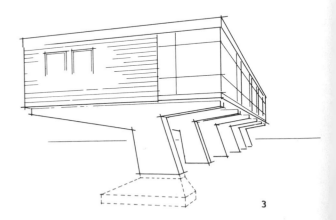

76.   A building on independent supports:
     1 To the eye it lacks stability.
     2 The bending moment diagram shows that the maximum moment is at the foot of the supports.
     3 A design that corresponds more closely with the actual distribution of forces.

Canopy in front of a school building in Cataguazes, Brazil [22]
Arch: Oscar Niemeyer

There are good reasons for setting back the upper stories of city buildings with respect to the first floor. The latter, which is wide open to the street, traffic and passers-by (show windows), serves as a link between inside and outside. The upper floors, removed from the bustle of the street, have other functions. Thus, it is reasonable to set them apart.

The idea of such setbacks is not new. It is a familiar feature of medieval timber frames. Structural discipline and the limitation of architectural detail to a scale that is technically "right" are characteristic of the honest old art of carpentry. This natural restraint is rare in modern skeleton construction.

A wooden joist, designed for maximum moment at mid-span, will carry the cantilevered load from an offset upper story, if the overhang "a" remains within reasonable limits. In old buildings the dimension "a" is generally less than the depth of the beam "h." This rule of thumb will generally enable the cantilever to support the loads from several stories. The floor joists and wall studs are relatively closely spaced. If the studs do not come down directly on a joist, a sill is used to spread the load fairly uniformly over the whole floor.

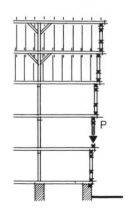

1

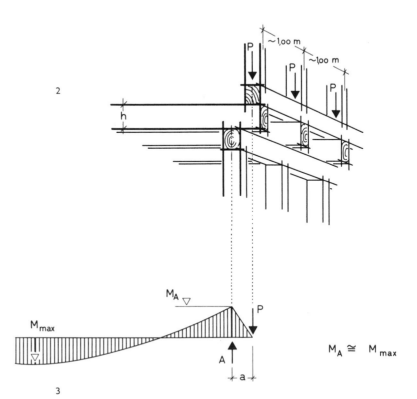

2

3

$M_A \cong M_{max}$

77. In half-timber construction each story is cantilevered beyond the one below.
   1 View and section.
   2 The ends of the joists are more or less equally loaded.
   3 The cantilever bending moment is approximately the same as that at mid-span. The strength of the floor system is efficiently exploited.

In reinforced concrete construction the columns can be spaced further apart. The loads on the individual columns increase roughly linearly with the distance between them. These loads are no longer uniformly distributed over the outer edge of the floor, but are concentrated in narrow zones at the base of the columns. Whereas in old timber buildings the outside wall acts as a line load, uniformly distributed along the outer edge of a joist floor, in concrete structures the cantilevered floor has to support relatively heavy, concentrated loads acting at greater intervals. However, the slab has only a limited ability to resist concentrated cantilever loading and its capacity cannot be indefinitely extended by adding reinforcement. The stresses in a cantilevered floor slab increase with increase in the length of the overhang, the distance between columns and the number of stories. For slabs of normal thickness "h" these stresses soon become unmanageable. In these circumstances the problem ceases to be one of an offset outside wall, as it is in timber buildings and concrete buildings with relatively narrow column spacing. It becomes instead a problem of individual columns offset with respect to each other.

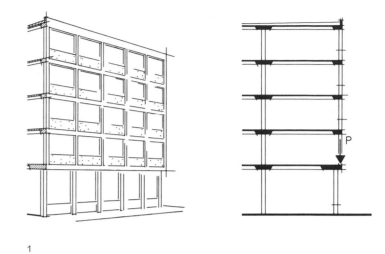

1

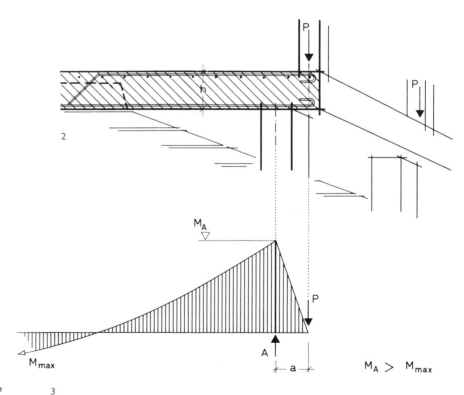

78. Setbacks in reinforced concrete construction:
     1 View and section.
     2 The loads on the cantilevered floor slab are concentrated at the columns.
     3 The cantilever bending moment is much higher than that at mid-span. The floor slab is locally overstressed.

$M_A > M_{max}$

3

At the end of this train of thought we find a new kind of V-support (Fig. 79). Such supports are normally employed where the upper floors are clearly offset with respect to the first floor and the usual solid floor slab is not strong enough to act as a cantilever carrying the concentrated loads from widely spaced columns. Offset V-supports of this description have to be tied back to counteract the overturning moment due to the eccentricity of the vertical loads. An equal but opposite moment is needed to restore equilibrium. As a rule, the tensile forces are dissipated in the floor slab, which must, in its turn, be secured against lateral displacement. These are the conditions for an offset V-support. In multistory buildings these conditions are often satisfied, so that an offset V-support, as defined above, may be fully justified.

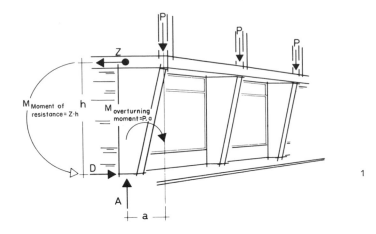

1

2

79.   The offset V-support:
       1 The offset causes an overturning moment that has to be dissipated in the
         floor slab.
       2 Some typical examples.

Unfortunately, the structural form of an offset V-support is often imitated without its function being understood. The building illustrated in Fig. 80.1 has V-supports at first-floor level. They appear to be offset. The cross section reveals, however, that the load-bearing exterior columns in the upper stories are, in fact, continuous with the V-supports at the first floor, though the loads come down on the inside edge of the latter. The outside edge, which remains unloaded, ends in a strip of floor slab expressly provided for this purpose. At each end of the building this strip of slab is continued as a projecting fin, which runs into a corresponding overhang at the roof. This continuous strip forms a purely decorative "frame." As used here, the word has nothing to do with a frame as the engineer understands it (cf. pages 88 ff.). It merely suggests a picture frame and thus betrays the non-structural character of the design (see also chapter 1, page 75).

Because the street front is closed in, the observer can only get a frontal view of the false V-supports. The dubious nature of this form is more clearly revealed, when the columns are exposed from the side, as in the corner building illustrated in Fig. 80.2. Once again the upper floors are not actually offset. The corner view discloses the ambiguity and irrationality of the treatment. The disquietude experienced by the observer coincides with the unfavorable judgement of the structural analyst.

The entrance to the building shown in Fig. 80.3 is "architecturally" accented by means of two tapered fins. These fins carry no load. The thin canopy, in which they terminate, is cantilevered from the roof.

The irrationality of this form is well revealed by the crass examples shown in Figs. 80.4 and 80.5. For structural reasons it was desired to avoid a rigid connection between columns and floor slab. In order to be able to make the floors in prestressed concrete, it was necessary for them to be simply supported. By notching the heads of the columns the engineer provided a virtual hinge. The architect consented to this, without realizing that it made formal nonsense of the V-shape, on which he had set his heart.

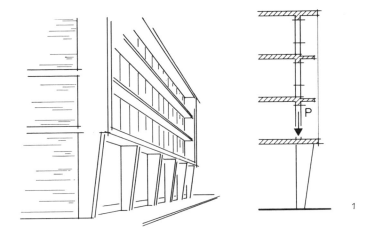

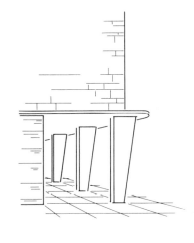

1

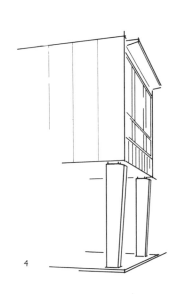

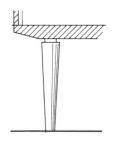

2

3

4

5

80. False offset V-supports:
  1 The load from the upper floors comes down near the inside face of the column, the V-shape of which has no structural significance.
  2 A corner view clearly shows the irrelevance of the V-supports.
  3 Decorative, non-structural V-supports.
  4 and 5 A V-support notched at the top is self-contradictory.

If two offset V-supports are opposed, given a symmetrical distribution of the loads, the forces will tend to balance out. Le Corbusier has used this technique in tall apartment buildings in Nantes and Berlin [23]. In both buildings the upper floors are carried on bearing walls, which divide one living unit from the next. To have carried these walls down to the foundations would have prevented the full utilization of the available space. It would also have been a solution lacking visual interest. Accordingly, at ground level, where the full cross section of the walls was more than was structurally necessary, Corbusier reduced them to a series of inclined fins, sloping alternately inwards and outwards. In this way he opened up the area underneath the building. The structure is symmetrical about the longitudinal axis so that supports tilted outward pull against each other, while those tilted inward lean against each other (Fig. 81.1). All the supporting elements work together to resist lateral wind forces, acting like a rigid space frame. Here the alternation of inward and outward sloping fins proves its structural usefulness. If all these fins sloped in one direction, which would be quite conceivable for symmetrical vertical loading, the system would become unstable the moment the loads were applied asymmetrically. The necessary transverse rigidity could then be achieved only by introducing a horizontal member, capable of resisting shear, between pairs of wall elements or by fixing the feet of these elements in the foundations. As it is, however, we get the much simpler and more stable system illustrated schematically in Fig. 81.2. It is characterized by rigid members in a triangular configuration.

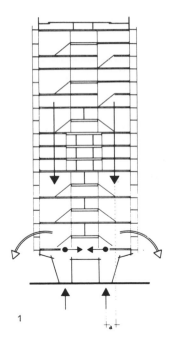
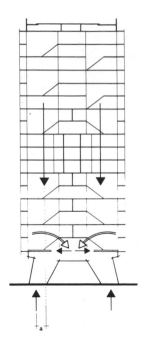

1

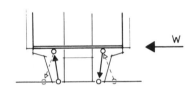
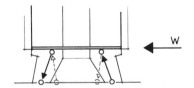

2

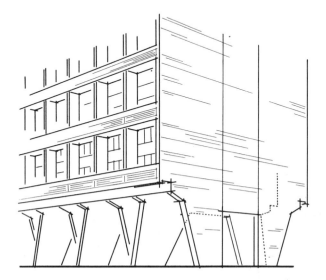

3

81. Offset supports arranged in pairs in apartment buildings designed by Le Corbusier [23].
1 The outward tilted supports are tied together, while the inward tilted supports lean against each other.
2 Together with the rigid floor slab, the alternating pairs of supports form a sort of triangular space frame that gives the structure lateral stability.
3 Perspective.

Multistory apartment building in Berlin raised on tilted supports [23]
Arch: Le Corbusier ▶

In certain circumstances the bracketed V-support develops into a new structural unit. As with the rigid frame, its efficacy depends on achieving the structural continuity between beam and column only possible in steel or reinforced concrete. Its function will be best understood with reference to the series of diagrams in Fig. 82. As the overhang increases, so does the overturning moment and with it the taper of the column, which soon assumes proportions that can no longer be considered satisfactory (Fig. 82.2). The forms shown in Figs. 82.3 and 82.4 develop perfectly organically, as a function of the load and the overhang. Finally, we are left with a V-support and a cantilever. In the extreme case the cantilever no longer supports a point load but the distributed load from a roof. It is not easy to say, as a general principle, just when one form or another is appropriate. The forms can be varied quite freely without infringing the structural principle. One rule, however, is clear: the cantilever and column moments increase linearly both with the load and with the span. Hence, only short cantilevers will take the heaviest loads from multistory buildings, while the longest cantilevers will only carry light loads. The lower series of diagrams in Fig. 82 graphically illustrates this relationship between load and span.

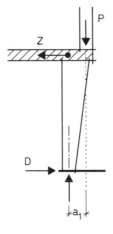

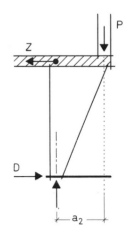

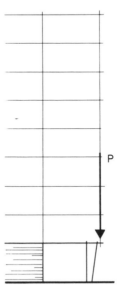

1

2

82.   V-supports with cantilevers:
      1 and 2 As the eccentricity "a" increases, the proportions of an offset
      column become distorted.
      3 and 4 Continuing the process gives a V-support with a cantilever.
      5 Large cantilevers are only feasible if the loads are light. They are not
      suitable for multistory buildings.

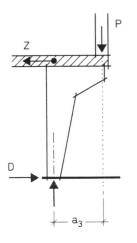

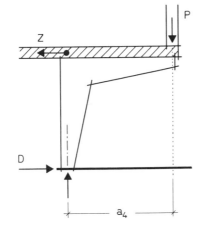

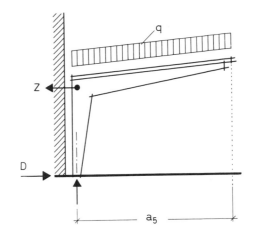

a_3

a_4

a_5

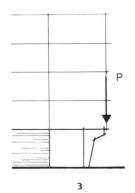

3

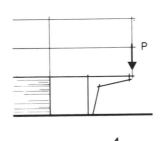

4

5

123

The combination of V-support and cantilever is suitable for canopies that back up against a larger structure (Fig. 83). The more clearly the canopy is separated from the main structure and the neater the tie detail, the more intelligible, and therefore the more significant the design. If the separation between canopy and main structure is blurred, the total impression will lack precision.

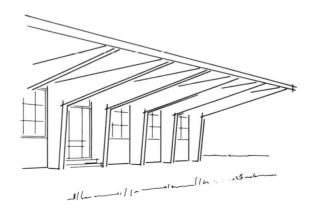

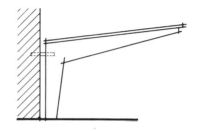

83.   The canopy is neatly separated from the main building. Its structure is clearly expressed.

In Fig. 84, for example, it is uncertain whether the cantilever forms a structural unit with the V-support or whether it is a continuation of the roof. The mere fact that the observer experiences this uncertainty clearly demonstrates the superiority of the previous design. The section (Fig. 84.2) shows that the cantilever reinforcement has been extended into the roof structure, so that the V-shape has only a decorative function.

1

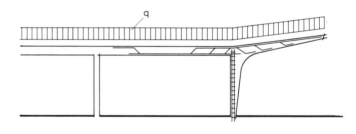

2

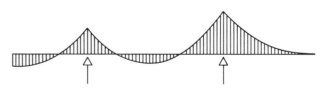

3

84.   The main building and the canopy are not cleanly separated.
       1 It is not clear whether the cantilever moment is transferred to the column
         or the roof structure.
       2 The section and the arrangement of the reinforcing show that the cantilever
         is continuous with the roof rather than with the column. The tapering of
         the columns is meaningless.
       3 Bending moment diagram.

Fig. 85 shows a few examples of relatively long cantilevers with correspondingly light loads. The two elements of the light shelter in Fig. 85.3 maintain equilibrium through direct contact. The structural principle of the free-standing support with a cantilever is the same as that illustrated in Fig. 83.

1

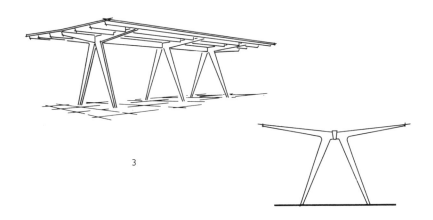

3

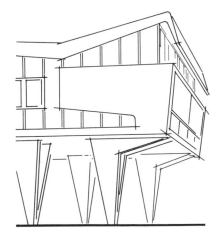

2

85.   V-supports with wide cantilevers and light loading.
     1 and 2 Cantilevers supporting one story only.
     3 The elegance of this cantilever is made possible by the lightness of the shelter roof.

In Fig. 86 the broad overhang of the second-floor cantilever seems incompatible with the very heavy loads imposed by the five floors above. The explanation becomes evident from a study of the cross section. The gable wall, which led us to believe that the loads from all the upper floors were concentrated on the cantilever, is not a bearing wall at all. On the contrary, it is supported at every floor. This support is provided by the floor structure, which is itself designed to cantilever beyond a row of columns set back inside the building. The inside face of these columns is flush with the inside face of the V-supports at the first floor. The second-floor cantilever does not receive any load from the upper stories. It has no more to carry than any single beam ·in the floors above. Its tapered· form is sheer ballast and the V-support, out of which it appears to grow, has no structural significance. This is a typical instance of a structural form being faked. The desire to achieve a contemporary idiom has merely produced a decorative gesture. The practiced eye will easily detect the inherent ambiguity from the exaggerated overhang, so incongruous in a building of this height. For the layman, however, modern architecture presents difficulties. How can he make such fine distinctions without specialized knowledge? How can he arrive at an independent judgement? The confusion generated by the mishandling of structural forms is particularly disturbing to such a person. Just what is he to think, when forms which he believes to be a structural necessity turn out to be specious ornament? Especially after being persuaded that one of the principal tenets of modern architecture is the rejection of formalism!

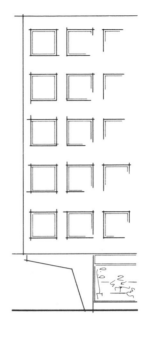

1

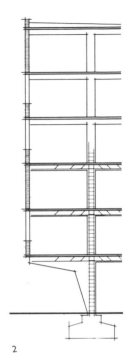

2

86. Wide cantilevers in multistory buildings:
   1 The length of the cantilever is out of all proportion to the apparent load.
   2 In actual fact the structure is cantilevered at every floor. The V-support and tapered cantilever at first-floor level are not strictly necessary.
   3 Presumably the visible cantilevers do not carry the loads from all the floors. The relationship between the depth of the cantilever arm and the load it carries fails to convince.

3

STADIUM ROOFS

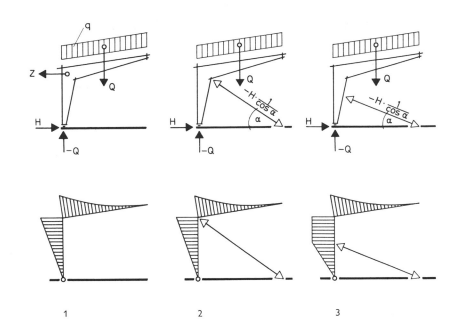

1   2   3

In the preceding section it was shown that in certain circumstances a V-support can conveniently be combined with a cantilever. In fact, V-supports are often used in conjunction with cantilevered stadium roofs. Among the many structures of this type that have actually been built a number are so significant that they deserve a special section to themselves.

Let us start with a V-support and cantilever tied back at the top (Fig. 87.1). Replacing the tie at the rear with a strut in front does not affect the loading diagram or the distribution of forces (Fig. 87.2). Even if the point where the strut meets the V-support is dropped (Fig. 87.3), the statical system remains the same. Sports stands erected in Augsburg (87.4) and Basle (87.5) are representative of this type of construction [25] [26].

The strut, however, may also perform another important function. It can be used to carry the tiers of seats. The originally independent elements—V-supports and cantilevered roof, on the one hand, and inclined struts, on the other—become fused into a new functional unit. Originally the two sets of elements only achieved equilibrium by leaning against each other. Now V-supports, cantilever and ramp together form a new statical entity. This new entity, however, demands a new, appropriate structural form. Obviously, the forms in Fig. 87 are not yet wholly in harmony with the play of forces. The important point where the strut and the V-support meet is not yet adequately expressed.

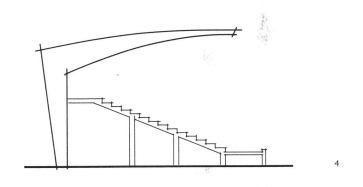

4

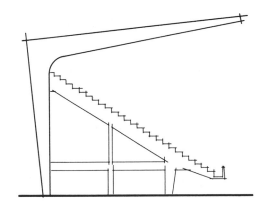

5

87.   Stadium structures based on V-supports with cantilevers:
       1 The frame can be tied back at the rear or
       2 propped up in front.
       3 Angle of the prop reduced.
       4 and 5 In the stadia at Augsburg [25] and Basle [26] the props also act as
         stand beams.

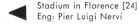
Stadium in Florence [24]
Eng: Pier Luigi Nervi

Fig. 88 shows how this form might be developed. An initial structural analysis suggests two possibilities (88.1 and 88.2). Both recognize the appropriateness of the V-shape for resisting the moments and the importance of its point of intersection with the strut. In 88.2 the kink introduced into the support indicates that the form is approaching maturity. When the stand beams, or struts, are combined with the supports below the kink to form a single member, we get the new configuration shown in 88.3. This system is still unstable and the sloping portion of the V-leg is still too short and too steep to carry the arena seating. By lengthening it and reducing the slope, we arrive at the form adopted for the stadium in [27]. The structure as a whole is made stable by mounting it on a frame. The result is an appropriate and convincing structural form.

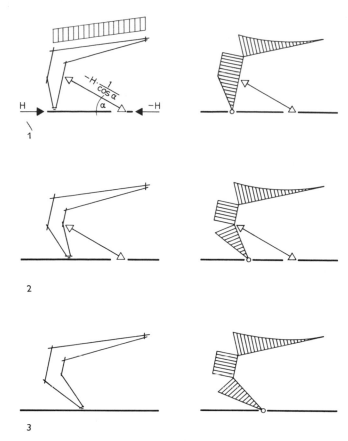

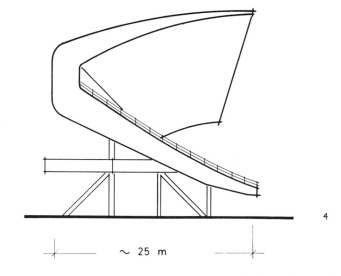

88. Stages in the design of the grandstand of the Caracas arena [27]:
1 The shape of the V-support reflects the bending moment diagram.
2 The point of support is emphasized by introducing a kink.
3 The lower part of the V-support is combined with the prop and the sloping stand beam. The structure is still essentially unstable.
4 The final stable form is arrived at by supporting the structure on a frame.

~ 25 m

Stadium at Caracas, Venezuela [27] ▶
Arch: Villanueva

The series of diagrams in Fig. 89 provides us with another important example [24]. The starting point of the stand design is the same basic structure as before, a V-support and cantilever, strutted in front instead of being tied back behind. In order to understand the structure, it is necessary to imagine the solid fins which form the cantilever and the support cut away to leave a triangulated frame. The strut retains its former function. It still has the character of an auxiliary member. There remains a division into main and secondary elements. Unity is still lacking. In an effort to bring order into the design, the diagonal member and the strut are then aligned. In this way, the functions of strut and stand beam are merged, while at the same time harmony is achieved among the various elements of the system. By resolving the cantilever and the support into a truss, the bending moments are transformed into tensile forces in the upper and compressive forces in the lower chords. The triangulation of the structure is in keeping with the principle of economy. If members are necessarily deep, using the truss form will save material. However, where the chords converge at an acute angle, at the end of the cantilever, for example, it is more convenient to fuse them together. Thus, the final design is the outcome of a logical train of thought, devoid of formal intent. Nervi has perfected it in his sports stadium for Florence. This structure appears to be totally unrelated to that in Caracas. Nevertheless, we recognize the same source of inspiration and can trace it through to the independent conclusion. The building owes its quality not least to the clarity of the construction and the unity of materials, form and function.

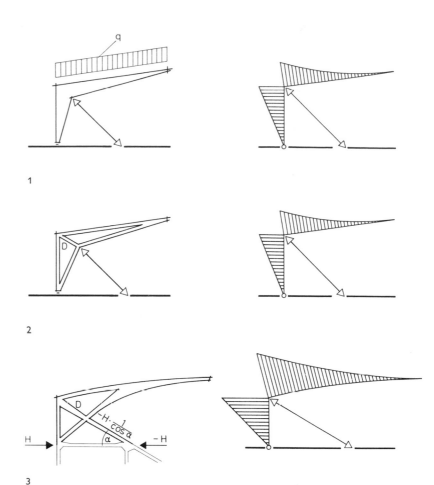

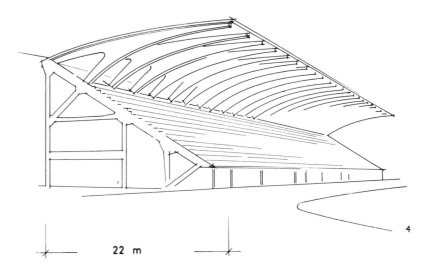

89. Stages in the design of a grandstand in Florence, Italy [24]:
1 The basic shape, a propped V-support with cantilever.
2 Triangulation of the V-support and cantilever.
3 At the end of the cantilever the top and bottom chords are run together; the sloping stand beam is combined with the "D" member.
4 Final form.

22 m

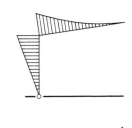

The stadium in Rabat (Fig. 90) includes a stand structure designed on quite a different principle [28]. It recalls the hinged T-frames already discussed. Fig. 74.5 illustrated the stabilization of a cantilevered roof, supported on hinged V-members, by means of a tie in the rear. In the case of the Rabat stadium a row of supports in front would have obstructed the view. Accordingly, a rear tie is justified. The broad overhang ensures the stability of the structure, even when wind loads produce uplift. The short rear cantilever is just long enough to shelter the gallery and anchor the tie rods. There is an obvious reinforced concrete hinge at the foot of the V-support. By raising it slightly above the gallery level, it is given the formal emphasis that its structural importance warrants. All the functional and structural elements fit smoothly together.

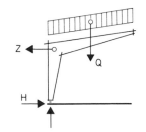

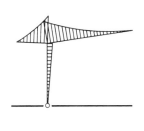

1

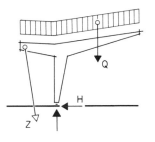

2

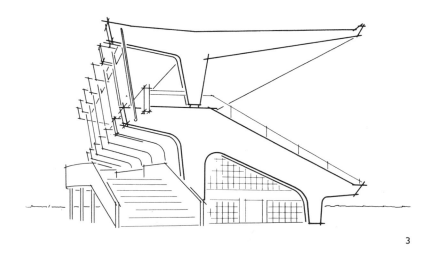

90. Stages in the design of a grandstand in Rabat, Morocco [28]:
    1 The basic frame stabilized by tying it back in the rear.
    2 The horizontal tie can be replaced with a vertical tension member attached to a short rear cantilever. This tension member is in equilibrium with the load.
    3 The final form is a sort of T-frame (cf. Fig. 74.5).

~ 17,5o m

Nervi's grandstand design (Fig. 89) introduces the idea of a trussed V-member. In principle, the most striking feature of the roof construction, the bifurcation of the cantilever, can be incorporated in any V-support. The result is a forked column.

Primitive forms of forked column have been known for a long time. Crossed poles for supporting climbing plants and strutted posts and masts (Fig. 55) are forked columns, though in these crude examples the fork points downwards. In our new world of structural forms the reverse is usually true. The modern forked column converges towards the base, that is, the prongs point upwards. Structurally, it is a V-support and obeys the same laws. To this extent it requires no further explanation. However, the basic idea is so fruitful and its applications so numerous that a separate section devoted to the forked column does not seem out of place.

If we think of the forked column simply as a variant of the V-support (hence its place in this chapter), then, logically, it should also be possible to use it as the leg of a rigid frame. This is the part it plays in the bridge design shown in Fig. 91 [29]. This bridge is a purely utilitarian structure without any formal pretensions.

The long span, the heavy live loads and the great stiffness of the abutments compared with the deck mean correspondingly high stresses in the squat, compact support, which, if it were a solid V-support, would be a massive triangular slab almost as broad as it was tall. It is therefore advantageous to replace the heavy, solid slab with a triangular frame. The bending moment is then transformed into a couple and the structure is resolved into clearly defined tension and compression members.

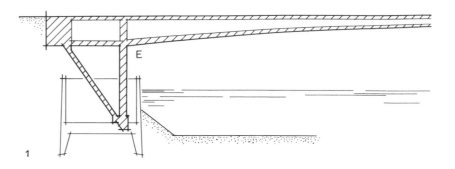

1

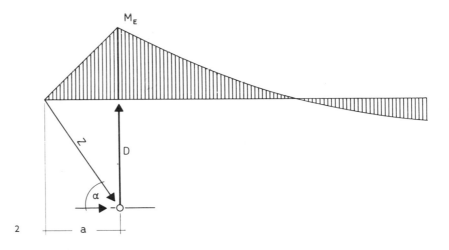

2

91. When the tapered legs of heavy rigid frames are triangulated, forked columns are formed.
1 The Rohrdamm Bridge in Berlin is a rigid frame with forked legs [29].
2 Bending moments and forces in the forked leg.

In bridge construction a forked column, acting as the leg of a rigid frame, is subjected to very heavy stresses. Yet exactly the same form is used in furniture-making, where the loads are extremely light. The only difference is that in bridge construction engineering considerations take precedence, whereas in furniture-making greater importance is attributed to esthetic values. The leg of the bridge frame is designed to restrain the girders and reduce the stresses at mid-span. It is able to do this thanks to the great stiffness of its broad, triangular form and its hinged feet standing on rigid foundations. As far as the table is concerned, there is no question of relieving the stresses in the horizontal member, i.e. the table top. Moreover there is nothing to prevent the lateral displacement of the feet. When the table top deflects, they yield sideways. Yet lateral rigidity is of great importance. The table designer can achieve it very simply by attaching forked legs to the table top, to form a joint comparable with that at the corner of a rigid frame (Fig. 92.1).

The extent to which the elementary laws of frame construction apply to the table is shown in Figs. 92.2 and 3. If the top is too thin, even forked legs will not make a long table stiff. In the first place, the top (horizontal member) is too flexible compared with the legs (vertical members) and, secondly, the ends of the legs (hinged feet of the frame) are not anchored to rigid foundations. They cannot get a purchase on a smooth floor.

The table also provides a good illustration of the need for three-dimensional stability. The elementary structures discussed so far have clearly all been so-called "plane" structures, that is, structures acting in two dimensions only (length and height). It was tacitly assumed that stability in the third dimension was ensured by other means, independent of the structure in question.

The table is a simple but striking example of how little a forked support affects the stiffness at right angles to its plane of action (Fig. 92.4). The forked leg contributes a great deal of stiffness in one direction but hardly any in the other. In order to overcome this deficiency, the furniture industry has devised a variant of the forked leg that is equally effective in both directions (Fig. 92.5).

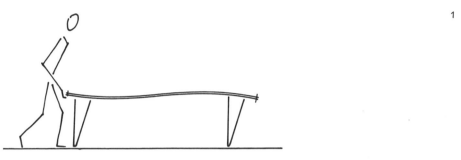

1

3

4

5

92.   A table with forked legs provides a clear illustration of the elementary laws of rigid frame construction.
  1 Forked legs give a table considerable stiffness in the plane of the fork.
  2 and 3 If the table has a top that is too long and too thin, even forked legs will not make it stable.
  4 Forked legs offer no resistance to deformation in a direction at right-angles to the plane of the fork.
  5 Only legs forked in both directions give a table all-round stability.

Like most structural forms, the forked column can be used merely for the sake of its decorative effect. Ignorance of its true structural significance leads to the artificialities characteristic of so many of the canopy structures that embellish the entrances to our commercial buildings, schools and hotels (Fig. 93).

For example, how often do we see a forked column turned at right angles to the front of a building, representing a stiffening function that is entirely superfluous. The building itself is infinitely more rigid than a forked column ever could be. Moreover, the canopy slab is often far too flexible to act as the horizontal member of a rigid frame. The analogy with Fig. 70.2 is unmistakable. Structurally, the forked column is just as inappropriate here as was the V-support under the balcony slab. In most cases neither its orientation nor its position nor the angle between the prongs aim at anything more than a purely decorative effect. The forked column, however, is primarily a structural form. To the technically conscious observer its triangularity conveys the idea that something is being stiffened. If its fails to convey this, it conveys nothing.

How much more impressive, compared with these structurally feeble, pseudo-technical frills, is the vigorous formalism of a nineteenth century design by Viollet le Duc [30]. With visionary power he has grasped the structural logic of the forked column 100 years in advance. Outwardly, it is true, the building is a flowery example of the prevailing style, but the structure is genuine and forceful. Modern forked columns are too often simply a concession to the "technological" taste of the day; the structure is false and the effect weak and spindly. It is both interesting and important to compare these two possible kinds of formalism. To us modern technical formalism seems the greatest of all such evils. It is the main object of our criticism and we are bent on its overthrow.

93.   Formalistic use of forked columns.

Design made by Viollet le Duc in 1864 [30].

A good example of a forked column clearly understood and master-fully applied is to be found in Favini's design [31] for a filling station on a highway leading out of Milan (Fig. 94). The roof is a corrugated reinforced concrete shell. At the back it is supported on a sturdy building frame of adequate stability. Accordingly, the front supports do not need to contribute any rigidity in the "y" direction. In the "x" direction the situation is different. In this case some extra stiffening is essential. Hence, the forked column has been combined with a deep diaphragm to form a half-frame (cf. Fig. 63), thus ensuring the transverse stability of the structure. Of course, two forked columns might have been used instead. The result would have been a two-hinged frame with even greater stiffness in the "x" direction. However, the stiffness of the half-frame is perfectly adequate to resist wind loads. There is no need to relieve the dead load stresses in the horizontal member, since its depth, determined by the height of the corrugations, is more than sufficient. The introduction of the half-frame reduces the structure to an elementary basic form. Its action and stability are perfectly obvious and the result is a design of limpid clarity.

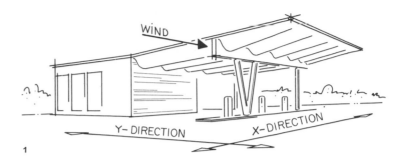

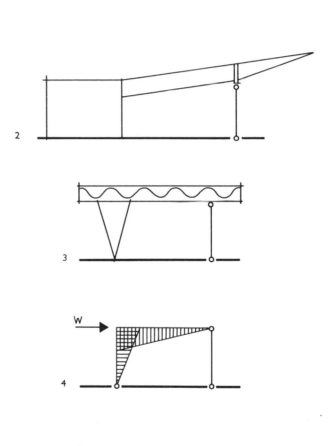

94. A filling station in Milan, Italy, an example of a building stabilized in two directions by different means [31].

1 In the y-direction the roof is tied back to the solid masonry structure in the rear. The front supports act as hinged columns. In the x-direction the forked column, the simple column and the horizontal member form a half-frame capable of resisting wind forces.

2 Structural system—side view.

3 Structural system—front view.

4 Wind moments in the half-frame.

5 A two-hinged frame might have been used instead of a half-frame, but this is not strictly necessary, since there is no point in relieving the stresses in a horizontal member that is already very deep.

Filling station in Milan [31]
Eng: Favini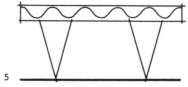

As already explained with reference to numerous examples, to make a two-hinged frame rigid, it is indispensable to stiffen not only the legs and the corners but the horizontal member as well (Fig. 95.1). If the latter is too flexible (Fig. 95.2), it makes no difference how stiff the supports are made. The structure will never offer much resistance to lateral loads.

Forked columns, however, can be combined in quite a different way. If the angle between the prongs is widened until successive members meet at the top (Fig. 95.3), a series of closed triangular frames is obtained. In this case the horizontal member can be relatively flexible, since it is no longer stressed in bending. Horizontal loads simply produce axial tension or compression in all three members of the frame. This is the significance of the substructure for the aluminum Dome of Discovery, designed for the London Exhibition of 1951 (Fig. 95.4). The relatively thin edge of the dome (Fig. 95.3) only makes sense as part of the triangulated system, which it forms in conjunction with the sloping struts. The feeling conveyed by the continuity of these struts is one of structural clarity and calm. The alternative form shown in Fig. 95.5 is not convincing.

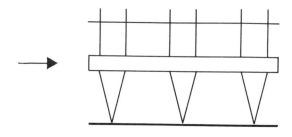

1

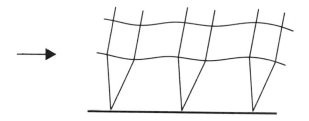

2

3

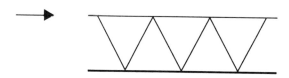

4

5

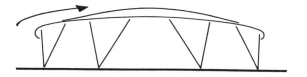

95. Rigid connections between forked columns and horizontal members.
  1 Lateral stability depends on the presence of a stiff beam.
  2 If the beam is flexible, even forked columns will not ensure stability.
  3 If forked columns are linked together to form a chain of triangles, the horizontal member will be free of bending under horizontal load.
  4 The thin edge of the Dome of Discovery at the London Exhibition of 1951 was similarly stiffened by triangulation [32].
  5 A ring of independent forked columns is neither esthetically nor structurally satisfactory.

Oscar Niemeyer often uses forked columns to support multistory buildings. He assigns them a role corresponding to that illustrated schematically in Fig. 95.1. Each forked column picks up the loads from two lines of upper columns within the thickness of the second floor and transfers them to a common foundation (Fig. 96.1). The heavy girder at the top of the forked columns is somewhat unexpected; nevertheless, although it may be assumed that this large building derives its rigidity largely from other sources, such as elevator shafts, stair walls, etc., binding the heads of the columns with a relatively stiff horizontal member sensibly adds to the stability of the design. The slender horizontal with no real stiffness, shown for the sake of comparison in Fig. 96.2, is far less satisfactory. We are left with the impression of a ragged edge, whereas a true structural form should be smoothly closed.

As far as the forked column itself is concerned, Niemeyer has succeeded in molding some very impressive plastic forms out of the simple prototype of the fork with two parallel-sided prongs. The density of these forms, that is the high degree of expressiveness they achieve with very economical means, must be acknowledged even by the critical engineer, though he may sometimes detect in them a measure of structural inconsequence. The detailing of the reinforcement in the forked columns of Niemeyer's hospital in Rio de Janeiro (Fig. 96.3) reveals the internal order as strikingly as an X-ray photograph [33]. There is no structural justification for the web of unreinforced material between the prongs. It is purely an architectural gesture. The reduced sections at top and bottom indicate three moment-free hinges. Thus, the diagonal members themselves transmit only axial forces and are not stressed in bending. Accordingly, in this case there is absolutely no reason why they should be tapered.

Later on, in connection with one of Niemeyer's buildings in Berlin, we shall see that under certain conditions this rather arbitrary solution may become a true structural form.

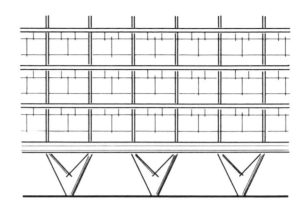

1

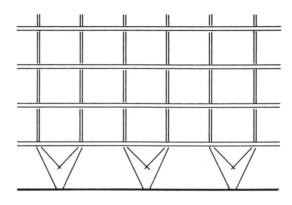

2

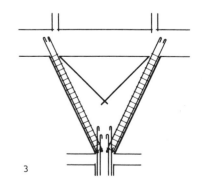

96.   Forked columns of a hospital in Rio de Janeiro, Brazil [33].
  1 The stiffening beam at the head of the forked columns is a satisfactory stabilizing element.
  2 A relatively slender beam does not convince.
  3 Detail of column reinforcement. The conical shape of the prongs is neither structurally derived nor statically exploited.

3

Outwardly, Niemeyer's apartment house for the 1957 "Interbau" development in Berlin [34] appears to resemble his building in Rio (Fig. 97). Here, however, the design of the forked columns is crisper, the spread greater, the hinges at the top more emphatic and the breadth of the base more pronounced. The two tapered prongs sprout from the base like growing shoots. They make it plain that they are not hinged at the bottom (a point the Rio design leaves in doubt) but firmly anchored in the foundation and well able to resist overturning. In this case the outward impression really is a reflection of the actual structure. The reinforcing detail (Fig. 97.2) reveals the true play of forces. The tapered prongs are reinforced across their entire width and resist high bending moments at the base. They actually make a decisive contribution to the lateral stability of the structure. The form of the structure is indeed determined by the nature of the forces it must resist.

At Belo-Horizonte [35] Niemeyer used a three-pronged column (Fig. 98). This form again speaks another language. Although, as a structural form, it is not as expressive as the column used in Berlin, its plastic contours neatly terminate this large building. The position of the prongs is unambiguous and correct; structurally it is the only position possible, the intersection of floor and bearing wall.

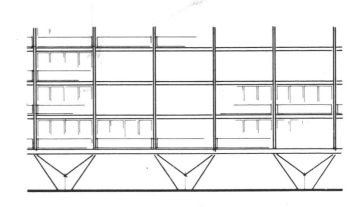

97 1

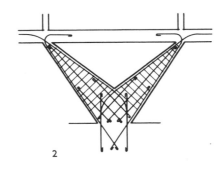

2

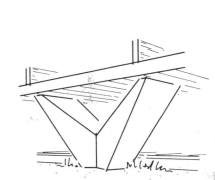

3

97.   Forked columns in Oscar Niemeyer's apartment house in Berlin [34].
        1 The broad base of the columns indicates that bending can be transmitted to the foundations.
        2 The reinforcing detail reveals the stiffening function of the fixed supports. The conical prongs are true structural forms.
        3 Perspective.

98.   Three-pronged forked columns at Belo Horizonte, Brazil [35]. Loads from the bearing walls in the upper stories are transferred to the tips of the prongs.

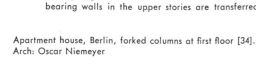
Apartment house, Berlin, forked columns at first floor [34].
Arch: Oscar Niemeyer

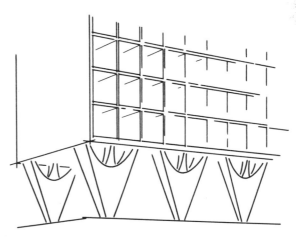

98.

The points of load transfer by no means always coincide so exactly with the tips of the prongs as in these examples of Niemeyer's work. The first impression produced by Fig. 99 is of a building in no way more arbitrary in design or less structurally coherent than the buildings of Niemeyer's we have just discussed. Column lines and floor bands divide the elevation into a regular grid. The points where the loads are concentrated are immediately obvious, but seem to be totally unrelated to the positions of the forked columns. The loads thrust between the prongs of the fork, apparently into the void. In actual fact the loads are transferred to the forked columns by means of a concealed, second-floor girder, designed to resist torsion and only recognizable in section (Fig. 99.2). The natural flow of forces is distorted. We miss the clarity of a genuine structural form. Moreover, the base of the column lacks elegance. A bent pipe might be suitable for furniture, but it is hardly compatible with the loads encountered in buildings. As a result of the curvature the longitudinal forces are transferred eccentrically to the pipe, developing bending moments far in excess of its capacity. Of course, if the architect insists, the engineer will always find a way out. In the last resort, the curved section can be made of cast steel. But is this really a solution? Does this drive out the dubious element and make the structure "right"? The technically pretentious modernity of such architecture remains inept and the structural gesture hollow.

2

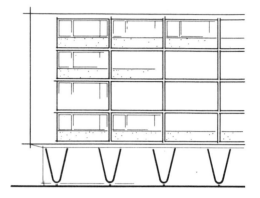

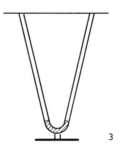

1

3

99.   Misuse of forked columns in tubular steel.
      1 The column loads come down midway between the prongs.
      2 The loads are transferred to the tips of the prongs by means of a concealed torsion beam.
      3 Rounding off the fork at the bottom aggravates the stress conditions. It becomes necessary to replace the curved tube with a piece of cast steel.

The simple, economical forked column with parallel-sided prongs has a legitimate place beside Niemeyer's more elaborate forms. Fig. 100 shows a box-type frame, in which each of the transverse bearing walls is carried by two forked columns [36]. At the same time, in conjunction with the extremely rigid bearing walls, the forked columns give the building its transverse stability. They perform this function better than ordinary vertical columns could. It is true that the forked columns do little to stabilize the structure in the longitudinal direction (cf. text page 135 and Fig 92). This must be achieved by other means, longitudinal stiffening walls, massive elevator shafts, etc.

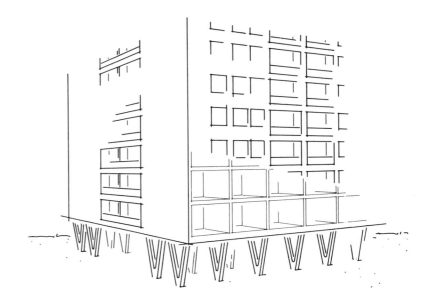

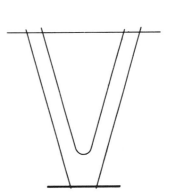

100. Simple forked columns with parallel-sided prongs combined with load-bearing cross walls [36].

Low industrial buildings are occasionally designed with shell roofs rectangular in plan and supported only at the four corners. As a result, clusters of forked columns are generated at these points. Structurally, these are not forked columns in the sense of our original definition, since they are formed by four independent columns from adjacent shells. How should they be interpreted in terms of design? The different shells may conveniently be treated as individual units separated by expansion joints (Fig. 101.1). The distance between edge beams is determined by the width of accessible gutter required or the necessary distance between opposite bands of glazing. The substructure must provide separate support for these neighboring but clearly independent elements. The loads descend at points too close together for it to be possible to provide four independent vertical columns. The space available is too cramped. At the same time, however, they are too far apart for the four columns to be combined into one. The only solution is to employ a cluster of columns to bring the loads from the four corners where they are concentrated down to a common base. Thus, whether the fork shape be the product of abutting independent, trestle-like structures with splayed legs in the manner of Fig. 101.1 [37], or whether the four corners of the room are carried on four-column clusters [38] (Fig. 101.2), in the long run the visual effect is more or less the same. The proper detailing of this structural form, however, presupposes a perfectly clear understanding of the function of the supports.

If the edge beam of the shell and two splayed legs are assumed to form a closed system (101.1), they can be made to act like a frame. In this case, however, the object is not to relieve the horizontal member (the edge beam is already stiff enough), but simply to give the structure lateral stability. Since the roof profile offers little resistance to wind, the lateral forces will be small and the splayed legs of the frame can be made relatively slender. Note, however, that these splayed legs are not tapered, nor do they form forked columns. The forked column effect is entirely due to the proximity of adjacent inclined supports. There is no question of a closed forked column. In detailing, therefore, it is correct to preserve a clear division between the prongs of the fork and to support them independently and neatly, side by side, on the substructure.

If the inclined supports are not regarded as the legs of a frame and there is no rigid connection between them and the shell edge beam, then they must be fixed at the base. Otherwise the structure will have no lateral stability. Adjacent columns may now conveniently be merged and the resulting form will be one resembling that illustrated in Fig. 101.2. In this case it is no longer appropriate to keep the feet of the inclined columns separate. On the contrary, good form now requires a node-like thickening at their base. At the top, on the other hand, the hinged connection can be expressed by means of a corresponding reduction in cross section. Although this is a convenient solution in the interior spaces of a large shed, it is hard to adhere to the same principle around the perimeter. There the arrangement shown in Fig. 101.1 has obvious advantages. The design of the Rhone Bridge (Fig. 101.3) [39] can be interpreted in more or less the same

way as that of the factory building in 101.1. Frames with inclined legs the same width as the girder follow one behind the other. Every pair of legs suggests a forked column. Since they are hinged at the feet, it is just as correct to taper the legs downwards as to thicken them at the corner of the frame, where the bending moments are greatest.

101.   Column clusters:
1 Splayed legs forming rigid frames with the edge members of shells. In this case the columns are clearly separated [37].
2 Three-dimensional forked columns formed where the corners of four shells meet. The roof loads are transferred to the columns through hinged joints [38].
3 The legs of abutting bridge frames give the impression of forked columns [39].

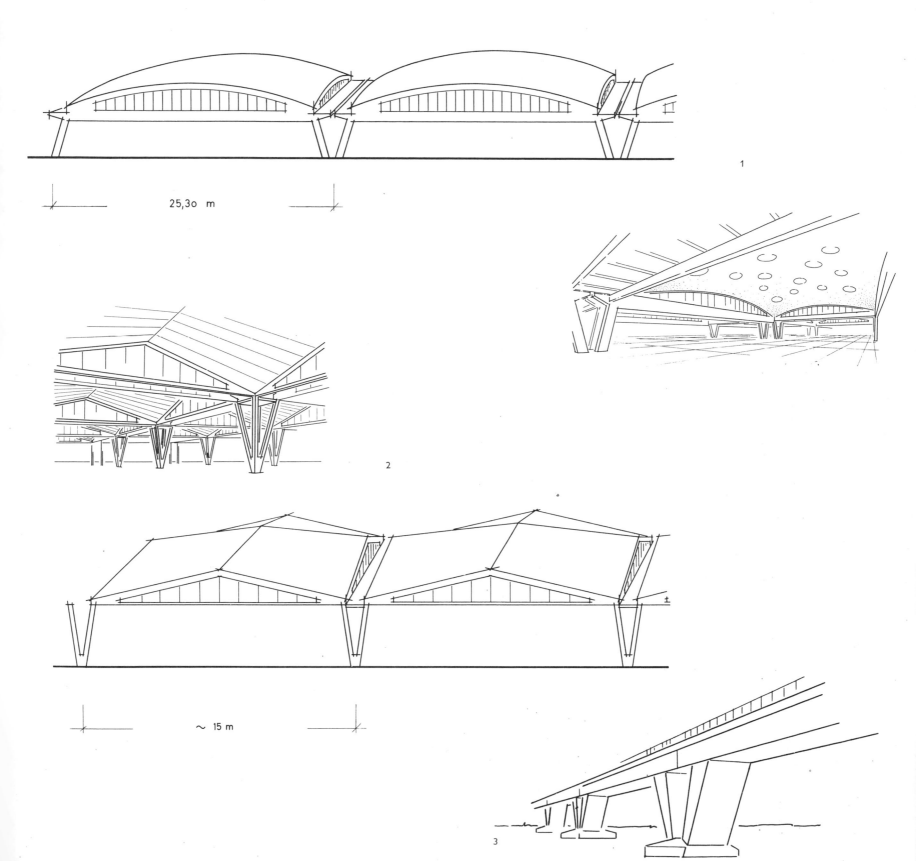

25,3o m

1

2

~ 15 m

3

147

At this point it seems appropriate to mention a form which, so far, has been little used. This form is characterized by a bifurcation beginning only half-way up the column. Thus, the column consists of a fork at the top and a relatively massive upright below. This idea has been incorporated in the design of the Birsfelden power station (Fig. 102) [40]. The straight part of the column is compact and rigidly fixed at the base. Together with a heavy crane beam it ensures the longitudinal stability of the structure. The spreading prongs of the fork, on the other hand, are surprisingly slim. Nevertheless, they carry the entire load from the folded-plate roof and are without the usual horizontal member at the top. This is only possible, because adjacent prongs are in direct contact with each other and form triangular frames, in the manner of the Dome of Discovery (Fig. 95). This explains both the delicate rim of the dome and the elastic edge of the folded-plate, which has no horizontal stiffener. The folded plate alone would be unstable in a direction at right angles to the folds (i.e. along the length of the building) (cf. Chapter 3, page 198 ff. Stability is restored by the crane beam and the slender but rigid triangulated forks. Folded plate, forked columns, crane beam and fixed legs form a structural unit, in which each part has its function and is logically integrated in the whole.

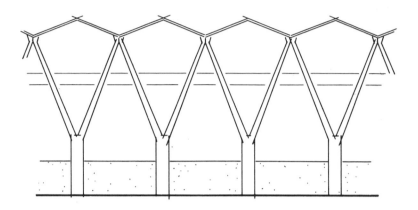

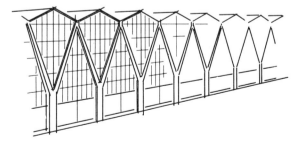

102. In the Birsfelden power station [40] the folded plate is stiffened by Y-frames, the legs of which are fixed at the base while the prongs meet at the top. The roof loads are transferred to the tips of the prongs.

The principle behind the Y-supports of Nervi's sports stadium in Rome [41] is the same (Fig. 103). As distinct from the Birsfelden power station, all the members are tapered. This suggests that the three outer joints are hinged and that the central joint where the three arms of the Y meet, is rigid. At Birsfelden the "plane" system meant that the columns had to be stiffened by fixing their feet and tying them to the longitudinal crane beam. In Nervi's design such measures are unnecessary. Together, the Y-frames, each one rigid in itself, form the base of a cone, which, in spite of the hinged connections at top and bottom, is a very stable structure. The Y-supports thrust against a ring beam buried in the ground. They have an advantage over forked columns that begin to spread just above the foundations in that the area beneath the fork remains free. They carry the circular dome on the upper ends of their tapered prongs. The points where the load is transferred are marked by a slight corrugation. This corrugation helps to prevent the edge of the dome sagging between supports. However, it also emphasizes the fact that in this design the edge of the dome need not be rigid at the fixed points where the prongs of the forks meet (cf. Dome of Discovery, London, Fig. 95, and Birsfelden, Fig. 102). In addition, the rippling of the roof admits extra light. Everything fits neatly together. Structure, function and form are one. All that is necessary has been provided, yet nothing is superfluous. The structure itself is decorative and elegant without sacrificing economy and utility.

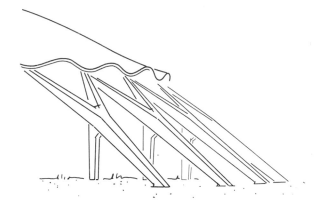

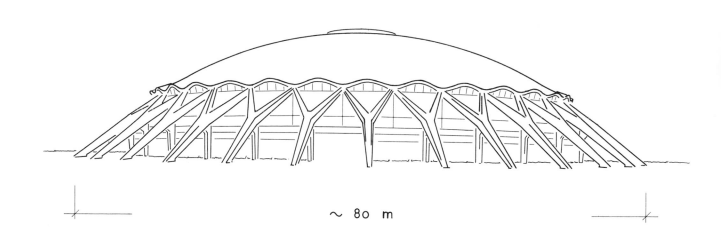

~ 80 m

103.   In Nervi's sports palace in Rome [41] the Y-frames are hinged at top and bottom. Nevertheless, the structure is stable because it forms a space system with three dimensional rigidity.

In this section on the forked column the author has again attempted to demonstrate the remarkable versatility of the V-support. It is precisely this versatility that makes the V-support difficult to handle. Really powerful and decisive forms, like some of those illustrated, are the exception rather than the rule. Engineers are not always interested in the esthetic aspects of the structures they design. They often think of their job as confined to making impeccable computations and are satisfied with almost any solution provided the calculations are correct. In reality, however, this is only part of the engineer's function. The engineer ought to do more than merely make sure that what the architect designs stands up. Even the most miserable structure may be statically irreproachable. But this is no help at all. On the contrary, the engineer should act as the architect's critical partner, objecting strenuously whenever the design offends structural logic. It should not be his ambition to squeeze everything into a framework of computation; instead he should try to make the significance of the structure and its behavior clearer to the architect, so that the latter can draw upon his understanding for inspiration in working out the final design. Most architects, on the other hand, appear to stand extraordinarily aloof from the problems of statics. They have little appreciation of the profounder questions of modern structural design, though these are at the heart of contemporary architecture. Too many have still to learn that artistic inspiration alone cannot produce genuine technical forms, whereas an ability to discern rational relationships is a prerequisite to inspiration. A mistaken idea has got about that, in this area, a systematic approach inhibits the imagination and the free process of thought. This is true only of petty computation. An investigation of the fundamental laws that govern the mechanics of forces and the evolution of genuine, powerful structures does not hobble the mind. On the contrary, it spurs the mind to discover new forms. The essence of the problem is really the individual's attitude to technology and, in particular, its significance for modern architecture. Hence it is a question of the time and education. Since the present generation is capable of recognizing structural problems, it has at least taken a great stride forward since the turn of the century. At that time the problem of modern structural form was still obscured by decorative whimsy. Even now we cannot expect to find general understanding; new technical ground is being broken every day. On the other hand, modern architecture owes its liveliness and extraordinary fascination largely to the inexhaustibility of the design possibilities upon which it can draw.

Olympic sports palace (Palazetto), Rome.
Column detail [41]
Eng: Pier Luigi Nervi

IMPROVED BEARING ON V-SUPPORTS

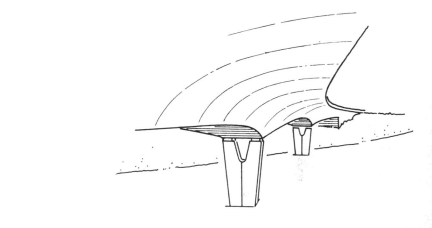

1

Our picture of the V-support would be incomplete, if we were to omit a description of another of its special functions, even though this function has little relevance to the discussion so far. Whereas in the earlier sections of this chapter our interest was entirely confined to the action of the V-support in the transverse plane, the plane in which the V-shape is expressed, in this section we are concerned with the improved bearing afforded by a V-support in the longitudinal direction. The broad top of a V-support offers a welcome bearing for wide beams, spanning at right angles to the plane of the V. A garage building in St. Gallen [42] (Fig. 104.1), bridge piers in Baden-Oos [43] and Paris (Fig. 104.2) and the unusual piers of Maillart's bridge over the Arve at Vessy-Geneva (Fig. 104.3) provide practical examples of V-supports used in this way. In the bridge over the Arve [44], however, the individual V-supports carry two narrow beams rather than a single broad one. To understand these forms properly it is necessary to consider the structure as a whole. The isolated form conveys very little. The important thing is whether it is correctly and logically incorporated in the over-all design.

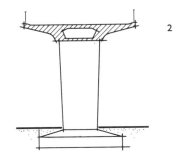

2

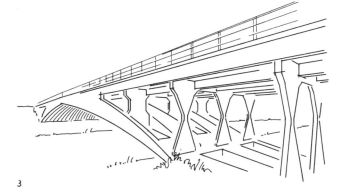

3

104.   Improved bearing on V-supports.
      1 Wide flat beams need correspondingly wide bearings. The plane of the
      V is at right-angles to the span and no frame action is developed [42].

 Bridge over the Oos-Tal at Baden-Baden [43]

An attempt has been made to classify V-supports according to their function and physical appearance. The material, however, is not amenable to strict classification. Certain special cases, though often of great interest, fail to fit in. Accordingly, we propose to round off the discussion by considering some of these exceptions. Treating all of them as V-supports means interpreting the definition rather broadly. This has a diluting effect, which, however, helps to offset the tendency to narrowness that characterizes any attempt to impose a system of order. Structural form never arises from rules and regulations alone; it tends instead to develop organically from a multiplicity of relationships, of which rules and regulations form only a part.

The Buttresses of Nervi's Hangars [45]

The historical V-support was briefly mentioned at the beginning of this chapter (Figs. 52 to 54). It always tapers upwards. The modern V-support, as so far discussed, tapers downwards. The difference appears to be a fundamental one, closely connected with differences in the historical and modern approaches to building. This, however, is not entirely true. Even today we find V-supports with a certain resemblance to the medieval buttress acting as members of modern rigid frames. Unprejudiced and impartial technical design is free from associations based on historical comparisons. Whatever is technically sound, structurally unambiguous and economical and practical as well will be good design, even in the light of modern ideas about form.

Nervi's work is free of inhibitions. Inevitably he arrived at a form for his hangar buttresses that departs radically from accepted notions. The result is not arbitrary or attributable to preconceived ideas about form, but the necessary consequence of observing structural laws (Fig. 105). To have used downward tapering V-supports here would have smacked of modern formalism. There is absolutely no possibility of forming a rigid connection between such a V-support and some horizontal element of the roof structure. The roof is a filigree of prefabricated parts. These parts are assembled into arch-like ribs that intersect to form a space frame. Statically, the finished structure behaves partly like a barrel vault and partly like a shell (see Chapter 3, page 192). In any event, the roof forms a compact unit so well-knit and self-sufficient that it would be neither structural logic nor intelligible design for individual elements, such as columns, to sprout from it. A point bearing on a few appropriately shaped buttresses is the only convincing solution.

The strength of a rigid frame depends on the flexural stiffness of the cross section. The strength of a vault, shell or catenary depends on its form. If it has the right form, a vault will stand, even though the cross section lacks stiffness. It arches itself against the loads, while the catenary droops between rigid supports. If the form is correctly chosen, both will be free of bending stresses. This gross simplification may perhaps serve to draw attention to the difference between arch and frame construction, which in this example is so decisive.

Thus, having little or no flexural stiffness, the arch cannot form a rigid corner like that of a two-hinged frame, and hence is unable to transfer bending moments to the supports. Without rigid corner connections and without the transfer of bending moments to the supports, the downward tapered V-shape makes no sense. The thrusts developed at the springings of an arch are mainly oblique, their direction being roughly tangential to the curve of the arch. The buttress must resist these oblique thrusts. This is the principal factor in its design.

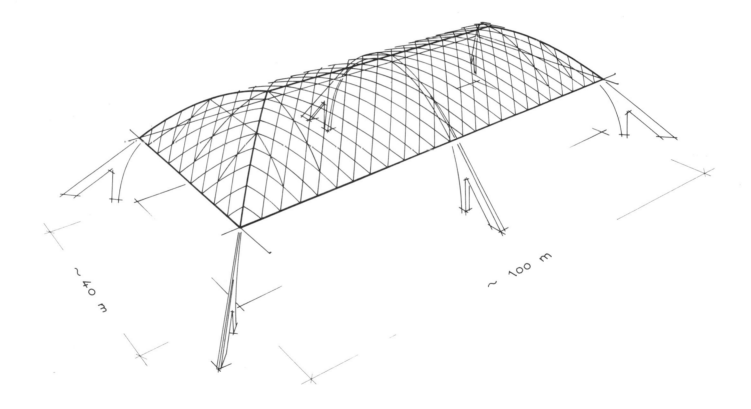

105.   The buttresses of Nervi's hangars are broad at the bottom and narrow at the top. They are inverted V-supports and have nothing to do with rigid frames [45].

In such hangars the chief types of loading are dead load and wind load. The vertical loading determines the shape of the arch. If the arch, when inverted, approaches the shape of a catenary, or suspended cable, the vertical loads will be resolved into normal compressive forces in the arch ribs and no bending stresses will develop. The buttresses are then required to resist thrusts of the type shown in Fig. 106.1. Thus, the vertical load, which determines the principal dimensions, can be carried economically. At the same time wind stresses cannot be ignored. In tall buildings, indeed, their influence can be decisive. The wind loads act unsymmetrically, from each side in turn. They modify the size and displace the line of action of the normal forces and thrusts, now to the left, now to the right. Fig. 106.2 shows both the thrust transmitted to the buttress for vertical load alone and the limiting values for dead load and wind together. The buttress must be adapted to these variations in the direction of thrust. The resulting shape is that of an upward tapered V-support. This is the shape of a cantilever element, firmly fixed at the base and acted on at the top by a lateral load of variable direction. The direction of the thrust due to the dead weight of the structure determines the center of gravity of the buttress design. The fluctuating effect of the wind transforms it into an inverted V.

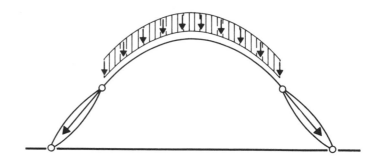

1

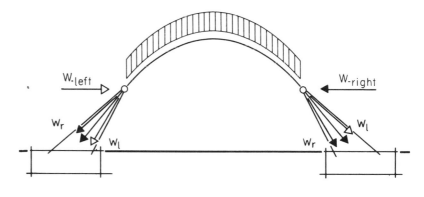

2

106.   The shape of the buttresses follows the line of action of the forces.
    1 The symmetrical, static load determines the principal direction of the forces
      in the supports. If the latter are hinged at both ends the structure is
      unstable.
    2 Wind loading from different directions causes the line of action of the
      forces in the supports to vary between certain extremes. These determine
      the shape of the buttress, which is made stable by fixing it at the base.

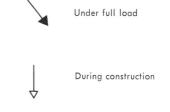

Finally, the shape of Nervi's buttresses (Fig. 107) can also be explained in terms of the triple relationship between load, distribution of forces, as determined by the laws of statics, and the practicability of the design. If we disregard everything but statics, i.e. the final direction of the forces, the inside limb of the buttress appears far too steep. It is hard to understand why. However, the direction of the forces under full load is not the only factor affecting the design, their direction during erection, before the vault is in place, is also important. In these conditions the buttresses must be prevented from overturning inwards. That is the reason for choosing this particular form.

At this point we may permit ourselves a further reference to Nervi's sports arena in Rome. Its forked columns are inclined at a very sharp angle in the direction of the thrusts from the dome. Fig. 103 shows how they are supported on a vertical prop, the direction of which deviates considerably from that of the forces acting on the buttress. This prop, too, is an erection aid. Nervi relates, not without regret, how erection considerations made this appendage indispensable. The finished building does not need it, even though the forked columns are hinged at all three ends. In a plane section the structure would appear unstable without these props; in three dimensions it is perfectly stable, since the forked columns lock together to form a rigid ring.

As far as the arched hangar is concerned, the buttresses do not form part of a rigid space frame and the structure shown in Fig. 106.1 is unstable. For this reason it requires inverted V-supports with their broad base fixed against overturning.

This is how we must interpret the buttresses of Nervi's hangars. The force and logic of the form have an immediate appeal. However, it is not enough to consider plastic qualities alone without reference to technical considerations. The form is inspired by its function and its full esthetic impact will be felt only by those aware of its appropriateness and strictly technical origin.

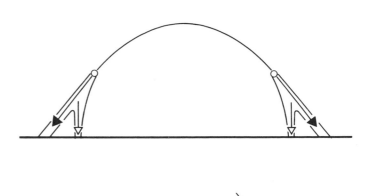

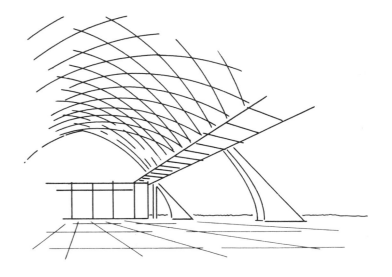

107.   To facilitate construction the buttress must be provided with an auxiliary strut or a steep soffit, since it is otherwise unstable without the vault.

A Design for a Church

It may seem rather strange to some that a section of this book should be devoted to a design for a church that has never been built. After all, there is no lack of finished buildings worth discussing. This, however, is not entirely true. Significant structures are really quite uncommon. We therefore consider ourselves justified in mentioning two projects of the Italian architect Castiglioni, a design for a church at Montecatini [46] and, later, a proposed station for Naples.

Castiglioni has a rare combination of talents; he is at once painter, sculptor, architect and engineer. The first three talents go together fairly often. The fact that the fourth, engineering skill, should have been added to the other three makes his case exceptional. Accordingly, unity of artistic and technical expression is one of the major characteristics of his work.

The bird's-eye and interior perspectives (108.1 and 2) show a nave dominated by the pregnant form of a three-hinged frame. This frame, however, does more than just enclose space and support the roof. It spans the nave, dividing it visually into a lower zone, in which the worshippers move, and a luminous upper zone, which seems to float above the first. The flood of light from above is broken, scattered and diffused by a cleverly conceived honeycomb grille. The hovering effect of this grille is achieved by means of an upper series of vaults, the springings of which are hidden from those inside the church. The vaults thrust against the shoulders of the frames. The provisions for countering this thrust form the main theme of the frame design. Instead of containing the thrust directly, by means of an obtrusive tie, the architect has diverted it through the tapered legs. This graceful yet powerful solution both justifies the taper and lends the structure as a whole its special charm.

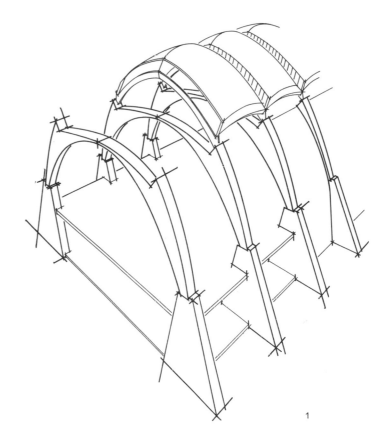

1

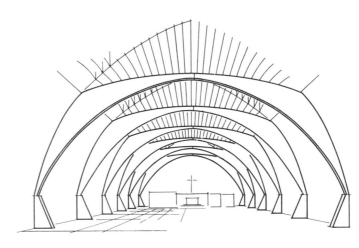

2

108.   This church design by Castiglioni is based on a three-hinged frame with tapered legs [46].
1 Bird's-eye view.
2 Interior.

The distribution of the forces is shown in Fig. 108.3. The direction of the thrust at the springings of the upper vaults makes plain the bracing function of the frame beneath. The loads acting on it include its own weight, the wind and the weight of the honeycomb vault. The first two loads are both small; that from the vaults above is critical. The most unfavorable combination of loads gives the bending moment diagram plotted on the tension side of the frame in Fig. 108.4. For the specialist these diagrams are a rich mine of information. Even the layman, however, will appreciate the relationship between their contours and those of the frame. This relationship reflects the complex of problems that extends from the underlying mathematical laws to their final architectural expression.

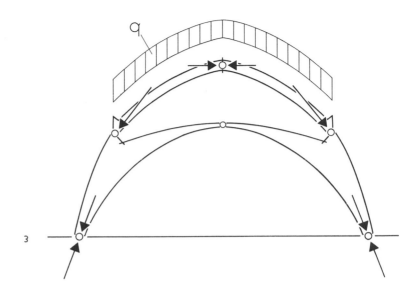

3

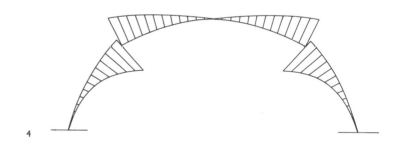

4

108.   3 The honeycomb grille forming the upper vault rests on the haunches of the
        three-hinged frames, the function of which is to resist the vault thrusts.
        4 The shape of the structure is clearly reflected in the moment diagram.

Maillart's Bridges

The bridges built in Switzerland by Maillart [47] include some of the finest examples of modern engineering. They are models of sound technical form artistically refined.

It is worth noting that Maillart's achievement has been acknowledged more readily among amateurs of art than in engineering circles. However rewarding this mutual contact may be and however well deserved the praise, occasional attempts on the part of architects to represent Maillart simply as an artist are quite misleading. No one will admit that a simple engineer is capable of creating such beauty. He must have been a great artist, it is suggested, even if he were not aware of it himself. Otherwise it would be imposssible to explain why his work has so much beauty. No comparison is too daring to be used in support of this contention. One of Maillart's reinforcing plans set against a well-known graphic composition, one of his bridges beside the work of some Constructivist, these may be ingenious associations of images, but nothing more. This kind of thing does not bring us closer to Maillart, the man, nor does it sharpen our appreciation of his achievement.

Maillart was a gifted engineer, but not the artist type, and never looked upon himself in that light. His creative talent and his sure feeling for economy in design are indisputable. Whether his idea of "economy" coincided with the definition attempted on page 100, however, is very doubtful. He probably equated economy in design quite straightforwardly with good value and simplicity of construction. At least, that is the opinion of those who knew him.

During his lifetime he was vigorously attacked by a number of well-known engineers. His seriousness was questioned, and he himself was called a "simplifier" who shunned rigorous structural theory. This was true to the extent that he did not care for so-called "exact," but laborious, methods of computation. He preferred rough, but penetrating, simplifications. He favored statically determinate, that is, simple systems. And this taste for simplicity was his source of strength. It made him a true designer. It would be wrong to assume, however, that Maillart's work was inspired by artistic impulses. His physiognomy and handwriting both refute this. We should try to understand his work, especially his bridges, from his personality and his manner of thinking and working and to see him as he was, not as one might have liked him to be.

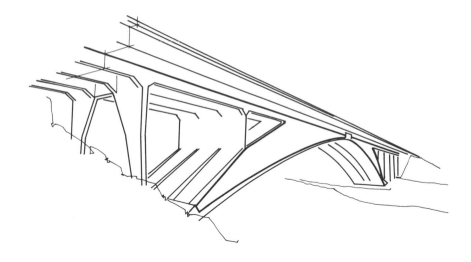

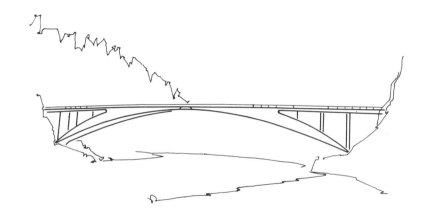

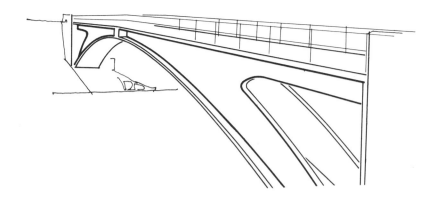

109.   Various three-hinged arch spans designed by Maillart [47], all conspicuously characterized by the structural form of the V-support.

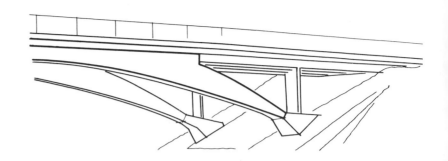

Let us consider his bridges without starting from an esthetic evaluation. Let us ask quite simply: What is that? Why is that so? What purpose does that serve? What are the mechanical principles underlying these unusually attractive structures? What relationship could there be between the mechanical principle and the outward form? How did the designer arrive at this solution?

Only then shall we have cleared the way for an esthetic evaluation, and we shall discover that our knowledge of the manner in which these structures behave has sharpened our insight and intensified our appreciation of their beauty.

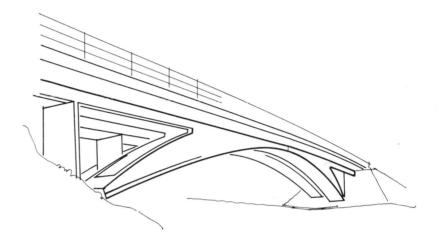

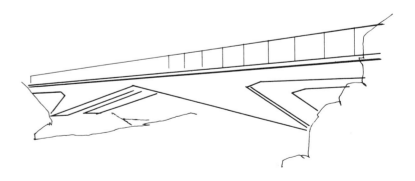

Thur-Bridge, Switzerland [44]
Eng: Robert Maillart.

Eng: Robert Maillart
Salgina-Tobel Bridge, Switzerland [44]

First, we must divide the structure of the bridge into two parts, according to function. The purpose for which the bridge is intended makes the deck system (Fig. 110.1) the more important. Its surface must adhere closely to the natural line of traffic. If there is nothing to prevent it, the deck should run straight and flat. It is primarily a part of the highway, not yet part of the bridge. To carry the deck system over the gulf, a supporting structure, the actual bridge (Fig. 110.2), is required. These two units, the deck system and the supporting arch, can be fused into a single whole. Maillart aimed at achieving this unity. He did so purely for reasons of economy. For him the bridge deck was not just so much weight; instead he saw it as an integral part of the supporting structure itself.

In order to understand his three-hinged arches, we must consider what constitutes the optimum form in the light of the laws of statics. Every arch that carries only its own weight, that is a dead load distributed more or less evenly over the entire span, has as its optimum form a line of pressure corresponding fairly closely to a parabola (Fig. 110.3). The line of pressure is best visualized as an inverted catenary, the form assumed by a chain suspended from each end. Just as the links in the chain sag under their own weight to form a curve, in which all are stressed only in tension, the elements of an arch form a line of pressure, along which all the forces are compressive. Every departure from the line of pressure introduces bending stresses into the arch and makes it necessary to strengthen the cross section. Adhering strictly to the line of pressure gives the most economical

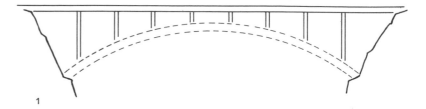

1

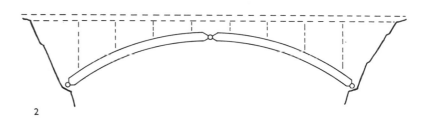

2

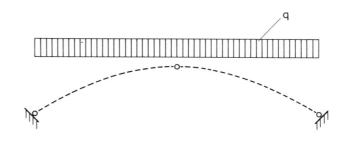

3

110.   The close relationship between structural form and statical principle demonstrated by means of a detailed analysis of the design of the Salgina-Tobel bridge.

1 The bridge consists of two main elements with different functions, the deck and

2 the substructure that supports it.

3 Under full static load the optimum form (line of pressure) of the substructure is an inverted catenary, a curve very similar to a parabola. Under these conditions there is no bending, the loads are transmitted in pure compression.

proportions. The line of pressure is decidedly a form that is structurally "right." It was not used with any consistency by the builders of the past. The Romans preferred the semicircle, a geometric but not a structural form. The pointed Gothic arch approximates more closely to the line of pressure, but the form was first consciously exploited by modern engineers, especially in bridge design. As a practical solution it is obviously "right," and hence appropriate and beautiful.

This simple correlation between the line of pressure and the arch, however, only holds true for a symmetrical dead load, for example, the dead weight of the bridge alone. The variable live load may be imposed in an infinite variety of asymmetrical combinations. If the live load is applied on one side of the bridge only, the arch will deform by yielding on the loaded side and thrusting upwards on the other (Fig. 110.4). If the loading is reversed, the process will be repeated in the opposite sense. If the lines of elastic deformation due to both cases of asymmetrical loading are superimposed, a lens-shaped zone is formed on either side (Fig. 110.5). To an exaggerated scale, these zones roughly represent the limits within which the bridge will deform under the action of maximum asymmetrical loading. The largest deformations occur about halfway between the springing and the crown, i.e. at about quarter-span. Large deformations indicate large bending moments and large bending moments require large cross sections.

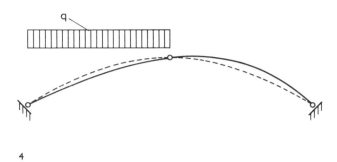

4

5

110. 4 Under asymmetrical loading an arch rib of optimum form is subjected to additional bending stresses and the corresponding elastic deformations.
5 If each half of the span is loaded alternately, the deformation will vary between certain upper and lower limits. The latter define lens-shaped elements which indicate schematically the degree of deformation, the intensity of bending and hence the logical shape of the arch.

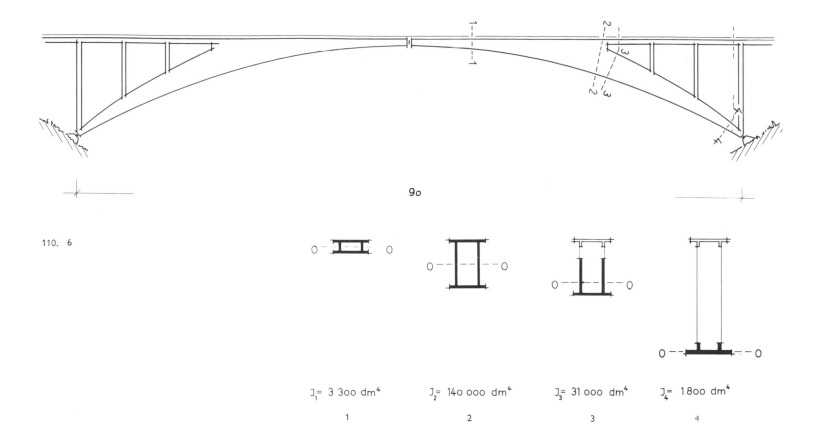

90

110. 6

$J_1 = 3\,300 \text{ dm}^4$

1

$J_2 = 140\,000 \text{ dm}^4$

2

$J_3 = 31\,000 \text{ dm}^4$

3

$J_4 = 1\,800 \text{ dm}^4$

4

There is an obvious correlation between the lens shapes of Fig. 110.5 and the form of the arch (Fig. 110.6). This form is pleasing to the eye. It clearly expresses the robust strength of the arch and, in particular, its ability to withstand the asymmetrical type of loading so critical in arch design.

Once mastered in principle, the form must be adapted to immediate practical requirements (Fig. 110.6), chief among which is the support of the deck system, already mentioned, the form, position and proportions of which are predetermined by its function. Towards the middle of the bridge, where the deck and the arch converge, a box section develops. The top flange is the deck, the bottom flange the arch slab and the twin webs connecting walls (section 1-1). The stiffness of this box-section increases as it grows deeper, until it reaches a maximum at section 2-2, close to quarter-span, the point of maximum bending moment. If it is to reflect the shape of the lenses (Fig. 110.5), which indicate the degree of bending along the arch, the stiffness of the section should fall off again towards the abutments. In fact, just beyond section 2-2 the deck and the arch part company and the box section becomes an inverted double-Tee. This sudden transition makes a big difference to the stiffness of the arch (cf. the moments of inertia of sections 2-2 and 3-3). To compensate for this, the webs of the double-Tee 3-3 are made substantially thicker than

those of the closed section 2-2. The depth of these elements gradually decreases towards the abutments to conform with the tapering of the lenses. At the abutments themselves the cross section of the arch is reduced to a minimum. Once more the observer will recognize the outline of the V-support, although this time it has yet another function.

The abrupt transition from box section to double-Tee has another interesting application to the relationship between form and statical principle. The lens shapes in Fig. 110.5 correspond schematically with the zone of elastic deformation of the axis of the arch under alternating asymmetrical loads. At the same time they correspond roughly with the intensity of bending experienced by the arch under these conditions, always assuming that under static loading the basic form of the arch closely follows the line of pressure. For reasons of practical necessity (for example, the need to integrate the deck slab with the rest of the structure), however, the actual arch and the line of pressure will occasionally diverge. The positions of the centroids of the adjacent sections 2-2 and 3-3 differ considerably. Thus, at this point there is a distinct jog in the centroidal axis of the arch (Fig. 110.7). The departure of the latter from the line of pressure is accompanied by a linear increase in the bending moments, the bending moment diagram losing the smooth shape of a lens and assuming a form that changes between sections 2-2 and 3-3 just as abruptly as

166

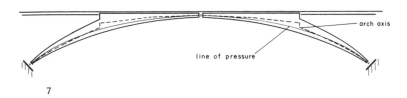

7

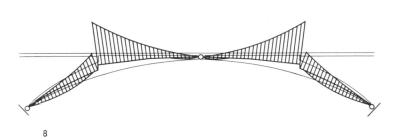

8

the form of the arch itself (Fig. 110.8). The structurally determined discontinuity of the form means a corresponding discontinuity in the bending moment diagram. The discontinuous moment diagram is the justification for the form. The circle is thus complete. The diverse elements of the problem, the function of the bridge, the necessary distinction between deck system and substructure, the action of the arch and its adaptation to practical needs, have been expertly reconciled in accordance with the principle of economy. The result is a unit, in which the parts live in the whole and the whole in its parts. The intimate fusion of practical requirements, laws of statics, and the structural possibilities of the materials has produced a work of great harmony and beauty. The perfection of the form resides in its lucid internal order. It would be wrong to ascribe it, as so many have done, to an artistic streak in Maillart's personality. The structural pattern is far too well-defined, too exact and too demonstrably "right"; it is far too clearly a genuine engineering achievement for anyone to drag in hypothetical artistic impulses. In fact, it is an accomplishment that proves that technology and down-to-earth, purposeful construction are in themselves capable of beauty.

It is clear that technical knowledge alone, masterfully grasped and consistently applied, can produce work of considerable esthetic merit, even masterpieces of design. Maillart has expressed his own ideas as follows: "Thus, the engineer . . . may escape from the old forms, characteristic of traditional construction, to exploit his materials to the full in perfect freedom. Then, perhaps, like the aircraft and automobile industries, we shall achieve beauty and a new style appropriate to the materials we employ. We may then reach a point where public taste will have become so sophisticated that reinforced concrete bridges built in the traditional manner will be regarded in the same way as automobiles built at the turn of the century, the prototype of which was the horse and carriage" [48].

If we have devoted so much attention to Maillart, it is because his work is of fundamental importance to the theme of our discussion. It proves that what we have termed "structural form" has an existence of its own and can inspire solutions of unusual merit. It proves that the design of structures is determined primarily by a knowledge of necessary relationships. Architecture, of course, is a discipline of a higher order of complexity than the design of bridges. But architecture embraces structural forms that obey laws as strict as those that govern a bridge. In fact, insofar as they are capable of being considered in isolation, they present the same problem as a bridge does. To the extent that they cannot be "dissolved out," they may be more difficult to recognize and also more difficult to master. However, they will never be mastered simply by being negated. As the modern architect cannot manage without the engineer or without modern materials and techniques, he must acknowledge and respect "structural principles" in architecture. Otherwise, he will find himself unable to participate in the discovery of Maillart's "new style, appropriate to the materials we employ."

110.   6 Sections 1 through 4 show how the bridge deck and the substructure are combined.
    7 The abrupt transition, due to practical construction requirements, from section 2 to section 3 produces a discontinuity in the axis of the arch, which thus deviates from the line of pressure.
    8 This discontinuity corresponds with a similar discontinuity in the bending moment diagram which, in its turn, coincides perfectly with the abrupt change in section.

V-Supports in Three Dimensions

The reinforced concrete frames that support the Unesco Building in Paris [18] have already been mentioned on page 100. We now return to discuss the unusual plastic treatment of their tapered legs (Fig. 111). Their vitality is not entirely derived from acting as part of a frame. They are plastic forms with clearly differentiable functions in two directions. In the plane of the frame (Fig. 111.1) they are broad at the top, where the critical corner moments occur, tapering downwards in the manner of a V. In the longitudinal direction of the building they are broad at the bottom and taper upwards. Firmly anchored to the foundations, they lend longitudinal stability to the structure. As in the case of Nervi's hangars, the bending moment diagram proves that here the inverted V is a logical and structurally meaningful form.

Nervi had no precedents for his design. He derived his inspiration solely from an understanding of structural laws. For him the problems of longitudinal and transverse stability were inseparable. He had them simultaneously in mind and thought them out as a single whole. In this way he arrived at a combined solution, in which the two functions are clearly differentiated, by reversing the V-form of the supports in the two principal directions. The continuous rounding of the edges and the neat detailing of the diagonals contribute greatly to the success of this unusual solution. Nervi has said that, essentially, form is not a product of "computation." Other proportions could have been adopted without prejudice to the statical integrity of the structure. For example, the fact that the columns designed to impart longitudinal rigidity are so numerous would easily have permitted a reduction in width at the base. However, to use Nervi's own words, it is not merely a question of exact computation, but of a design that makes the strongest and most pregnant statement.

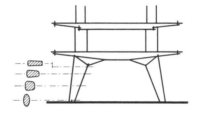

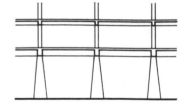

1

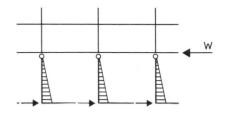

2

3

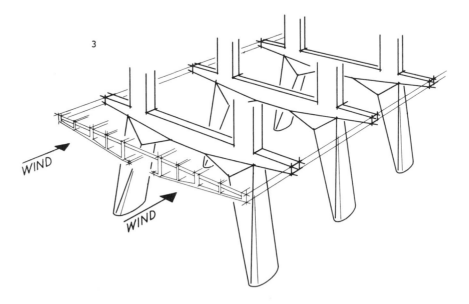

WIND

WIND

111.   The shape of the V-supports of the Unesco Building [18] expresses their different functions in different directions.
   1 In the transverse direction the supports act as the tapered legs of two-hinged frames.
   2 In the longitudinal direction the supports help to resist wind forces, acting like columns fixed at the bottom and pinned at the top.
   3 An oblique view reveals the plasticity of the form.

Unesco, Paris, Secretariat Building
Detail of leg of rigid frame [18]
Arch: Breuer, Zehrfuss. Eng: Nervi

Another remarkable example is provided by the War Memorial in Milwaukee [49]. Here on a splendid site, Saarinen and the engineers Amman and Whitney have used a similar form as a very prominent feature of the design. In this case, however, the V-legs do not form part of a two-hinged frame but support massive bearing walls, acting as offset columns tied back at the top. In the other direction they have the form of an inverted V and stiffen the structure against wind.

So far the use of V-supports seems to have been a privilege of the Old World and South America. The fact that United States architects have largely ignored such forms raises the suspicion that perhaps the V-support is a rather frivolous device alien to the sober North American. South American architects attribute North American antipathy to lively and dynamic structural forms to the Anglo-Saxon's general distrust of daring plastic invention. Perhaps it is a symptom of a subsequent change in taste that this suggestion has been debated in an American architectural journal [50] in a spirit of decided self-reproach. Changed attitudes are also reflected in more recent developments, including the Milwaukee War Memorial. In the United States the predominance of steel construction and the secondary importance of reinforced concrete appear to be the main reasons for the absence of the V-support, which, of course, is a form ideally suited to the latter material. As the use of reinforced concrete becomes more widespread, the V-support will inevitably become an accepted structural form in the United States too.

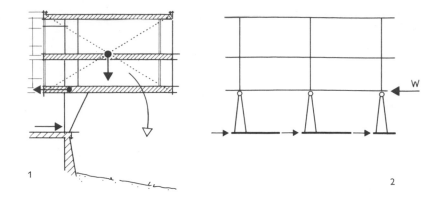

1

2

3

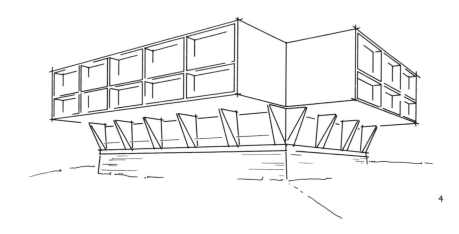

4

112. The V-supports of the Milwaukee War Memorial [49].
      1 In section the column is seen to be an offset V-support tied back at the top.
      2 In longitudinal section it is fixed at the bottom.
      3 Oblique view from the courtyard and
      4 perspective, showing the different functions in the longitudinal and transverse directions.

Milwaukee War Memorial [49]
Arch: Eero Saarinen ▶

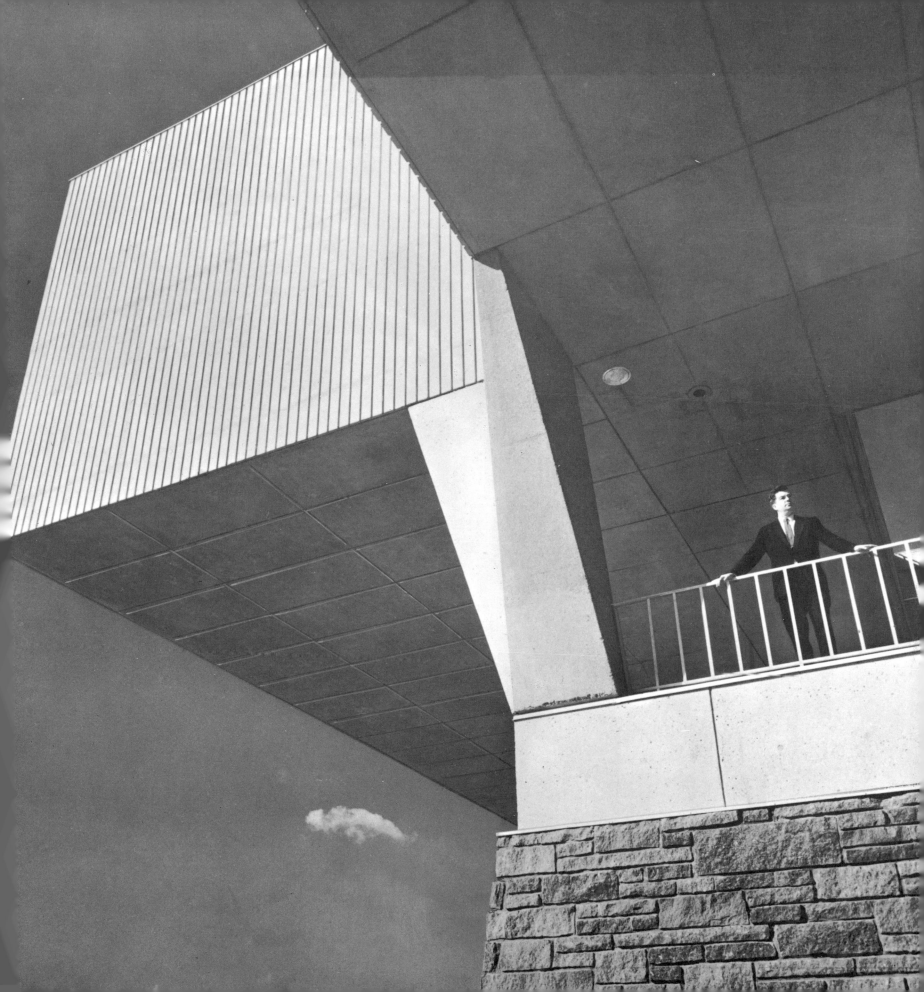

Design for a Railroad Station in Naples

We conclude this discussion of special variations on the theme of the V-support with a description of Castiglioni's original design for the Naples railroad station competition [51]. This design was not awarded a prize, but it was widely reported and much discussed.

Castiglioni wanted to create "a friendly, informal space that would serve to give strangers a warm and natural introduction to the city." He wanted the opposite of a barrier in concrete and steel. He pursued this goal by designing a gently undulating shell roof that was to grow organically out of a series of three-pronged forked columns. The latter are the reason why we have chosen to comment on Castiglioni's proposals in this section. They cannot be separated from the design as a whole. With the roof they form a unit and it is only in terms of this unit that they can be understood.

The three-pronged forked columns are laid out in a triangular grid. They each support a shell roof element, likewise based on the shape of an equilateral triangle. Between every three such columns and the triangular roof elements they support (1, 2, 3) a fourth roof element (4) is suspended (see the view from below, Fig. 113.1). Thus, the same grid is repeated in the pattern of the roof.

So much for our attempt to explain the geometry of the system. The space frame and the interconnection of the parts, particularly the way the roof shell grows organically out of the ends of the trident supports, are hard to describe in words. The section (Fig. 113.2), the perspective drawing of a shell element (Fig. 113.3) and the photograph on page 174 are far more eloquent. In spite of the complexity of the subtly interweaving plastic forms, the clarity of the geometrical conception and the naturalness with which the various elements combine are wholly convincing. Developed from a rough outline (Fig. 113.4), the final form has all the perfection of organic growth (Fig. 113.5). The forked columns are an important part of the structure as a whole. Each of their prongs thickens towards the root. This suggests that they strain against each other and are rigidly joined at the base, where they rest on a specially designed, raised pier, forming a hinge. The three-dimensional spread of the three prongs, the upper ends of which merge smoothly with the shell elements of the roof, ensures the general stability of the system, in spite of the hinged connection between piers and columns. It might be asked what purpose is served by tapering the prongs. If the forked columns rest on hinges, it is not immediately obvious what advantage is achieved. Compare what was said about Niemeyer's forked columns on pages 141-4.

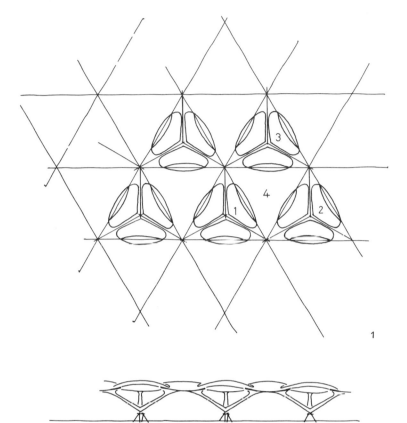

1

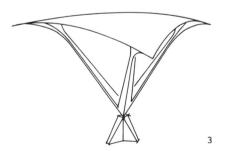

2

3

113.   Design for Naples railroad station, Italy [51].
      1 Basic triangular grid superimposed on a view of the underside of the roof. Three-pronged forked columns support triangular shell elements (1), (2) and (3). A fourth shell element (4) is hung between the other three.
      2 Section.
      3 A single three-pronged forked column with its corresponding roof element.
      4 A simplified view.
      5 Attempt to represent the view from the front.

Structurally this is a critical point, an element of the design of extreme importance to the whole. It is true that three-dimensional stability is ensured by virtue of the contact between the prongs of the forked columns and the roof. However, this is not a positive connection, since the two elements merge in supple curves. The elasticity of the roof, the visual effect of which is reinforced by rounded surfaces, depressions, notches and light-flooded slots, therefore demands a higher degree of stiffness from the supports. These demands are met by the form selected, with its three branches steadily broadening towards a rigid node.

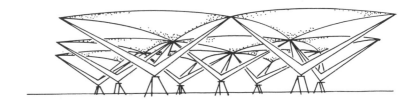

4

This chapter is entitled "the V-support." To many a reader the theme may at first have meant little or nothing. The author himself confesses to having first thought of the V-support as a marginal topic. However, as he plunged deeper into the material and his notes accumulated, he began to realize that the V-support is more than a peripheral phenomenon. Both its popularity and versatility and its frequent mishandling suggested that it would be well worth while to attempt a fundamental and comprehensive analysis of the form. In order not to weary the reader, however, it was obviously necessary to confine the discussion within certain limits. The material has therefore been grouped and subdivided on the basis of related forms, rather than subordinated to an abstract theory. The reader who insists on a strictly scientific treatment of those borderline topics may perhaps object to this approach. He may not consider it feasible to sketch out design possibilities theoretically, starting from the laws of statics. He may argue that the end and scope of such an undertaking would be uncertain and that it would be hard to avoid the unfortunate impression that an attempt was being made to solve problems of design by exclusively scientific methods.

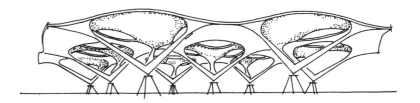

5

The author has preferred to bring actual structures into the foreground. The image of the typical form, noted daily by the alert observer, has been left to determine the theme and has led to a graphic system of classification. Certainly, a great deal is still lacking. Certainly, the interpretation we have attempted is not the only one possible. Too much of what we have to say is not the result of technical and computational considerations alone, and thus lacks the obviousness of $2 \times 2 = 4$. Accordingly, not all our conclusions can claim the force of proof. In actual fact, this is not the point. It is much more a matter of showing that in the border zone between technology and art the conclusive argument *also* counts and that unambiguous interpretations of "right" and "wrong" must *also* be thrown into the balance of judgment. It is a matter of showing that a sober, intelligent analysis will clear the ground for the discovery and understanding of more significant structural forms and that genuine and impressive new forms, like the V-support, must first have their structural principles laid bare, before they can be developed, judged and truly understood.

Design for Naples railroad station [51]
Detail of support.
Arch: Enrico Castiglioni.

Every structure is by nature material and three-dimensional, and hence, in fact, a space structure. What then is the special significance of the "space structures" described in this book? How do they differ from other systems like the skeleton frame or the V-support?

In spite of their natural three-dimensionality, historical timber and masonry buildings and the skeleton and rigid frame buildings, described in the first two chapters of this book, are *not* "space structures." The carpenter's roof, the modern reinforced concrete building frame, even the ancient vault, are imagined resolved into non-three-dimensional, i.e. plane systems. In designing a traditional timber roof, the first step is to calculate the size of the rafter (1) in the transverse plane "y." The second is to find a suitable section for the purlin (2), which runs at right angles to the rafters in the longitudinal plane "x." The fact that in reality these two members, the rafter and the purlin, interact in space is deliberately disregarded. This is done not only to simplify the calculations but because in "classical" structures introducing a three-dimensional effect makes practically no difference in the end result. The time spent on computation would be out of all proportion to the advantages obtained.

In designing the structures discussed so far, skeleton and rigid frames, there is no point in working out the consequences of three-dimensional action. A design based on plane sections has been shown by experience to be entirely adequate. The engineer can be confident that structures analyzed in this way will have perfectly definite reserves of strength. If, for example, the framing of a timber roof still holds together, although ruined walls hardly give it any more support, and if, when brick buildings are burnt out, the towering chimney stack, with its stiff box section, and the corners, where walls intersect, still stand, this is because of their extra three-dimensional rigidity, which in classical structures, and even in modern skeleton construction, is not usually exploited.

Apart from certain exceptions, such as the thin mud domes of the Middle East, the architectural history of the world up to recent times contains no examples of buildings, in which three-dimensional rigidity

114.   The essential difference between "plane" systems and space structures.
1 The engineer does not treat the traditional timber roof as a space frame. He first designs the rafters (1) in the "y" plane and then makes separate calculations for the purlins (2) in the "x" plane. Each member is designed independently to carry its own loads.
2 The mud dome of the Middle East, one of the few known historical examples of a space structure. Its stability is derived entirely from its three-dimensional action. These domes cannot be resolved into parts nor can they be divided into a system of planes for design purposes.

has been made the essence of the design. This is precisely what is both new and typical about modern space structures. A "space structure" is one in which the three-dimensionality, inevitably present, is of such importance that it cannot be disregarded without discarding the rational basis of the design. The internal order and outward form of such structures are essentially the result of their three-dimensional action.

Today, when the study of structural forms has only just begun, and especially when the technical disciplines are developing so rapidly, it may seem presumptuous to venture to define the formal characteristics of space structures. Nevertheless, occasional experimental lectures and the reactions of the very open-minded younger generation have encouraged the author to take the risk. If he does no more than arouse interest in the subject, he will still have achieved a great deal. Critical awareness is the first prerequisite for fighting the modish formalism which is already beginning to affect the design of space structures.

Common utensils have always provided examples of three-dimensional structure. Such objects are the result, among other things, of creative instinct and the unique suitability of particular materials for satisfying particular needs. The clay or metal pot, the spoon, the helmet and the wheel with inclined spokes are ancient, simple forms that work in essentially the same way as a space structure. However, there are even more complicated objects, like forged armor and the wooden canoe, essentially fragile things that owe their considerable strength entirely to their three-dimensional rigidity and testify to man's early technical mastery of the form.

Today we are surrounded by objects designed on this principle. The self-supporting car body derives its great strength from pressed sheet metal. The same idea is utilized in the design of ships and aircraft. The telephone receiver and the lamp bulb are simply variations on the same theme. Wherever thin sheet or plate is molded into a rigid shape the inspiration derives from the three-dimensionality of the "space structure."

115. Certain ancient utensils and modern industrial products make use of the space structure principle. Both clay pots and sheet-metal car bodies possess great rigidity.

It is the same inspiration that has led architects and engineers to develop new and unusual building forms. A web of steel tubes, a freely undulating shell, or a mesh of cables suspended like a great sail over a column-free arena, all stand by virtue of their three-dimensional action. We are confronted by a new world of forms, with boundaries that cannot yet be ascertained, an order that is still unfamiliar and design principles that for many remain an enigma. The revolutionary element in these new plastic values is indisputable. But we are still unable to manipulate them with confidence and understanding. The following pages are an attempt to clarify the position.

Good form is the key to the development of new structure. While the technical solutions remain as hotly debated as they are today, it will in many cases be impossible to pass a final judgment. Nevertheless, a discussion of structural form will contribute to the clarification of certain unanswered questions. In fact, the structural designer may well reap some advantages from an analysis of form carried beyond the stage reached by structural theory. True form is a mirror to the laws of statics, and occasionally the mirror image is better visible than the object itself, depending entirely on the direction in which we are looking.

Any attempt at interpretation must be methodical. It will be necessary to group related elements together. In what follows we shall distinguish between four such groups:

1. *Space frames* are composed of large numbers of individual members. These members are stressed axially, that is either in tension or compression. They are braced against each other in a three-dimensional system.

2. *Folded plates* derive their strength from the stiffness of the folds. The elementary slabs are stressed in tension, compression and shear in their own plane and in bending in a direction at right angle to this pane.

3. *Shells* are thin, curved surfaces in which, in the ideal case, the stresses are limited to normal stresses and shear, bending being excluded.

4. *Suspended roofs* are formed of cables, steel nets, fabric or thin sheet. They are stressed exclusively in tension. Supporting elements capable of resisting compression or bending necessarily from part of the over-all design concept.

The various structures are grouped according to form. Occasionally, however, neat classification is impossible. The boundaries are too fluid. The future will show whether any serious gaps have been left and whether boundaries, which today appear well-defined, will subsequently become blurred. For the time being, however, the system of classification adopted should permit a sufficiently comprehensive treatment of the subject.

 **SPACE FRAMES**

Trusses are composed of vertical, horizontal and diagonal members. They are a common feature of medieval roofs and wooden trestle bridges. The plane truss is not much used by the modern architect. Mies van der Rohe's design for a theater in Mannheim [52] is one of the few attempts that have been made to exploit the truss as an element in an architectural design. It is true that architects are being increasingly attracted by the neat detailing possible with steel construction and are showing a tendency to use trusses in schools, halls, and so on, as well as in industrial buildings; however, it is impossible to think of the truss as a structural form capable of satisfying the most exacting architectural demands.

All the trusses mentioned so far are "plane systems" in the sense we have defined. This is revealed particularly clearly in half-timbered and trestle-bridge construction, in which the different structural planes are easily distinguishable. Each of these planes defines a separate statical system. It is not as immediately obvious that the same principles apply even to the modern carpenter's roof. Rafters and struts, running in all directions, give an observer the impression of a space frame with three-dimensional rigidity. In fact, some such rigidity is actually present, but the crudity of the connections and the difficulty of the analysis prevent us from designing and stressing such roofs as true space frames. Accordingly, even modern engineers and designers usually regard the wooden roof as a two-dimensional rather than a three-dimensional statical problem. Resolving the structure, and the forces acting on it, into a system of planes at right angles is one of the elementary rules of practical statics. This rule, however, does not apply to the space structures, with which this chapter is concerned.

1

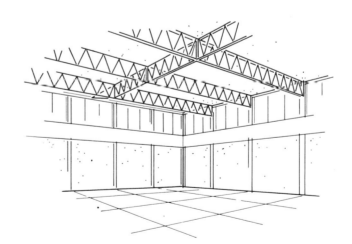

2

116.   Plane trusses are not much used in modern architecture.
    1 Mies van der Rohe's design for a theater in Mannheim, Germany [52], is a rare example of the architectural exploitation of trusses.
    2 A school in England with exposed lattice joists.

The structure of the human hip bone [53] is eminently suitable for demonstrating the mode of action of a space frame. The weight of the body rests on a rounded knob at the end of a "cantilever." With respect to the axis of the hip bone, we get a bending moment $M = P \times a$. This moment, however, is not constant. It varies with the forces developed as the body moves. The position of the body and the degree of rotation of the joint affect the direction of the resultant of the loads. The bone is splendidly designed to withstand all these fluctuations, since it has a system of support available for every form of loading. These multiple systems are fused into a single three-dimensional unit. Interpenetrating, they reduce the effective lengths of the individual members, stiffen them, absorb some of their load, and thus help to increase the strength of the unit as a whole.

Nature does not need to solve higher-order differential equations in order to give this complicated network of members the right proportions. Everything develops organically in continuous adaptation to the variable static and dynamic loads. It is perfectly obvious that instead of acting in a *single* plane the bone structure is flexibly adapted to resist forces coming from any direction, depending on the movements and position of the body. Thus, nature has designed her space frame without right angles and without a single straight line, yet most beautifully and probably much more economically than man ever could. The fact that in bone the "members" are more like hardened, horny membranes than structural sections does not affect the basic issue. It only shows that organic nature prefers more complicated, more beautiful and probably stronger building elements. Of course, the designer is handicapped from the start. His numerical techniques are poor substitutes for the subtle powers of natural growth. His work will probably always lag behind the achievements of nature. Nevertheless, the resemblance between the space structures produced by nature and by man is startling, and at the same time encouraging.

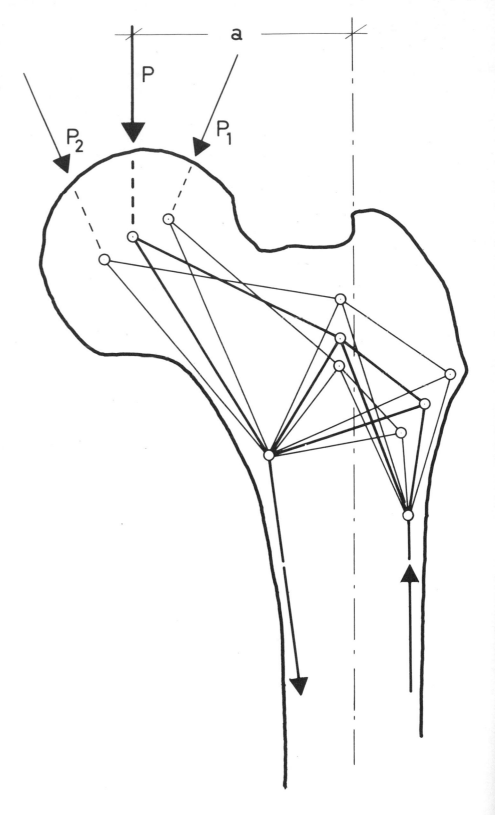

117.　The human hip bone is a highly expressive space structure. The diagram shows how the bone is organically adapted to changes in the direction of the applied force [53].

Sections through the human hip bone [53]

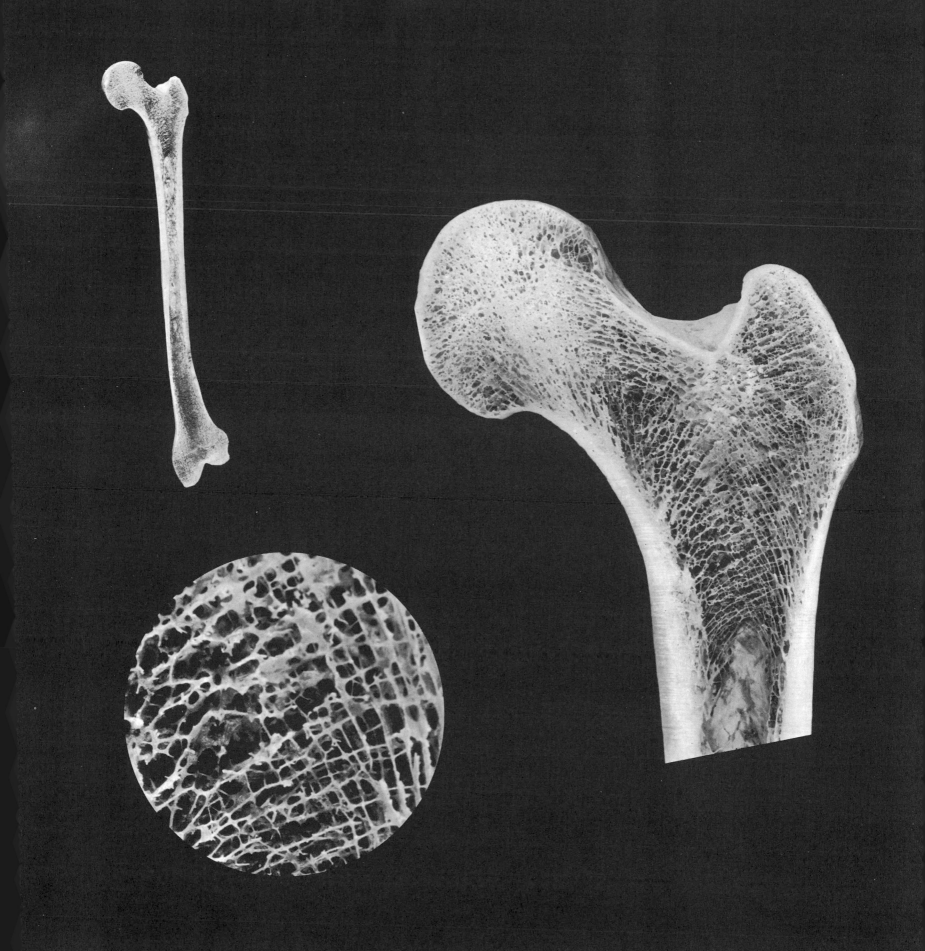

The "three-dimensional" forms, preferred by nature, are more expressive than the "plane" structures devised by man. They are ideally and materially at a higher level of creation. The recognition of this fact is linked with a contemporary reorientation in engineering thinking. Future historians will probably talk of a "breakthrough" from two-dimensional to three-dimensional design. This will bring the engineer to the fringes of the architect's domain, the shaping of space. It is to be hoped that, in the future, the two will meet there more and more often.

The Mannesmann system of tubular scaffolding [54] is based on the use of arbitrarily selected lengths of tubing of standard diameter connected at any angle by means of clamps. Although the strength of a *single* length of tubing and a *single* clamp is limited, there is no limit to the number of pieces of tubing than can be effectively clamped together. Accordingly, this system has a high degree of adaptability to different tasks and varying loads. It thus becomes possible to develop structures with a flexibility somewhat akin to that possessed by organic growth. In this way, simple elements, combined in a sort of prefabricated assembly, can be made to yield lively and expressive structural forms. For a long time, however, tubular construction has been confined to temporary structures and scaffolding. Apparently, architects have yet to discover the esthetic charm and rich variety of such forms. One of the reasons for this is probably the fact that the joint details necessarily still have a mobile, flexible character, while the parts, being designed for repeated use, are not yet as refined as they otherwise might be. Finally, from the structural point of view the system has the disadvantage that the connectors always transmit the forces eccentrically, so that the tubular members are never free of bending.

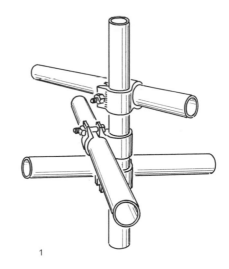

1

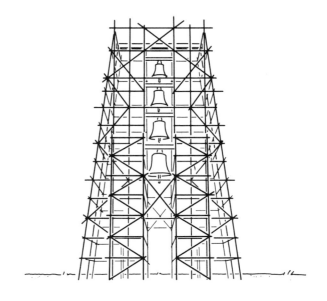

2

118.   Tubular steel scaffolding with clamped joints (Mannesmann System) [54].
    1 Tubes can be connected at any angle. It is possible to use any number
    of tubes of any length.
    2 A temporary bell tower in tubular steel.

Mannesmann scaffolding [54] ▶

184

The Mero system [55] employs a limited range of members, which screw into well-designed spherical connectors to form "nodes" where no bending can develop. Up to 18 members can meet at each node; their directions are clearly defined by three principal axes at right angles and by intermediate diagonals at 45°. The resulting structural forms are characterized by a severe geometric regularity, enlivened by numerous overlapping perspective effects. Interesting combinations are sometimes to be seen in temporary exhibition buildings. Statically the carrying capacity of the system is limited. The members are standardized and therefore, like the connectors themselves, only capable of resisting specified loads. Clearly, the strength of the system as a whole is determined by the strength of the most highly stressed individual element.

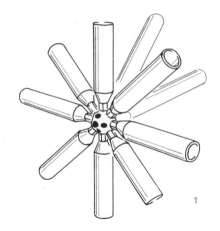

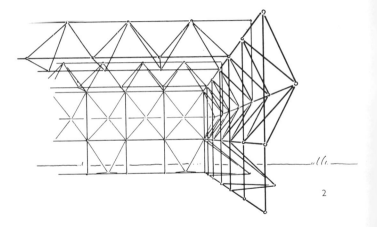

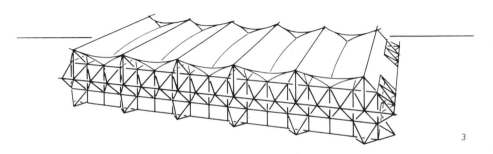

119.   Structural system based on steel tubes and threaded connectors (Mero System) [55].
        1 Up to 18 tubes can be connected at any joint.
        2 and 3 Structures erected at the Interbau Exhibition in Berlin 1957 [56].

In America the Unistrut system [57], using prefabricated parts made of light bent plate, has been developed for permanent rather than temporary construction. It has been employed, for example, in an extension of the Faculty of Architecture of Wayne University, Michigan, and, as illustrated below, to build a covered playground for children. The actual structure is a space frame, braced in several directions and more than three feet deep. The connectors, specially formed plates, are convincingly simple; the joints are bolted. The carrying capacity of the system has been established on a purely empirical basis. It is claimed to be capable of withstanding loads of about 300 kg/m² over a clear span of 12.5 m in both directions. A span of 15 m in both directions is considered possible. The empirical determination of the carrying capacity of the structure suggests that a theoretical analysis would not be easy. The pyramidal broadening of the column heads draws attention to the difficulty, typical of this class of structure, of concentrating the forces at the supports. If the roof were to have a point bearing on a narrower support, the members immediately adjacent to the head of the column would inevitably be overstressed. So far the system has not been extensively adopted. Whether the costs are too high, compared with conventional construction, whether esthetic prejudice is proving an obstacle, or whether there is still no clear insight into the advantages of "mobile" construction remains uncertain. At any rate, the corresponding structural form is new and very expressive, and therefore deserves a place in this chapter.

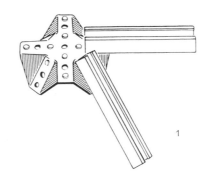

1

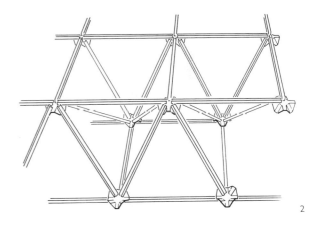

2

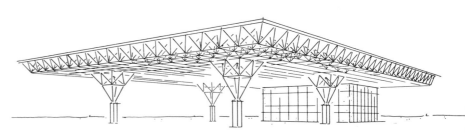

3

120.   Prefabricated construction employing light bolted sections (Unistrut System) [57].
1 A connector.
2 Space frame detail.
3 Children's recreation pavilion, Wayne, Mich. [58].

Here, too, belongs Mies van der Rohe's design for the Chicago Coliseum [59], dating from 1953. Although this design does not make use of mass-produced prefabricated parts, like the Unistrut system, and although a span of about 220 m in both directions naturally makes it impossible to determine the stresses by means of a full-scale experiment, the structural principle is still the same, namely that of a space frame that sheds its loads in several different directions. The roof structure was intended to be about 9 m deep and the building as a whole 36.5 m high. The structural form is the same as with Unistrut but on a larger scale. The extent to which the attractive perspective effects produced by the criss-crossing of so many slender members might have been expressed in the finished building would have depended very much on how the underside of the roof structure was treated. It would also have depended on lighting requirements and the architectural handling of the thirty feet of space occupied by the roof trusses themselves. The elevation of an alternative design shows clearly how van der Rohe tried to make the inner structure discernible on the outside.

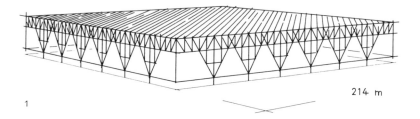

214 m

1

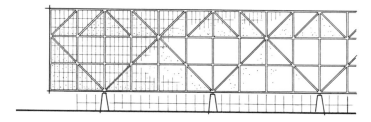

2

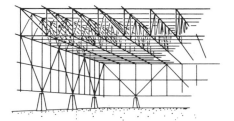

121.   Design for a convention hall by Mies van der Rohe [59].
        1 Oblique view of the model. Floor area about 214 x 214 m, height 36.5 m, depth of trusses about 9 m.
        2 Alternative design showing structure exposed in elevation.
        3 Interior view showing the web of steel in the roof.

3

Working in America, Konrad Wachsmann has developed an easily erected, prefabricated, tubular system for building cantilevered hangars of enormous size [60]. The design was conceived as a space frame. The intention was to roof an area of about 116 x 245 m with a limited number of supports down the center of the structure. What is so impressive about this project is the fact that the structure was to be made of prefabricated parts so that it could easily be dismantled, transported and re-erected at another site. Striking photographs of the models have been published in architectural and engineering journals all over the world. They have stimulated many to think and plan in terms of space frames of this kind. How far such daring projects are capable of realization is still uncertain. To what extent they will be frustrated by fundamental difficulties, inherent in the very nature of the problem, namely the reconciliation of mobility with construction on such a scale, remains to be seen. Our experience is still too limited. Unfortunately, in spite of considerable publicity, we have so far heard nothing more about the development of this project or the problems that attend it.

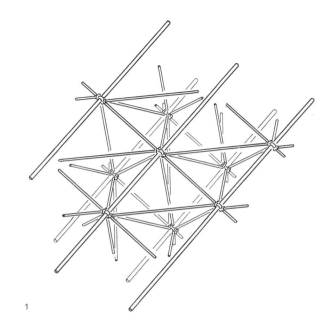

1

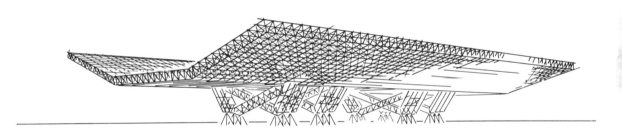

2

122. Design for a demountable tubular steel structure by Konrad Wachsmann [60].
   1 In the direction of the main span the top and bottom chords are continuous tubes to which the diagonals are joined by means of ring connectors.
   2 Oblique view of an aircraft hangar with a floor area of nearly 30,000 sq. m.
   3 Cross section through the hangar.

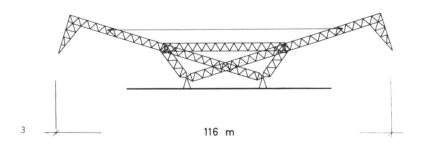

3

116 m

Summing up, we shall attempt to throw some light on the typical characteristics of space frames designed to be assembled from prefabricated parts.

1. If all the members in a given structure are identical, or if there are only a few standardized types, apart from sheer coincidence and deliberate repetition, only one member of any particular type will be fully exploited statically and economically. Thus, out of 1,000 identical elements, used in different positions in a structure, 999 will *not* be fully stressed. Accordingly they will be over-dimensioned. By way of contrast, we note that in bone there are no two fibers alike; the form of each is wholly adapted to its specific task. Thus, assembling a building from identical prefabricated parts is obviously not an economical way of utilizing material. This applies particularly to frames that are primarily stressed in bending. The stresses in the individual members vary considerably. It is not true of arched systems, like Nervi's hangars (see Figs. 105 and 124).

2. In order to get an accurate erection fit, the individual elements must be fabricated to tolerances closer than the accuracy of the finished construction warrants. Every production engineer knows that fine tolerances are dearly bought. As far as possible he tries to avoid them. In this case, simply for erection reasons, the designer is obliged to adopt tolerances of fractions of a centimeter, which go far beyond the requirements of the finished building. Tolerances of a few centimeters are normally quite good enough. Doubtless, the high degree of technical perfection that can now be achieved in every branch of industrial production exercises a fascination and encourages the development of structures of this kind. However, it should not be forgotten that inappropriate refinement and exaggerated accuracy contradict the principle of economy.

3. Unavoidable slip in the individual connections accumulates over the structure as a whole. The risk of permanent, excessive deformation due to the yielding of the connections is not to be underestimated. Particularly close attention must therefore be paid to the question of slip in the joints of demountable systems.

4. The elastic deformation and, hence, the behavior of structures with such a high degree of statical indeterminacy is very difficult to predict, if it is amenable to analysis at all. Even the much-mentioned possibility of using electronic computers to work out the stresses is no panacea.

   The expense of such methods must bear some relation to the results. Although it is possible to determine the strength of small-scale systems empirically, this is impossible where large structures are concerned.

5. Increasingly complicated construction techniques will take over the whole roof space and make it necessary to introduce a suspended ceiling. The undesirable tendency of truss construction to act as a dust trap also points to such a solution. To cover up a space frame in this way is, of course, to sacrifice the expressiveness of the form.

6. Like bone, the space frame has the advantage of being able to adapt itself to the most varied types and directions of loading. Heavily stressed areas are smoothly relieved by the adjacent material. The structure has built-in reserves of strength to enable it to deal with local overloading. In ordinary buildings this special characteristic of space frames is rarely utilized. Floor and roof loads are uniformly distributed. The local concentrations of load, typical of bridge design, are uncommon.

7. Their only undoubted asset is rapidity of assembly and disassembly, hence space frames have usually been designed for conditions in which mobility is a real advantage, or else where it is worth paying for. Small movable buildings will probably receieve more attention than larger structures. Where a mobile space frame is a really rational choice, its characteristic structural form will be quite spontaneously adopted.

The structure illustrated in Fig. 123 makes a fitting conclusion to this section and a neat contrast with the more ambitious projects discussed so far. Designed by the Italian architect Castiglioni, it shows how versatile the space frame really is. Castiglioni uses these welded-rod constructions for fences and gates [61]. Because he applies the principles of the space frame logically and naturally, he achieves a structure which is dainty and delicate, yet surprisingly rigid.

123.   Photo: Welded-rod space frame for gates and fences
Arch: Castiglioni [61].

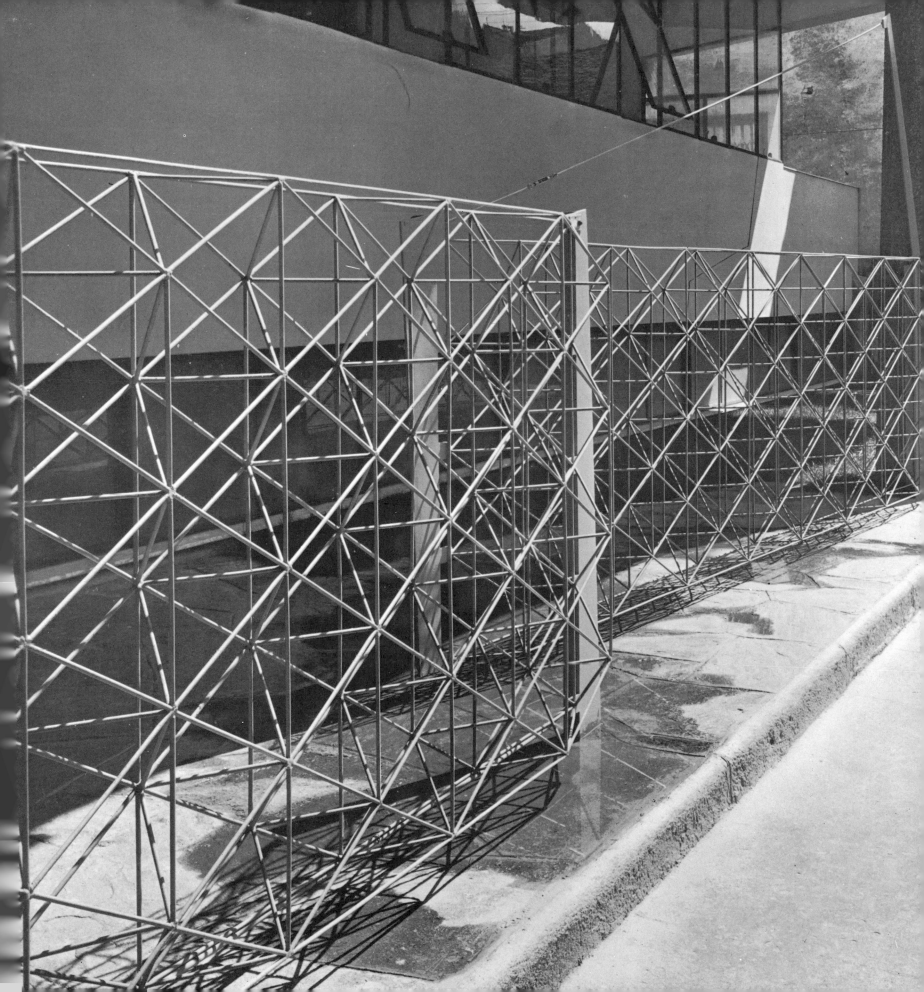

So far the discussion has been confined to space frames, in which, though the individual members may intersect at a variety of angles, the structure as a whole forms a kind of flat roof. Space frames, however, can be used to create more subtle shapes. The members can be made to follow curved surfaces that directly determine the form of the structure. If these surfaces are curved in one direction only, the resulting shape is cylindrical. In the Twenties German engineers designed a number of cylindrical, steel lamellar frames which acted as self-supporting falsework for the construction of reinforced concrete shells (Fig. 124.1) [62]. Nervi has employed similar systems, using prefabricated reinforced concrete lamellas left permanently in place. The roofs of his aircraft hangars [45], the buttresses of which were described in Chapter 2, are space frames of this type. The "members" are prefabricated reinforced concrete elements tied together at the nodes and later grouted. In these buildings the general contours are curved rather than angular. The effect is produced by a large number of individual elements organized in a curved surface.

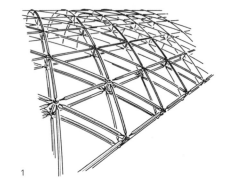

1

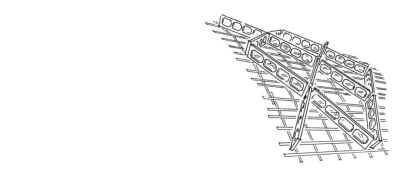

2

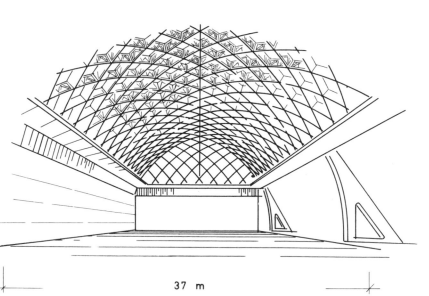

3

124.   Cylindrical space frames.
        1 Steel lamella vault used in 1927 as falsework for one of the first cylindrical concrete shell structures, the wholesale market in Frankfurt-am-Main, Germany [62].
        2 and 3 Precast concrete aircraft hangars designed by Nervi [45].

37 m

The next step brings us to the doubly curved surface, which gives a space frame of maximum rigidity. The resulting architectural form is a dome. It is worth noting that the potentialities of this kind of structure were discovered at the beginning of the twentieth century by rather a devious route. The Zeiss Works in Jena needed a surface corresponding as closely as possible to a perfect hemisphere on which to project an image of the heavens [63]. In view of the level of technology at the time, this was by no means an easy proposition. Prof. Bauersfeld, the author of the planetarium idea, also suggested a means of solving the structural problem. He designed a network of members (a space frame) that described the hemispherical shape desired. He had the position and length of the individual members determined with mathematical accuracy and then had an iron frame built to the closest tolerances. The surface of the frame was covered with fine wire mesh and gunited.

This was the beginning of the development of modern shell construction, which had its structural origin in the design of steel space frames. Subsequently, such frames were occasionally used as falsework (cf. Fig. 124.1), but they lost their importance as an element in actual shell construction as soon as the simpler round reinforcing bar was introduced.

Meanwhile, Buckminster Fuller was approaching the problem of the framed dome from quite another angle. His thinking was primarily colored by ideas of prefabrication and easy assembly. Quite rightly, he anticipated that space frames could be used to span large areas with a structure of minimum weight. He pursued his goal for many years with great energy. He also had a talent for enlisting the aid of enthusiastic and equally determined young men.

Today Fuller can point to an impressive number of domes all over the world built in accordance with his ideas [64]. He prefers to suspend the roof itself, a skin of molded sheet metal or plastic film, inside the actual frame, an arrangement that does much to improve the legibility of the structural form. Many exhibition halls, including the Ford Rotunda in Detroit with its famous aluminum dome, not to mention many interesting radar structures, owe their inspiration to Fuller's space frame principle. There is another point worth mentioning in connection with the Fuller system. Together with maximum economy in material (so characteristic of natural structures), the inherent rigidity of the geodesic dome makes possible some unusual methods of erection. The Ford dome [64] was erected from the head of a mast, that is from the top down. As it was also capable of rotating, any part of the suspended dome could be reached from a single erection ramp.

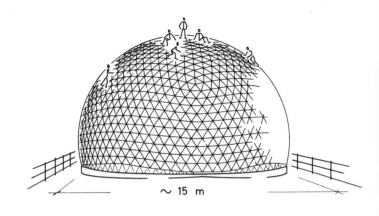

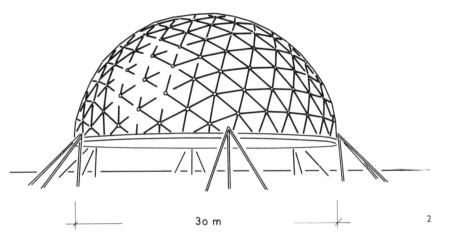

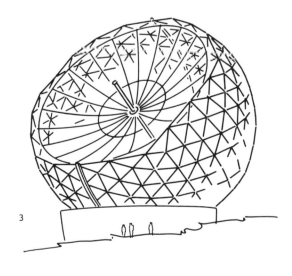

125. Space-frame domes.
  1 Skeleton of the first planetarium dome, Jena [63], showing the irregular subdivision of the surface.
  2 A Buckminster Fuller dome [64].
  3 Radar structure.

Since then, other domes have been successfully erected with the aid of inflatable balloons. The inflated balloon takes the place of scaffolding. Erection begins at the crown, proceeding downwards, and, as the space frame grows, the balloon is pumped higher and higher. When erection is complete, the balloon is deflated and removed.

For all its good points, the space frame also has inherent shortcomings. In Fuller's designs we admire the orderly subdivision of the spherical surface, which can never be successfully dissected into perfectly equal parts in accordance with a geometrical law. A glance at the armor of a giant armadillo shows how Nature, too, has failed in its attempts to solve a comparable problem. The geometry of the irregular polyhedra that can be inscribed in a sphere is not amenable to simple, straightforward treatment. We know that the icosahedron, with twenty faces, is the largest regular polyhedron that can be thus inscribed. Every attempt to cover a hemisphere with a closer network of equal, regular polygons is equivalent to an attempt to square the circle. We also know that regular hexagons can be combined to form a plane. If we try to force them into a spherical surface, we are obliged to twist them into irregular, three-dimensional curves. This can be clearly seen in the photograph on page 195. Determining the lengths of the edges accurately is a difficult problem in spherical geometry. The edges are *not* all the same length. Hence, members of different lengths must inevitably be used in the construction of such domes. The final form and the erection process are very sensitive to inaccuracies in the dimensions of the individual parts. For this reason it is necessary to work to tolerances far in excess of the order of accuracy of the building as a whole. This, of course, complicates the fabrication process.

The range of possible forms is limited. The structures built so far have almost without exception been spherical domes. Functionally, the spherical dome is an inflexible form; it has few applications other than in roofing large, centrally oriented buildings, like exhibition halls and arenas.

If, however, we indulge in a little technological optimism about the space frame, we may envisage a future in which:

a) The length of the individual members is variable and capable of simple adjustment to any desired dimension.

b) The strength of individual members can be varied, within reasonable limits, by modifying the cross section or combining members in clusters.

c) Any number of members can be connected at any angle at universal joints, without introducing bending.

d) Computers are used to master the geometry of doubly curved surfaces so that the lengths of individual members can easily be calculated with the accuracy required for fabrication and erection.

e) The stresses in all the members of a space frame can be computed with certainty.

If these conditions were satisfied, it would be possible to build structures of any shape from prefabricated parts, and reliably predict their statical behavior. If the designer had such material to work on

and if, instead of pursuing arbitrary formalism, he remained intent on the quest for genuine structural form, it is conceivable that man-made space frames would advance much closer to the ideal of organic structure.

Today these speculations may still seem utopian. If, however, technology should ever reach this goal, it will be largely due to the efforts of those who are even now trying, energetically and consistently, to realize the idea of the space frame, even though the conditions in which they work are far from ideal.

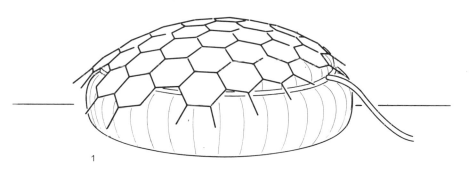

1

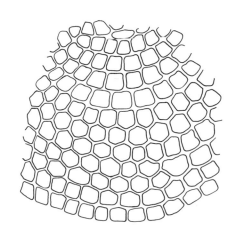

2

126.   1 Erecting a dome from the top down by using a balloon instead of scaffolding [64].
      2 Even nature has not succeeded in dividing a spherical surface into a large number of equal parts (the armor of a giant armadillo).

A Buckminster Fuller dome with aluminum panels suspended on the inside [64] ▶

194

The folded plate is something new. It is not an historical form. Among everyday objects only the folding screen and the bellows of the accordion suggest a similar principle. A few plants grow ribbed or fanned leaves. Elsewhere in nature structures resembling the folded plate are scarcely to be found. It is therefore difficult to make the idea understood by means of historical or natural analogies. Some theoretical introduction is unavoidable. It is best illustrated by describing a series of experiments on a model.

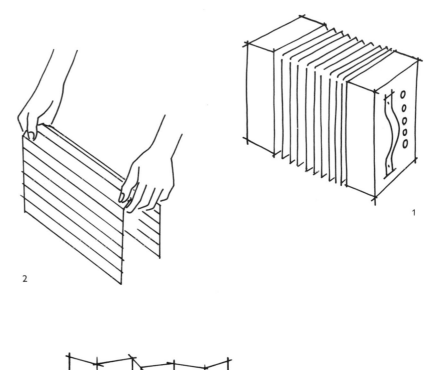

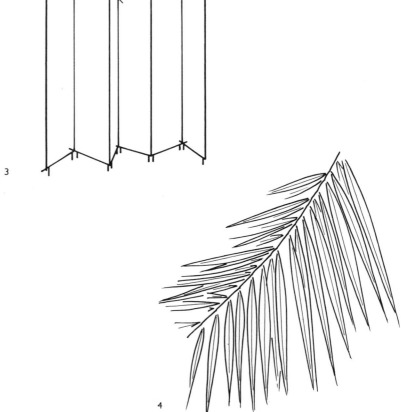

127. Folded forms, natural and man-made:
1 The bellows of an accordion.
2 A table mat.
3 A folding screen.
4 Leaves stiffened by folds.

A flat sheet of paper, laid across a gap between the ends of two boards, will collapse. It has hardly any strength in bending (Fig. 128.1).

If it is folded in the direction of the span in a series of parallel folds, like the bellows of an accordion, it acquires stiffness. In this form it will easily carry one hundred times its own weight (Fig. 128.2).

If the load is increased to breaking point, the structure will fail as a result of the collapse of the folds (Fig. 128.3).

There is a simple means of preventing the folds from collapsing. Each end of the sheet must be reinforced with a strip of cardboard (or stiffener). The sheet will then be capable of withstanding further increases in load. It is assumed that the reinforcing strip rests on the supports. Transverse stiffeners of this type are essential in folded plate construction (Fig. 128.4).

The behavior of the paper model corresponds to that of a full-scale structure. The material, however, must be one that is strong in bending, that is, capable of resisting tension, compression and shear at the same time. Theoretically, there is no reason why wood should not be used, but, in practice, large wooden plates are difficult to fabricate and complications arise in detailing the ridge and valley joints. Accordingly, relatively few folded plates have so far been built of wood.

Because of their high strength, steel and aluminum are used in sections so thin that there is a risk of local buckling in panels of the size needed to fabricate a folded plate, unless special double-walled panels are employed. Development in this direction has only just begun. Thus, for the time being we are left with reinforced concrete for folded plate construction. It is the ideal material for the job.

1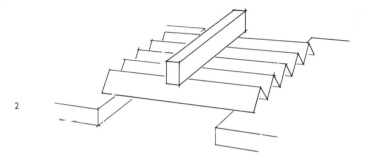

2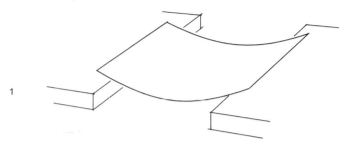

3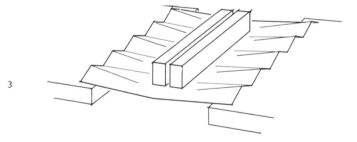

4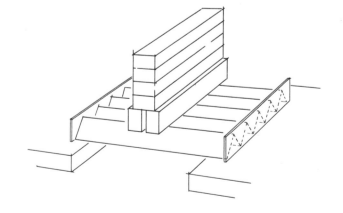

128. A paper model of a folded plate.
1 A flat sheet of paper has almost no resistance to bending.
2 Folded it can support a certain load.
3 If overloaded, the folds collapse.
4 Diaphragms, glued to each end, stiffen the folds and increase their carrying capacity.

For purposes of analysis, the action of a folded plate can be divided into three parts.

1. The action of the plate between folds in the transverse direction. In the transverse direction the folded plate acts like a crimped, continuous reinforced concrete slab spanning between a series of alternately high and low supports (Fif. 129.1). We are able to assume that the slab is supported at these points thanks to the stiffening effect of the upper folds at the ridges and the lower folds in the valleys.

2. The action of the plate parallel to the folds in the longitudinal direction.

   The folds (ridges and valleys), acting as supports, pick up the loads from the continuous crimped slab. These loads are resolved into components, the magnitude of which is determined by the pitch of the elementary inclined slabs, which together form the folded plate. These elementary slabs are now assumed to behave like thin, deep beams, leaning one against the other and spanning in the longitudinal direction between end supports. The strength of these beams increases with the depth of the plate, that is with the pitch and projected height of the elementary slabs. If the pitch is too low, the plate as a whole loses its effectiveness. In the typical case the simple beam analogy is sufficiently exact and experimentally substantiated. However, it does not apply to the end slabs of a folded plate or unsymmetrical folds. In these circumstances the edges of adjacent elementary slabs tend to deform in different ways, but the opposing tendencies are resisted by the continuity at the ridges and in the valleys. Only then are the reserves of strength that make the typical space structure superior to one designed for plane bending only actually brought into play. This point will be discussed in greater detail in connection with the cylindrical shell.

3. The action of the transverse stiffeners.

   The object of the stiffeners is to hold the folds firmly together at the supports. If the folds flatten out, the depth of the plate will be reduced and the structure will collapse. The simplest and most reliable stiffener is a continuous diaphragm that completely encloses the end of the folds. Such a diaphragm will effectively preserve the true shape of the plate.

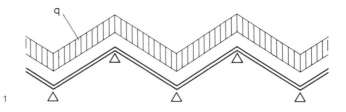

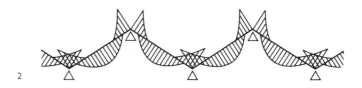

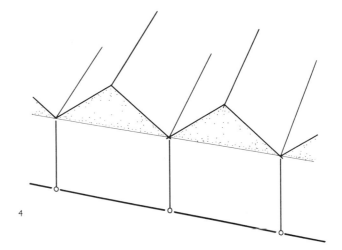

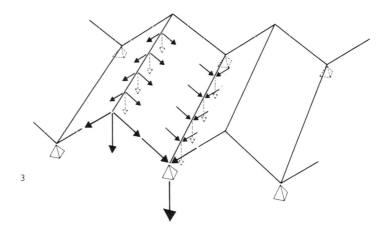

129. How a folded plate works.
   1 At right-angles to the span the plate acts like a continuous crimped slab supported at the folds.
   2 Bending moments in the crimped slab.
   3 In the direction of the span the surfaces between folds act like inclined beams, leaning one against the other.
   4 The shape of the folds must be preserved by introducing stiffeners at the supports.

There are many variations possible within the framework of the three elementary functions mentioned above. The most important factor is the nature of the folds. The relationship between their height and pitch and the span determines the rigidity and strength of the structure. The proportions of the individual folds, the form of the stiffeners and the treatment of the edges are the means by which the action of the folded plate is expressed. Employing them rationally leads to genuine structural form.

The stiffeners may also be replaced with ties, if the folded plate is supported at the low points, where ties can be introduced, and if the edges of the plate are suitably thickened. It is also possible to use a form like a broad arrowhead with two rigid, tapered barbs, a compromise between a diaphragm and a tie. This type of edge element is illustrated in the student's project shown in Fig. 130.2. We can identify the same element, somewhat modified, in the University Hydrotechnical Institute in Haifa (Fig. 130.3) [65]. In the student's design (Fig. 130.2) the folded plate is supported at the low points, while in the Haifa Institute it is suspended from the high. Either solution is possible.

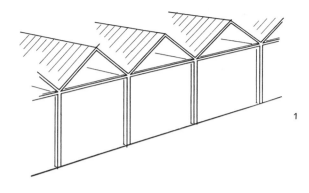

1

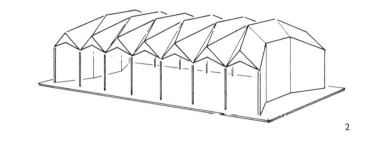

2

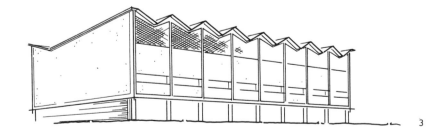

3

130. Various forms of stiffener:
 1 Tie members between supports.
 2 Arrowhead stiffeners supported at the low points.
 3 Arrowhead stiffeners supported at the high points.

At this point we must return to the Birsfelden power station, previously mentioned in Chapter 2. The treatment of the edges of the folded-plate roof is surprisingly light. There are no stiffeners and no ties to obscure the crisp undulation of the slab. If we consider for a moment the main reason for introducing an edge element, namely to prevent the folds from spreading sideways, we see that the problem has been solved by different means. The forked columns intersect at the roof and form a chain of fixed points that prevent any lateral movement of the folds. In the student's design illustrated in Fig. 131.2 the folded-plate roof of the stand is supported in such a way that at one end stiffeners are unnecessary. The stability of the substructure is again attributable to forked columns braced against each other to form a series of rigid triangular frames (see Chapter 2, Forked Columns, page 140). At the other end the roof rests not on triangular frames but on hinged columns. Accordingly, an edge beam is required to stiffen the folds.

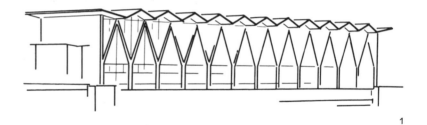

1

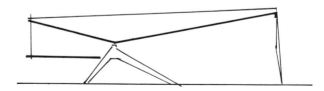

2

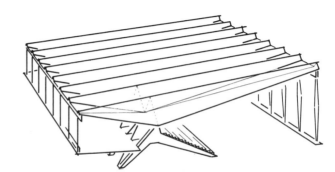

131.   Fixed supports instead of stiffeners:
       1 The Y-frames of the Birsfelden power station, Switzerland [40], form a
       chain of stable supports for the roof.
       2 The substructure of the sports stand (student project) provides a series of
       stable supports for the folded plate.

In the simplest form of folded plate the folds are parallel (Fig. 132.1). If the floor plan is trapezoidal, a fan shape suggests itself. As the folds fan out, they become broader, and hence deeper (Fig. 132.2). If it were necessary to keep the depth constant, the surface of the folds would have to be warped. It is debatable whether this would not mean sacrificing the essential character of the folded plate. Possibly the crystalline sharpness and meaningfulness of the form would be better preserved, if the folds were composed entirely of plane surfaces. However, the future will show where the true path lies and whether such distorted forms are likely to assume any importance. If warping the surface of the plate were to bring statical advantages, by substituting membrane action (see Shells, page 238ff) for slab bending, with corresponding economies in construction (thinner plate), then the above considerations would undoubtedly have to yield to the compelling logic of a new structural form.

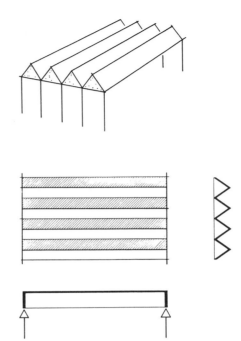

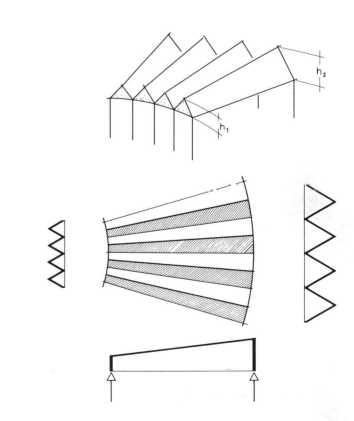

132. Variations on the folded plate:
1 Parallel folds.
2 Fan-shaped folds.

In addition to parallel and fan-shaped folds, we have folds that run counter to each other. They either span the entire distance between supports (Fig. 133) or interpenetrate over shorter sections, forming kinks in the structure (Fig. 134). These kinks can be developed into sharp-angled bends. The result is a rigid corner and the folded plate becomes a rigid frame. This, however, depends on the folds being held in shape at the corners of the frame, in the same way as the paper model was restrained at the supports.

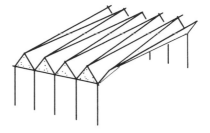

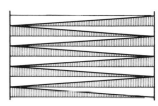

133.   Another variation—counter-folds.

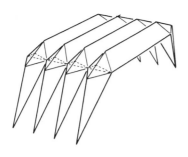

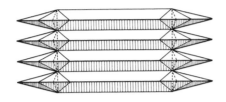

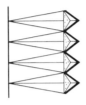

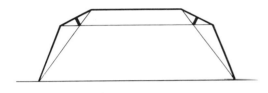

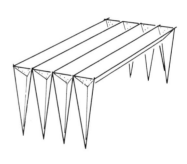

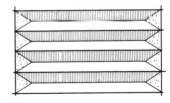

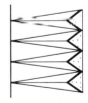

1

134.   Folded plates developed into rigid frames:
       1 Feet of the frame in the same plane as the ridge.
       2 Feet of the frame in the same plane as the valley.

2

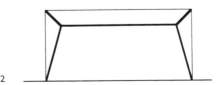

The Unesco Congress Hall in Paris [18] is an example of this kind of design. The fan shape was derived from the trapezoidal floor plan and the frame construction from the joint between the roof and the folded walls. In this case the frame has three legs. The general form of the bending moment diagram is different from that which we have learned to associate with the two-hinged frame (Chapter 2). At the corners, however, the pattern is very much the same. The greatest bending moments are concentrated at the corners and at the center of the longer span, with a maximum over the interior support. The design of the members is determined primarily by the fact that the bottom of the section is in compression at the corners and at the interior support, while the top is in compression in between, particularly at the center of the longer span. The ridges and valleys have only a limited moment of resistance. Therefore they have been strengthened by means of a solid slab which runs between the folds, following the line of maximum compression. At the corners and over the interior support it lies at the bottom of the section, swinging upwards into the compression zone at the center of the span. This undulating form is also exploited for its architectural effect. However, its true justification resides in its structural logic. Running right across the folded plate, the curved slab not only helps to resist the compressive forces, it also stiffens the folds over the entire width of the roof and thus contributes to the general stability of the structure.

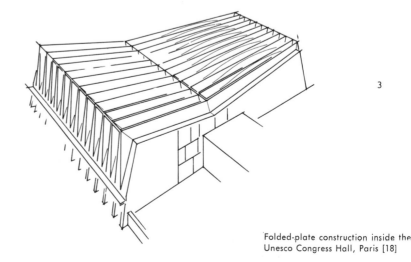

1

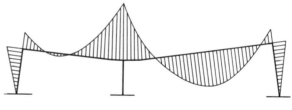

26,7o m   39,6o m

2

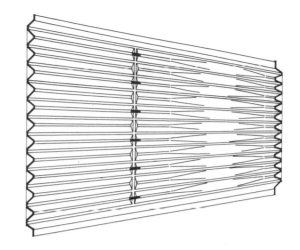

3

135. The Unesco Congress Hall, Paris [18].
      Arch: Breuer and Zehrfuss. Eng: Nervi.
      1 The trapezoidal plan.
      2 The roof is a series of three-legged frames built as folded plates. The folds are intersected by a solid slab which follows the curve of maximum compression. At the corners the frames are reinforced by means of inclined stiffeners. Over the center supports the roof is stiffened by a transverse beam.
      3 Perspective.

Folded-plate construction inside the Unesco Congress Hall, Paris [18] ▶

Marcel Breuer's design for the St. John's Abbey Church in College-ville, Minn., is a variation on the same theme [66]. Obviously influenced by the Unesco building, Breuer has developed the folded plate into a series of two-hinged frames that dominate the interior of the church.

Belloni's project for a sports arena in Pavia [67] is characterized by an imaginative crystalline form expressive of the southern temperament. Here the play among opposed, conically interpenetrating folds is pushed to the extreme, yet the resulting shape, far from being arbitrary, is obedient to geometric and mechanical laws. The telescoped folds merge into a vault. In the direction of the vault the folds give the system necessary stability. In the transverse direction the slender feet are bound together and the folds prevented from spreading by a lateral tie. The thrusts from the vault are resisted by tapered buttresses. No doubt, this kind of form still seems rather strange, but its "rightness" is confirmed by exact analysis. In no circumstances, even in so dynamic an example as that illustrated in Fig. 137, can the folded plate be dismissed as a mere frivolity. It is a type of structure that has been suggested by the new possibilities presented by reinforced concrete. It should be developed and encouraged with perfect open-mindedness. However, its crystalline severity and unique architectural atmosphere must not be abused, although it seems inevitable that the urge to be up-to-date and structural ignorance will together produce some singularly inappropriate designs. Certain irrational tendencies in the application and evaluation of folded plates are already becoming apparent.

For example, when an American publication, under the title "Toward an architecture for enjoyment," talks of "new directions" in modern architecture in connection with some recently completed folded plates, it looks very much like an attempt to establish a new architectural fashion. Reserve, modesty, the avoidance of all ornamental tendencies and some restraint in announcing "new directions" are the surest means of learning to master the problem and of getting both a structural and an esthetic grip on the forms. On the other hand, the worst thing one can do is to use them indiscriminately at every opportunity.

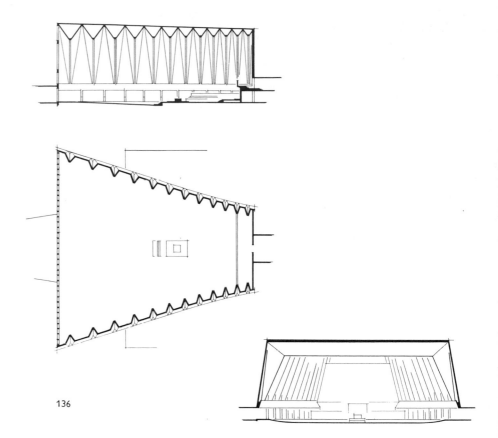

136

136. A church by Marcel Breuer with two-legged frames in folded-plate construction [66].

137. A sports stadium in Pavia, Italy [67], with a vaulted roof composed of interpenetrating folds.

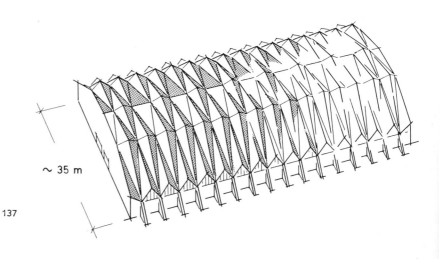

~ 35 m

137

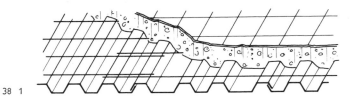

Where the folded plate is used for purely practical purposes, with no architectural pretensions, true structural form will develop quietly and without fuss. Sheet piling, some wall panels, and many types of steel decking derive their stiffness from folds and corrugations. Here the purpose is so transparent, and the scale so immediately familiar, that we are hardly aware of the novelty of the form.

If we explore deeper into the world of familiar shapes, we shall recall the northlight factory roof as another decidedly practical form of a related type. The northlight roof, of course, was first adopted in industrial construction, which is free of esthetic prejudices. Since then it has been an object of contempt, a "merely" utilitarian device. And a project that dares to incorporate a northlight roof is inevitably dismissed with the comment: "It looks just like a factory." We must never forget that in searching for new structural forms the preservation and accentuation of simplicity is most important. This will do more to encourage development than any premature esthetic classification.

138 1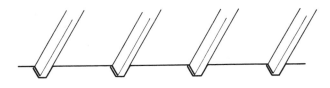

2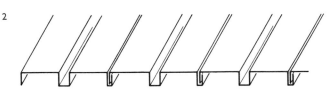

3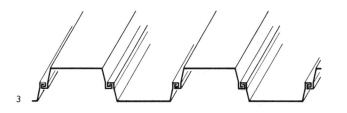

138.   Simple corrugated building elements:
        1 Combined forms-and-reinforcement for reinforced concrete floors.
        2 Corrugated wall panels.
        3 Sheet piling.

139.   The northlight factory roof can also be regarded as a folded plate, insofar as there are no structural members acting in a vertical plane.

139

Probably one of the noblest architectural applications of the folded plate so far is the McGregor Memorial Conference Center in Detroit [68] by Yamasaki. The perfectly clear and simple form of the concrete frame sets the theme for the building as a whole. The many difficult details that result from the numerous oblique intersections with the structure are nowhere concealed and have been mastered with admirable integrity. Yet the limitations of this type of construction are equally clear. The severity and crystalline sharpness of the forms dominate the human activities within. The building, intended as a center of learning, becomes a monument. Those entering it instinctively feel obliged to speak in hushed tones. The severe, geometric order of the folded plate is imposed on every detail. Windows, doors, skylights, in short, every part of the building owes its form not primarily to its function but to its inescapable subordination to the system of geometry that has been made the principal element of the design. This all-pervasive geometry dominates not only the Center but its environs as well, isolating the building and monumentalizing it.

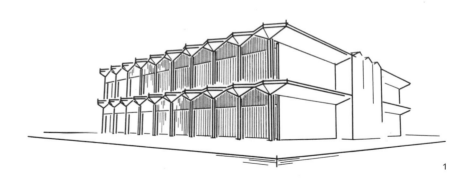

1

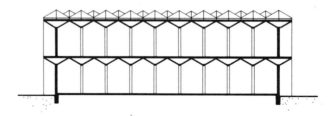

2

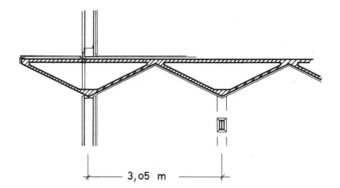

3,05 m

140. In the McGregor Memorial Conference Center in Detroit [68] Yamasaki has developed folded-plate construction into a refined form of architectural expression.
1 Elevation.
2 Longitudinal section and details.

The unusual forms of a new church in Royan [69] radiate a similar influence (Fig. 141). They also emphasize the monumentality of the design, which in this case, however, is more appropriate. The effect may appear too bold or too calculated, but really it is only new and unusual.

A conclusive esthetic judgment cannot be made without a knowledge of the structural background of the forms. The exterior walls consist of piers with a broad V section opening towards the outside. They stand independently, side by side, separated by vertical strips of glazing. These piers are stiff because they are folded. They are bound together into a three-dimensional structural unit by horizontal galleries, which are expressed in the façade. Those who planned the church (the architect Gillet and the engineers Lafaille and Sarger) have raised the basic structural idea to the status of a design motif. Thus, they have simply done in reinforced concrete what the master builders of the Middle Ages did with the arched buttress in masonry. They have attempted to let the substance of the structure speak for itself, without interference. The rough concrete surfaces have been left as they were when the forms were stripped. The structural inevitability of the form is all that matters, the treatment of the surfaces relatively unimportant. We must admit that this church makes an important contribution to the development of the folded plate. In this context questions of taste are more or less irrelevant.

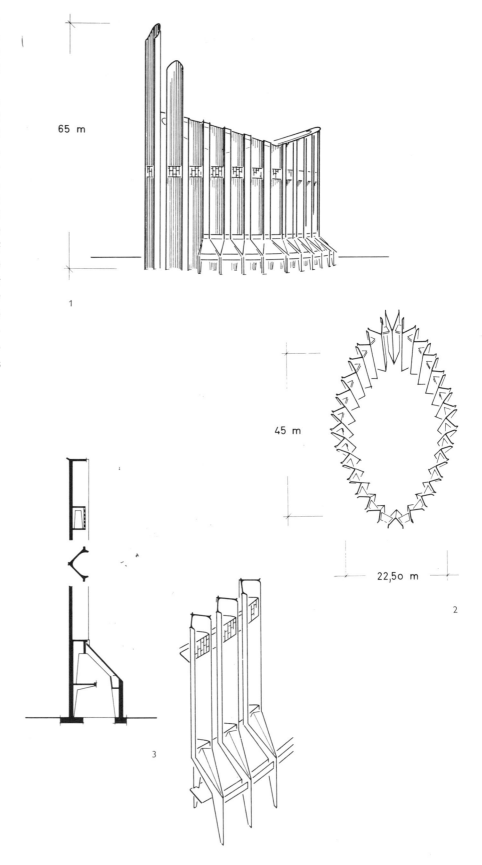

141.   The church of Notre-Dame in Royan, France [69].
       The tall outside walls are folded to increase their rigidity.
       Arch: Gillet. Eng: Lafaille and Sarger.
       1 General view.
       2 Plan showing the folds in the outside walls.
       3 Details of a fold.

The need to strengthen the ordinary folded plate has occasionally led to some significant modifications. An example of this is provided by the roof of the Sears Tampa Store [70]. By concentrating material at the ridges and in the valleys, where, in accordance with the beam analogy, the maximum bending stresses are to be anticipated, the strength of the folded plate can be effectively increased. In this case horizontal strips of slab have been inserted between the folds. The same reasoning has produced the familiar corrugated wall panel (Fig. 138.2). A slightly different form, reminiscent of the roof structure in Fig. 142.1, is used for self-supporting formwork for concrete floors (Fig. 138.1). In these modifications we may perhaps discern a new point of departure in the development of the folded plate. Intended, in the first instance, simply to increase its strength, they also suggest new possibilities with respect to design.

For example, the same tendency to develop the form is evident in the ribs of Nervi's Exhibition Hall in Turin [24]. Here, it is true, the structure is essentially an arch, rather than a folded plate, but in section the arch ribs are to be interpreted in exactly the same way as horizontal folds. They give the arch the necessary stiffness. The sections clearly reveal the concentration of material at the ridges and in the valleys. That Nervi should have seized on this idea so early (the Turin Exhibition Hall was erected in 1948) is not surprising.

1

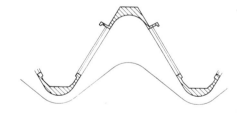

2

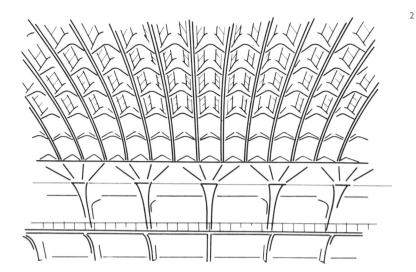

142. Further development of the folded plate:
1 The carrying capacity can be increased by introducing horizontal slabs at the ridges and in the valleys [70].
2 A section through the roof of the Turin exhibition hall [24], designed by Nervi, shows how the material is concentrated at the points most heavily stressed, the ridges and the valleys.

The notion of stiffening a plate by folding it is so elementary and so persuasive that one is inclined to ask why it was not exploited long ago. The answer is probably that there were no suitable materials available. We now have reinforced concrete and will probably develop other materials with similar characteristics. Attractive new possibilities open up before the imaginative architect. But imagination alone is not enough. If the geometry of the folded plate is not mastered and if architects will not venture further into statics than many of them are at present prepared to go, the structural form of the folded plate will be overgrown with formalism, before it has even had a chance to develop.

The crystalline forms of all folded structures are very exacting. They are difficult to integrate in the general design. They exert a powerful and obstinate influence on their surroundings. These characteristics will often constitute a temptation to try a folded plate for the sake of the "architectural effect," in defiance of functional and structural principles. Moreover, the detailing of a folded plate structure is very delicate work and the difficulties are easily underestimated. More than almost any other structure, the folded plate derives its vitality from clarity of expression. It will tolerate no disguising. If we recall the virtually unavoidable density of modern mechanical installations, pipes, ducts and conduits, the need to insulate and drain the roof, to waterproof the valleys, to provide gutters and rainleaders, we shall have no difficulty in appreciating that, though a design may look very convincing as a model, it may easily fail when it comes to hard realities. Whoever balks at following the spartan road to large, bare, crystal-clear structural forms, as exemplified by the Unesco Hall (pages 204 and 205), would do better to forego the folded plate and its tricky detail altogether.

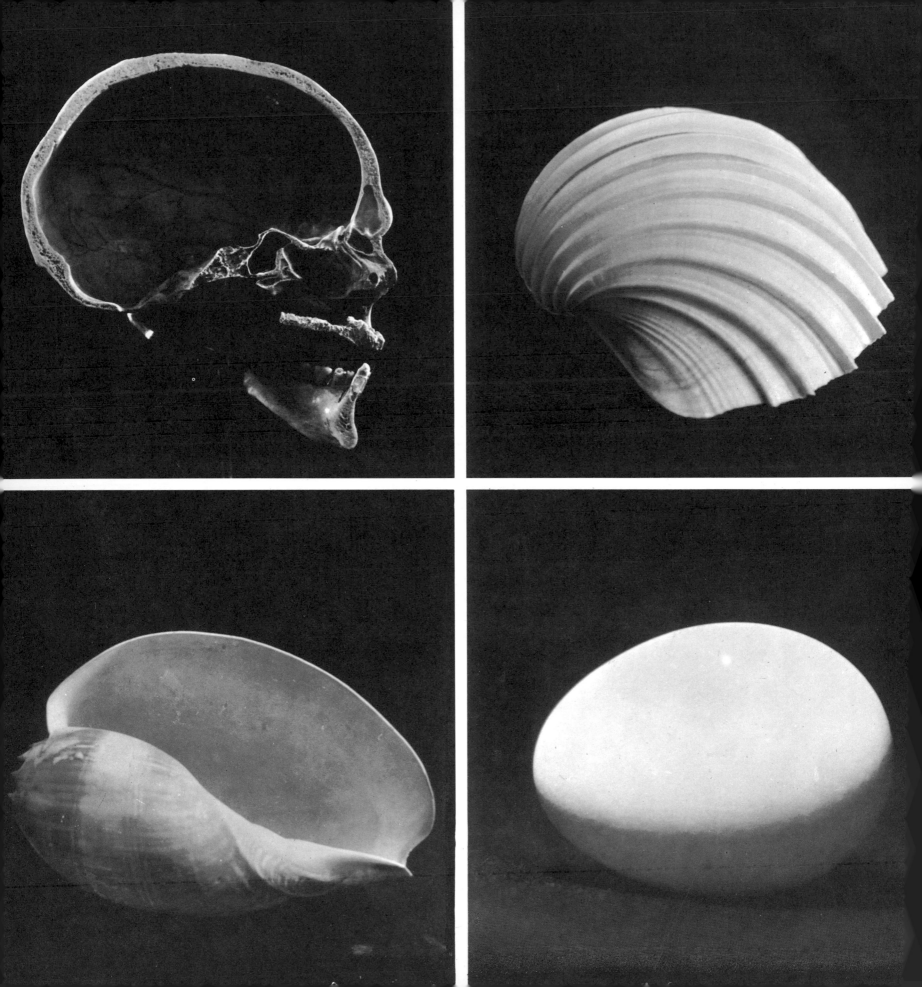

 **SHELLS**

Natural shell forms ◀

The word "shell" suggests a natural form, that of an egg, nut, crab or mollusc, a seed pod or the armor of insects. It is associated in our minds with two quite specific properties. Shells are *rigid* and *curved*. Plane surfaces can never form a shell, at the best a cell or box. Nature uses soft materials in a myriad forms, but not to make shells. Nor are fibrous materials like straw or pliable materials like leather and skin compatible with the idea of a shell, as we are trying to define it. Only "rigid," in the sense of hard and tough, satisfactorily describes the material of which a shell is built.

A "curved" surface and "rigid" material are the two fundamental properties of a shell in both its natural and man-made forms. It is no accident that the engineers who first grappled with this problem, whether English, French or German, borrowed the same natural image to describe the fruits of their work. The German word "Schale" is equivalent to the English "shell" and the French "coque." Perhaps this choice of terminology points to a future in which man-made forms will gradually tend to approach closer to those of nature. Architecture will be enriched with many previously impracticable, free forms, curiously related to organic growth.

Such reflections, however, easily lead to exaggerated and premature claims. This is still a matter for the future. We must complete the first step before attempting the second. If we are to build shells at all, we shall find ourselves obliged by practical necessity to add a number of other conditions to those of "curvature" and "rigidity" introduced above.

A shell must be "buildable," in the sense that it must have a manageable geometry. It must not overtax the normal facilities of workshop and site.

From the point of view of statics, the loads must be of the type a shell is best able to resist. Shells will not carry heavy point loads, unless specially reinforced. The inevitable concentrations of load at the supports make it necessary to modify the shell at these points, in order to control the forces and transfer them smoothly to the substructure.

The mathematician who analyzes a shell and predicts the stresses in it is concerned with those aspects of its form that are, at least in part, amenable to mathematical treatment. If his recommendations are disregarded, the considerable time consumed in calculation ceases to bear any proper relation to the economics of the design.

The mathematician will insist that, in principle, the shell must be "very thin" in relation to the span. In order to be able to formulate a theory at all, he needs to eliminate all the influences that produce bending in the shell. He would prefer the shell to act like a "membrane," in which all the forces are tangential to the surface. In order that the actual distribution of forces in the shell may correspond as closely as possible with the assumptions on which the theory is based, the shell ought to be made so thin that it is incapable of resisting any forces other than those acting in tangential directions.

For practical reasons, various parts of a shell often have to be thickened. These thickenings produce "disturbances" in the stress pattern, distasteful to the mathematician. For the sake of his computations he prefers the ideal case of a shell uniform in all directions. Any irregularity is for him a "disturbance."

These and similar considerations restrict the range of forms possible in modern shell construction. How far they are inherent in the nature of the problem itself or merely consequences of the crudity of our present techniques of computation is another question. Nature knows nothing of such limitations, and since we are interested above all in form, and in particular, in the significant structural form that can be derived from natural growth, which depends exclusively on natural

laws and not on a somewhat limited skill in calculation, we shall have to judge very critically all the possibly transitory limitations which today still hamper the development of shell design. Moreover, we are anxious to avoid burdening our exposition with inessentials. The only inescapable requirements, inescapable because inherent in the nature of the problem, are those outlined above, namely that the shell must be "curved" and "rigid" (that is able to resist compression, tension and shear).

The material in this section has been classified on the basis of form. We shall not inquire whether members of different groups all belong mathematically to the same family. It is more relevant to our purpose that they provoke similar reactions and behave in the same way. An arched barrel vault and a hyperboloid of revolution may look confusingly alike, yet mathematically they are totally different. We are not interested in whether a polygonal dome is better defined as a segment of a sphere or as a translational form. The principle of the egg is unaffected by the fact that no one egg is the same as another. Thus, two shells can have the same structural form, although mathematically they are constructed in different ways. What we call structural form has a broader base than this, namely a unity of function, material and statical principle. This trinity alone is the author of the form, the mathematical construction being merely a means to an end.

The laws of structural form will be explored with reference to a number of groups of similar, formally related examples. These examples have been chosen fairly freely. Clarity and simply expressiveness have been the chief criteria. They can be divided into five categories:

1. Cylindrical shells.
2. Shells of revolution.
3. Conoids.
4. Hyperbolic paraboloids.
5. Free forms.

Cylindrical Shells

Like the folded plate, the cylindrical shell has few counterparts in nature. The closed tube is represented in the stems of grasses and bamboos; it also has applications in technology. But the segment of a cylinder, the basic form in shell construction, is a building element used neither by technologists nor by nature. Its only importance is that which it has been granted by architects during the last twenty or thirty years. The segment of a cylinder is the typical shell form and the one with which this section is mainly concerned. If in what follows we refer concisely to "segmental shells," we have in mind a segment of a cylinder, not a segment of a sphere or circle, as might normally be the case. With the segmental shells we shall also include types which, strictly speaking, do not belong to this group, but for which, on account of their related form, there is no more appropriate place. Thus, we shall also discuss segments of cones, segments of cylinders curved in the direction of the axis and, finally, shells of a completely different mathematical character, for example, certain hyperboloids of revolution. Our main criteria will be similarity of form and structural action.

In spite of its curvature (cf. Fig. 146) the segmental shell has nothing in common with the familiar form or statical principle of the arch. It is something completely new. In order to make its action understandable without the apparatus of mathematics, we shall again resort to a paper model. A sheet of paper, normally almost incapable of resisting bending, can be made stiff by being rolled up. If the paper is unrolled and folded at equal intervals against the curve, we get a series of relatively strong segmental shells. Under heavy loads they spread sideways and collapse. Strips of cardboard glued to each end will preserve the shape of the shells and increase their strength.

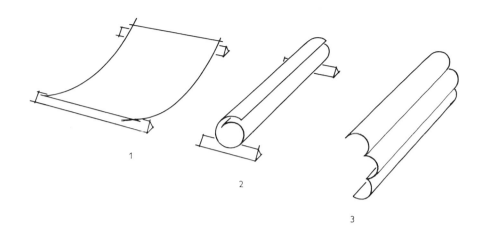

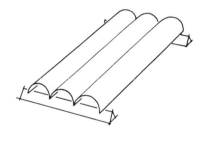

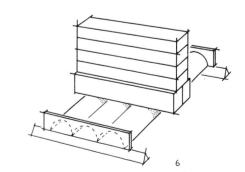

143.   Paper model of a cylindrical shell roof.
1 A flat sheet of paper has practically no resistance to bending.
2 Rolling it makes it stiff.
3 and 4 Folding it against the curvature produces a series of rigid segments of a cylinder.
5 When overloaded, the segments collapse.
6 Transverse stiffeners, glued to each end, preserve the shape of the segments and improve their carrying capacity.

If we try to analyze the action of a cylindrical shell in the same way as we analyzed that of a folded plate (cf. page 198), we again find ourselves able to distinguish three elementary functions:

1. The action of the curved surface in the transverse direction.

   First, let us imagine the cure replaced with a series of flat, parallel strips, i.e. a folded plate in place of the shell. If we also assume that these strips are sufficiently strong in bending in the transverse direction, then, as described in connection with the folded plate (Fig. 129), the distributed loads will be concentrated at the folds, which will act like ordinary supports (Fig. 144.1).

2. The action in the longitudinal direction.

   The loads concentrated at the folds can be resolved into components in the planes of the adjacent strips. These components represent the reactions on the strips, which now act as elementary beams spanning in the longitudinal direction (144.2). From the asymmetry of the system, at the edge A-B, for example, it is easy to see that the loading on the two elementary beams on either side of the edge A-B is not the same. Thus, at the edge A-B the two unequally loaded elementary beams will tend to deform in different ways. However, since the slab is continuous across A-B, the two beams must restrain each other's tendency to deform and along A-B the actual deformation must be a compromise between these two tendencies. The result is that the stresses at the edge A-B are mainly shear stresses, a type of stress that the thin shell is well equipped to resist.

   Now, if we imagine the strips made narrower and narrower, we soon arrive at the continuous curve characteristic of the true shell and it is easy to see that there is no fundamental difference between normal shell action and the action of the folded plate just described. The above-mentioned shear stresses make an important contribution to both.

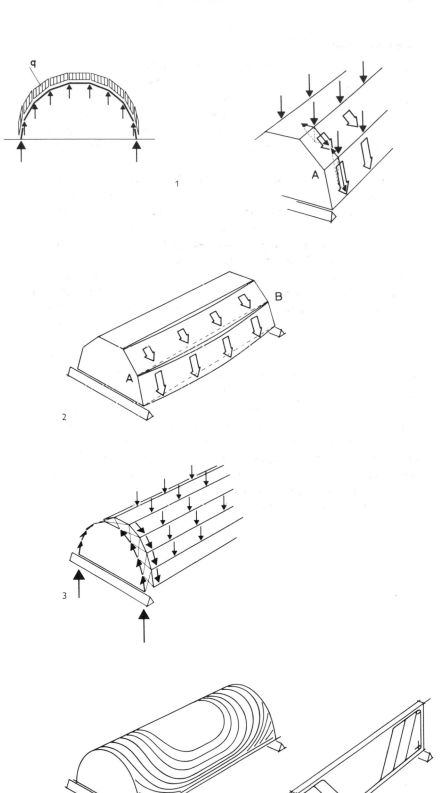

144. The action of a cylindrical shell can be understood by imagining it replaced with a folded plate.
   1 The loads are concentrated along the rigid folds (cf. Fig .129).
   2 In the direction of the span the flat elements between folds act like small beams, transferring the loads to points A and B. However, since they are continuous at the folds, they are capable of resisting shear. Accordingly, they mutually restrain each other's tendency to deform and thus increase the carrying capacity of the structure as a whole.
   3 The shape of the structure is preserved by means of transverse stiffeners at each end. The connection between these stiffeners and the shell must be capable of transmitting shear.
   4 The principal reinforcement in a cylindrical shell compared with that in a simple beam.

3. The action of the transverse stiffeners.

If a very thin shell is to act as described under 1 and 2, its initial shape must be rigidly preserved and lateral spreading prevented. The joint between shell and stiffener must therefore be capable of resisting shear. This joint is of critical importance. In Fig 144.3 it is approximately·represented by a symbolic lattice. It is obvious that the carrying capacity of the structure as a whole depends on the shear strength developed along the line where shell and stiffener meet.

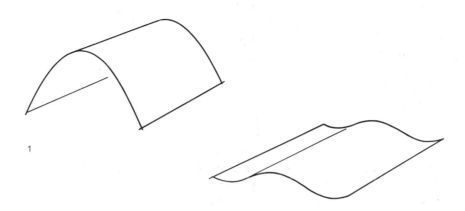

1

To summarize, the cylindrical shell behaves rather like a folded plate composed of numerous narrow strips. The loads are first transferred to the folds and are then resolved into components tangential to adjacent strips. In the longitudinal direction the latter act like beams, restrained from deforming freely because of the continuity with their neighbors (contrary to the simple beam theory of the symmetrical folded plate, cf. page 198). In general, the shell will only work if it is held in shape by stiffeners and if the joints between stiffeners and shell are capable of resisting shear.

If the cylindrical shell is viewed as a closed system, then, of course, we again get a clear analogy with the action of a beam (Fig. 144.4). There is an unmistakable resemblance between the patterns formed by the reinforcing in simple beams and cylindrical shells. The shell immediately becomes intelligible when seen as a beam with a thin, curved web.

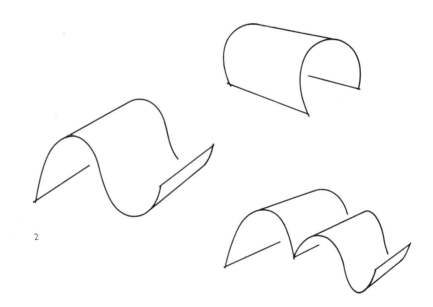

2

There is one more point worth noting. The approximately parabolic line of pressure, which so rigorously determines the form of the arch, is not typical of a cylindrical shell; in fact, it even impairs its strength [71]. If a cylindrical shell is given a cross section of the line-of-pressure type, the loads along the line of pressure flow straight down to the bottom edge of the shell, without being converted into shear forces on the way and thus transferred to the supports by the shortest route. Normally such shear forces are developed at the folds in a folded plate or along the curve in a shell, the curve of the shell being the more effective for this purpose the more it departs from the line of pressure. If the cross section follows the line of pressure exactly, pure beam action will develop at the bottom edge of the shell; this, of course, goes against the true nature of a shell, the carrying capacity of which is based on its ability to resist shear.

145.   Possible cross sections for cylindrical shells:
     1 The line of pressure is not typical. Unemphatic and feeble curves are wrong.
     2 Any cross section can be employed, provided the curve is strongly enough expressed.

Actually, the cross sections of most of the shells built so far have been arcs of circles. This is because such forms are geometrically simple, easy to build and mathematically tractable; there is nothing, however, in the nature of shell construction that dictates such a solution.

The building of cylindrical shells began in Germany in the Twenties with the famous Zeiss-Dywidag system. The Central Markets in Frankfurt and Budapest [62] were roofed with segmental shells of semi-circular cross section. The segments were tied together with large, beam-like edge members in the direction of the span. At first it was thought that these edge members were indispensable. Tilting the segments and introducing intermediate glazing gave the northlight shell, which has since become one of the typical forms of industrial roof. These early shell styles still convey very little of the inner tension and elegance of the structural concept. True shell designs only emerged later.

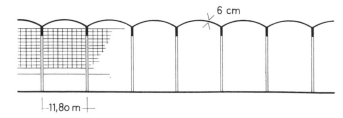

1

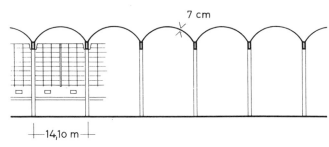

2

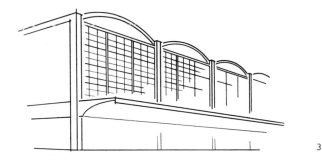

3

146.   Simple primary forms of cylindrical shell acting like beams spanning between two supports.
    1 Cylindrical segments with heavy edge beams placed side by side (cross sections correspond to Fig. 146.3).
    2 Inclined cylindrical segments forming a northlight roof.
    3 Elevations of the markets in Budapest and Frankfurt-am-Main [62].

The lightness and elegance of the shell are never more in evidence than when its curvature and astonishing thinness are fully exposed. This point is made particularly clearly by the cantilevered roofs of sports stands like those in Hanover [72] and Cartagena [73] (Figs. 147.1 and 2). The same effect, however, can also be achieved with simple shells, supported at both ends, by cantilevering the shell beyond the plane of the supports. The roof of the Bogotá bus station [74] (Fig. 147.3) is composed entirely of segmental shells and transverse stiffeners, which also act as beams. Thus, it becomes possible to omit alternate columns and add a freely cantilevered shell at each end. The whole building is nothing but structure and form.

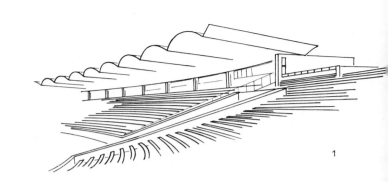

1

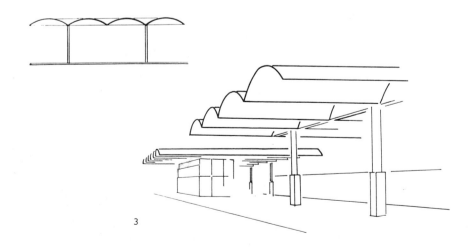

~ 18 m

2

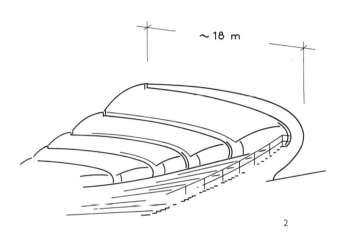

3

147.   Later use of cylindrical shells in cantilevered construction:
        1 Sports stand in Hanover, Germany [72].
        2 Sports stand in Cartagena, Colombia [73].
        3 Bus station in Bogota, Colombia [74].

Compositions in which segmental shells are arranged to form a space structure that gives a hollow effect when viewed from below can be both technically and formally interesting. The two water tanks in Fig. 148 consist of a ring of inwardly convex segments. The curvature of the shell is opposed to the pressure of the water. The tensile stresses in the shell, viewed as an element spanning vertically, are absorbed mainly by the projecting ribs (cf. Fig. 144.4) and the horizontal ring tension is concentrated in the outer edge of the chain of stiffeners. Thus, in addition to their primary function of stiffening the shell elements and holding them in shape, these members resist the ring tension like the hoops around a barrel.

These examples are pure civil engineering. They show that it is possible to do more with segmental shells than simply line them up side by side. Slight modifications of the basic form, for example, the conical taper adopted for a water tower at Caen [77], suggest a multitude of new possibilities, for architects as well as for engineers.

An extraordinary project, still awaiting realization, is the prize-winning design for a new city hall in Toronto [75] by the Finnish architect Revell. Here for the first time the hollow form of a segment of a cylinder has been used for the vertical frame of a tall building. The engineers confirm that the structure will be designed as a shell. Though this shell was originally intended to have two walls, it has been found possible to cantilever all 36 stories from one side of a single wall and still derive enough stiffness to resist wind forces from the intrinsic curvature of the form itself. In this case the floor slabs play the part of stiffeners.

How unprepared we are to accept such solutions was demonstrated by the extensive criticism that greeted this design. Most of the critics betrayed a complete lack of understanding of what was really at stake.

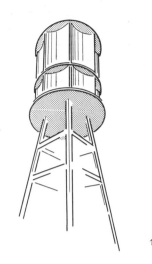

1

35 m

2

148. Water tanks based on combinations of shell segments:
    1 Water tank in Egypt [76].
    2 New water tower in the center of Caen, France [77].

Skyscraper design for Toronto city hall [75]
Arch: Viljo Revell

As a theoretical exercise, the Universal Atlas Cement Company recently invited certain prominent architects and engineers to prepare designs for a series of important projects, without any specific instructions as to type. The results, some of which are of great interest, were communicated to the public through the daily press, a piece of enterprise truly worth imitating. This series of designs, some of which have already had fruitful repercussions, included "Tomorrow's Auditorium" [78], the work of the Architects' Collaborative (TAC) in Cambridge—Walter Gropius' team—and the engineers Weidlinger and Salvadori (Fig. 149). The two groups of shells fan out over a strictly functional plan. The fanning effect is achieved by giving the individual shells a conical section. The carrying capacity of the shells remains unaffected.

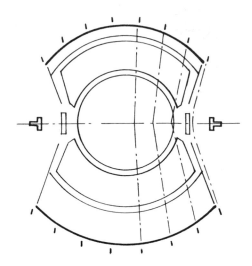

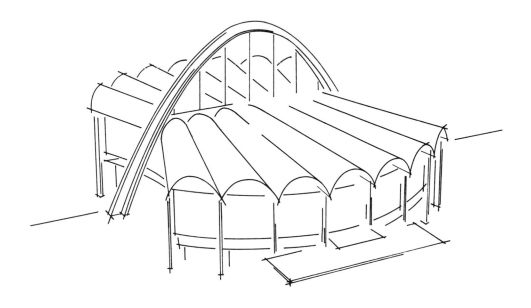

149.   Shells arranged in a double fan to form an auditorium roof. Arch: T.A.C. with Walter Gropius. Eng: Weidlinger and Salvadori [78].

In collaboration with Nervi the architects Hellmuth, Obata and Kassabaum have prepared a centrally oriented design for the St. Louis Priory in St. Louis [79]. It consists of two superimposed, concentrically arranged rings of conically sliced shells. The departure from the segment of a cylinder is more pronounced than in the project illustrated in Fig. 149. In fact, the individual shells are now curved in the direction of their longitudinal axis as well. Nevertheless, the design is mentioned at this point in order to show how one form evolves gradually out of another and how much the expressiveness of a shell depends on the way the edges are treated. Although, in this case, the edges of the shell are clearly related to forms already discussed, the radial arrangement and the double curvature of the individual elements indicate a development that we shall re-encounter, variously modified, among shells of revolution, hyperbolic paraboloids and free forms. Together, the shells, which taper inwards in section and in plan, form a sort of dome. They are rationally integrated in a broader structural conception in which the laws of the independent cylindrical shell are only partially observed. The extremely rigid gullies between the shells, to which we shall return later (compare the discussion on ridges and valleys in connection with interpenetrating forms, page 228 ff.), acquire the importance of stiffening folds. They are formed by the intersection of two adjacent shells. From what has already been said it would appear that some sort of diaphragm ought to have been provided over the supports to prevent the segmental shells from spreading. Here, for the first time, we find that the diaphragm has been omitted and the edges of the shells are free and unreinforced. This is only possible, because, in this particular case, the individual shells are not simply but doubly curved. The difference in the curvature of the segments on the outside and on the inside is clearly visible in the sketches. Thanks to this double curvature, about which we shall have a great deal to say later on, the shell is so stiff that it holds its shape without diaphragms, especially as, in this case, the loads tend to flow away into the rigid gully sections, which act like arch ribs, relieving the free edge. The parabolic form of the free edge is probably another factor that assists it in shedding load. In the neighborhood of the free edge the loads can be transferred to the supports by a form of arch action, without the shell as such being brought into play. In these circumstances the parabolic cross section, which we decided was not typical of the cylindrical shell, again becomes significant. In the following sections we shall return repeatedly to the question of its appropriateness in connection with shell design.

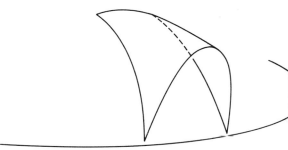

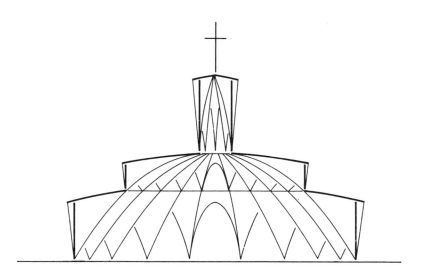

150. Circular arrangement of shell elements in which the cylindrical form has been abandoned. The subsequent development of doubly curved surfaces is suggested. Arch: Hellmuth, Obata and Kassabaum [79].

The "long" cylindrical shell curves at right angles to the direction in which it spans. This transverse curvature does not imply arch action. The shape of the curve is independent of the line of pressure (Fig. 151.1). There are other shells, however, in which the direction of curvature and the direction of span coincide. These shells, known as "short" shells, are stiffened by means of ribs introduced at relatively short intervals. Under these conditions the line of pressure again becomes an important factor. The short shell has a greater rise and is only rational where lofty spaces are required, as in central markets, arenas, hangars and so on. If the short shell is supported directly on the foundations at both ends of the curve, the forces will follow the shortest route to the supports, as they would in an arch, without making a detour through the diaphragm or stiffening ribs, as they must do in the long shells illustrated in Figs. 144 and 151.1. If the curve of the short shell corresponds with the line of pressure for dead load, that is, if it approximates to a parabola, the forces will choose this route without bringing the stiffening ribs into action at all. Every modification of the line of pressure, under wind loading, for example, (Fig. 151.3), interferes with this balance and would bring about the collapse of the thin, simply curved shell, if no stiffening ribs were provided. Wherever the line of pressure and the shape of the shell do not correspond, the shell must act to transfer the asymmetrical portions of the load to the stiffening ribs. These ribs must then perform the same function as the diaphragms in Fig. 144, namely, provide stiffness and preserve the shape of the shell. However, since, unlike the diaphragm, they do not close off the end of the shell with a solid wall, they must be given sufficient strength in bending to withstand every possible combination of loads. The work of the ribs is reduced to a minimum, when the dead loads are carried by the shell itself, and the ribs are left to absorb the variable loads due to snow and wind. This is the case when the shell has the same shape as the line of pressure. Thus, in short shells the parabolic line of pressure again becomes a form-determining factor. Hence, the form of the short shell adds nothing to what is conveyed by a simple arch. The element of true shell action, restricted in this case to the short intervals between ribs under asymmetrical loads, is not visibly expressed. Instead the design is controlled by the near-parabola of the line of pressure. Direct arch action is typical of the short shell.

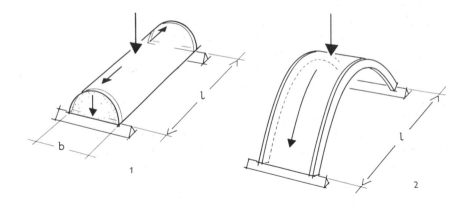

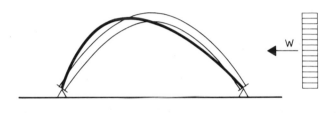

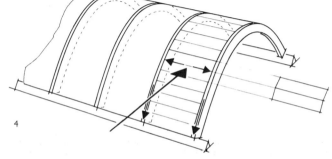

151.   The "short" shell is also a cylindrical shell but its structural principle is quite distinct.

        1 So far the discussion has been limited to cylindrical shells curved at right-angles to the direction in which they span.

        2 The "short" shell is curved in the direction of span itself, preferably following the line of pressure. The vertical loads are carried by arch action.

        3 Stiffening ribs preserve the shape of the structure when asymmetrical loading causes fluctuations in the line of pressure.

        4 The asymmetrical loads reach the stiffening ribs through the curved slab (which can be thought of as composed of a series of flat strips).

The short shell may well be appropriate for roofing wide, single-story buildings like the Central Market in Cologne [80] (Fig. 152.1). In a discussion of typical shell forms, however, it is of only secondary importance. The designer of the factory in Gossau, Switzerland, illustrated in Fig. 152.2, was able to give his short shells a circular form, rather than the parabolic form dictated by the line of pressure, only because he was able to provide a very rigid lattice girder as a stiffener [81]. This girder is capable of resisting the bending moments due to the deviation of the form from the line of pressure. At this point we ought to mention the pavilion designed by Maillart [82] for the 1939 Zurich Exhibition (Fig. 152.3). In this building the ends of the shell project far beyond the stiffening ribs on either side. In this way the thin edges are thrown into relief. The parabolic line of pressure which determines the form is clearly legible in the curve of the ribs. It is typical of the short shell.

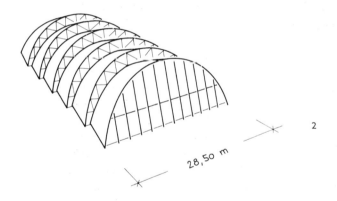

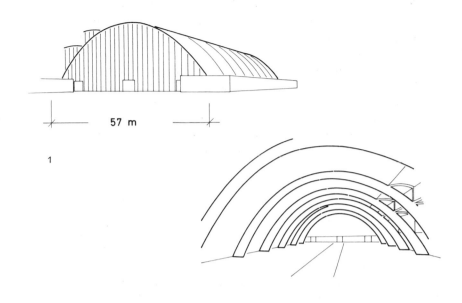

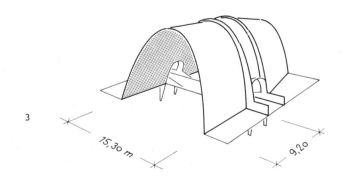

152. Buildings designed as short shells:
      1 Market in Cologne, Germany [80].
      2 Factory in Gossau, Switzerland [81].
      3 Exhibition pavilion designed by Maillart, Zurich, 1939 [82].

The flower market in Pescia [83] is a compromise between a shell and a vault. It is made of hollow blocks about 25 cm thick and is thus much stronger than a thin concrete shell would be (Fig. 153.1). There appear to be no stiffening ribs. Where they would normally be found, the cavities have been filled with solid concrete. Thus, the ribs are concealed within the thickness of the roof. Nevertheless, they still act to stiffen the vault against asymmetrical loading (cf. Chapter 2, page 164 ff.). A tilted arch, lying in the plane of the vault, spans longitudinally from pier to pier, replacing the continuous line support in which a short shell normally ends. By this means the structure is pared away, the interior better ventilated and illuminated, and the structural form rendered more intelligible.

It is important to draw a clear distinction between the "long" shell (Fig. 144) and the "short" shell (Fig. 151), because confusing these two forms seriously impairs our ability to develop and appreciate pure structural form. We shall illustrate this point by means of two examples. In Fig. 153.2 a large area is roofed by several shells of different size. The fact that the two outside shells are carried down to the foundations suggests that they span like short shells, in the direction of curvature. Significantly, they also have a parabolic form. The center shell has a circular cross section and, moreover, the length-to-breadth ratio suggests that it spans in the direction of the longitudinal axis, like a normal segmental shell. Apparently, then, this roof is a combination of short and segmental shells. Moreover, it is uncertain whether the end walls have a stiffening function or not. They ought to act as diaphragms for the center shell and stiffening ribs for the short shells at either side. Their transparent texture suggests neither of these functions. If they are not massive and do not act as stiffeners, then there are at least two supports missing, at A and B, as well as a diaphragm to develop the strength of the center shell. Furthermore, the outer shells lack the stiffening ribs that the short shell normally requires. All the shells are the same thickness. This thickness is too great for a long shell and not enough for the stiffening rib of a short one. There is no means of analyzing this design to improve our understanding of the way in which it works. It is not of structural origin. It may express certain plastic values but it has no place in building.

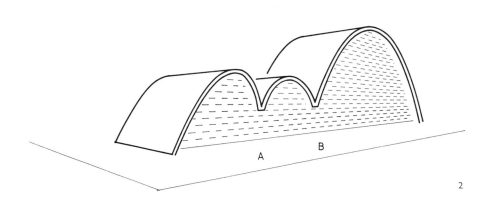

153.   Variations on the short shell:
   1 The flower market in Pescia, Italy [83], is a vault, built in hollow block, that acts like a short shell. The vertical loads are carried to the bottom edges of the shell where they are transferred to the independent supports by inclined arches lying within the thickness of the roof. Asymmetrical loads are resisted by stiffening ribs similarly concealed within the thickness of the shell.
   2 When the functions of short and cylindrical shells are not clearly distinguished, the result is structural ambiguity. The curvature of the shells, the direction in which they span, their thickness, the presence or absence of transverse diaphragms or stiffeners and the general structural principle remain obscure.

Similar criticisms apply to the roof structure shown in Fig. 154.1, although in this case the general pattern is easier to grasp. The supports at the corners of the center shells indicate that they span in the direction of the longitudinal axis, although no end stiffeners have been provided. The fact that one edge of the outside shells has been carried down to the foundations suggests that they behave like short shells, although there is no sign of stiffening ribs. The flaps added to the outside shells are flat and hence inappropriate both for shells and vaults. They can only be interpreted as slabs stressed in bending. The uniform thickness of the shells, revealed in the elevation, is once again too much for a long shell and too little for a stiffening rib. On closer inspection, the first impression of a coherent structure gives way to one of structural inconsequence. The stability of the system is derived entirely from the stiffness of the curved slabs, which are neither shells nor vaults and would be better suited to their purpose if they were plane instead of rounded (along the lines of Fig. 154.2). On the other hand, the design would gain in lightness, economy and expressiveness, if the curvature and thickness of the shells, the shape and position of their diaphragms and supports and the general direction in which they span were those of a shell of true cylindrical form (154.3).

The nature of building, of course, is too subtle for all the varieties of cylindrical shell to be compressed into the two types we have defined, the long shell, spanning in the direction of its axis, and the short, spanning at right angles to it. There is no doubt that various modifications, compromises and combinations with other systems are possible and that one day these may lead to valid new forms. However, future development can only proceed from forms that are in themselves mature, not from a formalism that is merely evidence of an ignorance of structural principles.

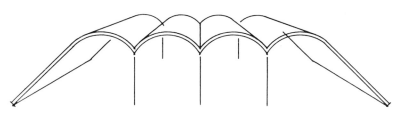

1

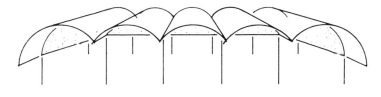

2

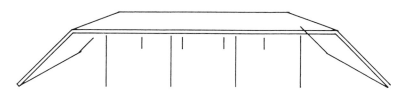

3

154.   Pseudo shells:
    1 The thickness of the slab, the lack of stiffeners and the flat sections at each end suggest a plate structure stressed in bending.
    2 In this case a flat slab design would be more convincing than a seeming shell.
    3 A suggested alternative, a series of true thin shells with stiffeners at the supports and end shells tilted.

The intersection at right angles of two segmental shells of circular cross section produces a form related to the cross vault (Fig. 155.1). The valley formed where the segments meet is comparable to a curved fold. It is very rigid. It helps to preserve the shape of the structure and stiffens the shell in the same way as a diaphragm or stiffening rib. Its stiffening effect depends largely on the angle at which the shells intersect.

The edge of the shell roof of the St. Louis airport building [84] is reinforced with a massive concrete rib about two meters wide and 45 cm thick (Fig. 155.2). This is the dimension visible from the outside, whereas the thickness of the shell itself is only 11 cm. Without this edge reinforcement, however, the shell, which is curved in one direction only, would not be stiff enough for the span, about 36 meters. At this point it is interesting to compare the St. Louis structure with the Maillart shell shown in Fig. 152.3. As we saw, this shell also has a free edge projecting far beyond stiffening ribs located in the interior of the building. Since the dimensions are relatively small, however, no edge reinforcing is required.

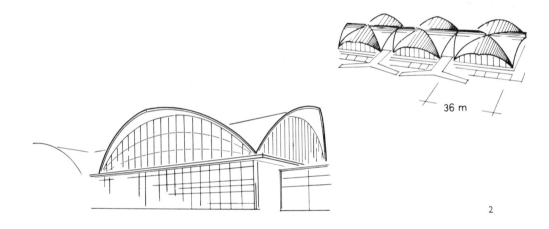

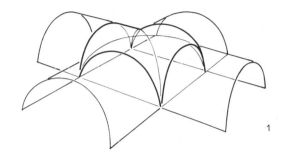

36 m

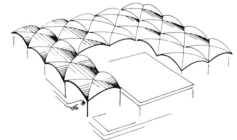

155.   Two cylindrical shells interpenetrating at right-angles:
        1 The result may be a form similar to that of the cross vault.
        2 The St. Louis air terminal [84].
        3 Warehouse at Menlo Park, Cal. [85].

Having dealt with two segments interpenetrating at right angles, the next step is to consider the multiple intersection of even greater numbers of segments. If, moreover, we form ridges rather than valleys, the result will be a dome. Structures of this kind were used at a very early stage in the history of shell construction to roof markets in Leipzig and Basle [86] (Fig. 156.2). The stiffening function of the valleys is now taken over by the ridges. Following the same elementary reasoning as that we employed in analyzing the distribution of forces in the short shell (Fig. 151), we can distinguish:

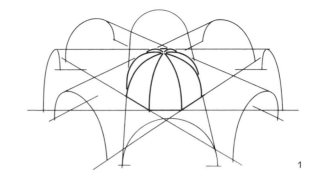

1. a curved shell in which the forces flow downwards in the same way as in arch construction. They bending introduced as a result of unsymmetrical loading or the departure of the curve of the shell from the line of pressure is resisted
2. by the stiffening effect of the curved surfaces, which also transfer the forces to the ridges. These surfaces can be thought of as a continuous series of plane strips. Finally, we have
3. the ridges, which take the place of stiffening ribs and preserve the shape of the shell.

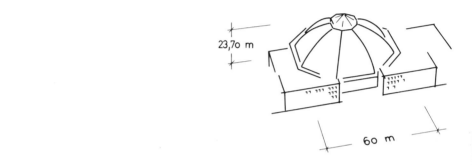

Visually these interpenetrating forms are not always very lively. On the one hand, they lack the austere simplicity of a linear arrangement of segmental shells, all curved about a single axis and all clearly oriented in the same direction. On the other hand, the radial plan which results from the interpenetration of identical segments is architecturally exacting and makes demands which surfaces curved in one direction only are unable to meet. The unidirectional curvature gives an impression of stiffness and solidified geometry.

Doubtless, however, the variations that can be played on the theme of intersecting segmental shells are still far from being exhausted.

156. Multiple interpenetration of cylindrical shells:
      1 In contrast to Fig. 155 this kind of interpenetration may also result in a dome.
      2 Wholesale markets in Basle, Switzerland, and Leipzig, Germany [86].
      3 We must again differentiate between the action of the curved slab (which may be thought of as composed of a series of flat strips) and that of the stiffening ribs, which in this case are actually the ridges.

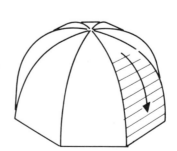

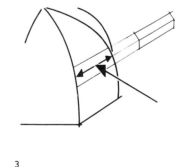

The proposed market in Tressanti [87] is a fine example of how an animated and vigorous building form can result from the interpenetration of a series of cylindrical segments (Fig. 157). Once understood, the idea that all ridges and valleys contribute stiffness can be applied to any set of interpenetrating forms. They provide a means of controlling the way a structure works and of making it more expressive. If the interpenetration of even the simplest segmental shells makes possible such dynamic, three-dimensional forms, it is certain that modifying the basic configuration of the shell by tapering it, making it asymmetrical, tilting the axis, etc. and causing elements thus modified to interpenetrate will give new forms in profusion.

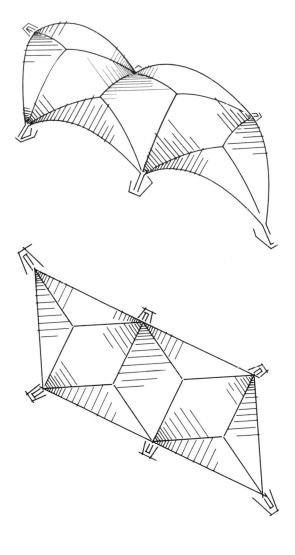

157.   Cylindrical shells interpenetrating at oblique angles. Market in Tressanti, Italy [87].

In this connection we should mention "Tomorrow's Airport" [88], another in the series of projects sponsored by the UACC (Fig. 158). The radial arrangement of shells is reminiscent of the cathedral illustrated in Fig. 150. In this case, however, the result is a great ring rather than a dome. Once again it becomes necessary to modify the cylindrical shell by giving it a tapered form, but this is not the most important feature of the design. The real innovation is the introduction of a second set of shells forming a ring that penetrates the first set at right angles. The result is a structural unit of increased size which derives most of its stiffness from the valleys where the two systems meet. At this stage the architect has merely sketched out an idea, which remains to be tested by rigorous statical analysis. Should the cross section of the shells be based on a parabola or on some other curve? Should the edges of the shells be free or reinforced with stiffening ribs? Can the crowns of the interpenetrating shells be raised to different levels without the unstiffened region in the crown of the higher shell being reinforced? These are just a few of the many points of detail that still await clarification. No doubt the engineers would soon find a way of building such a structure and making it stable, but as far as the structural form is concerned, many studies would remain to be carried out before the project approached maturity. Our reason for introducing it at this point is merely to illustrate the endless possibilities of creating novel forms based on geometrically interpenetrating shells.

This broad, largely untouched field offers a challenge to the skill and imagination of architects and engineers. The starting point of this section was the simple cylindrical shell. Its surface is curved in one direction but straight in the other. Hence, it is easy to build, and for the same reason it has been a popular form since shell construction first began. Whatever modifications the basic form may undergo, the essence of its action remains the interplay of forces between the thin shell, which in one direction offers almost no resistance to deformation, and the stiffening diaphragms or ribs, which help it to retain its shape. Only if both elements are present will the shell preserve its rigidity, strength and three-dimensional action. Alone, without stiffeners, the simply curved shell is no more a space structure than a stiffener without a shell.

158.   The more complex the interpenetration, the stronger the inducement to abandon the simple cylindrical form. Design for an airport building [88].

In discussing the cathedral illustrated in Fig. 150, we made our first reference to double curvature and the beneficial effect it had on the natural stiffness of the shell. Any further development in shell design leads inevitably to a doubly curved form.

The first and most obvious step in this direction is to take a cylindrical shell and introduce a second curve at right angles to the first (Fig. 159.1). We are aware that the resulting form is no longer, strictly speaking, a cylindrical shell. However, in view of our introductory remarks (see page 215), we shall take the liberty of including it in the same category.

The best we can do to define it is to call it an "arched segmental shell." The surface is curved twice, in both the longitudinal and transverse directions. The result is a shell of increased natural stiffness. Fig. 159.2 shows how a shell curved in one direction only will collapse, as soon as the stiffeners are removed, whereas a doubly curved shell will continue to offer a certain resistance to deformation (Fig. 159.3), rather like a piece of orange peel, which, though relatively flexible, is not easily turned inside out.

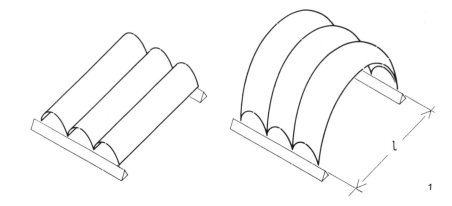

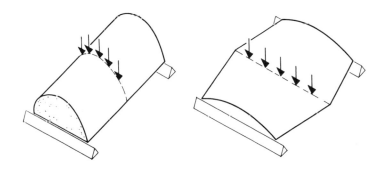

159. Cylindrical shells become doubly curved surfaces when arched in the direction in which they span.
   1 As distinct from straight shells, arched shells develop arch action in the direction of the span.
   2 Without transverse stiffeners the cylindrical shell is relatively unstable.
   3 Like a piece of orange peel, an arched cylindrical shell derives extra stiffness from its double curvature.

If its ends are firmly supported, an arched segmental shell will assume the general character of a vault, and thus the shape of the line of pressure will again become an important consideration. This is the type of construction used for a group of hangers built at Marignane in France [89] (Fig. 160). The horizontal thrusts due to the arch action are resisted by means of ties, which were poured on the ground together with the shell, the whole roof then being raised 19 m into its final position. Each hangar covers an area about 100 m wide and 60 m long. A shell thickness of only 6 cm, or about 1/1670th of the span, means an extraordinary saving in material. It also means, however, that the shell has to be braced at short intervals over its entire length. Though full of admiration for the skill of the engineers, we must permit ourselves some criticism of the form, since it is relevant to our present theme. The transverse curvature of the individual segments is of supreme importance to the action of the shell. Therefore it should be the determining element in the design. From a favorable position it can be seen as a silhouette at the crown of the roof. Still more important, however, are the supports, the points where the shells end and the substructure begins. Here the transverse curvature thins out into a straight edge. The transition is confused. The form is soft and looks flattened, although resistance to flattening is the essence of shell action. Furthermore, it is indecisive and fails to reflect the inner tension characteristic of both shell and the material of which it is made—probably the shells ought to end in a crisp slice that would reveal their shape and proportions (Fig. 160.3).

American engineers [90] have designed a building on the same principle, in which a span of 300 m is bridged by a shell only about 10 cm thick. It remains to be seen whether single shells of this size are sufficiently stable.

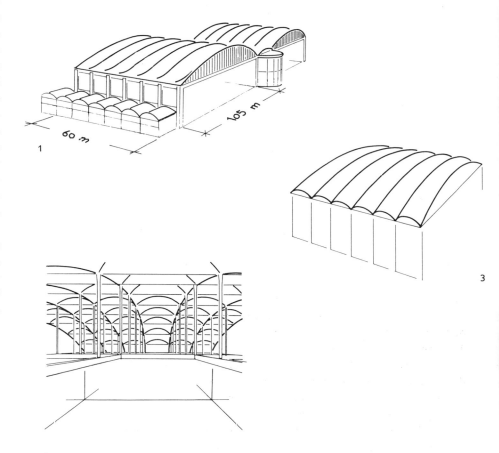

1

3

2

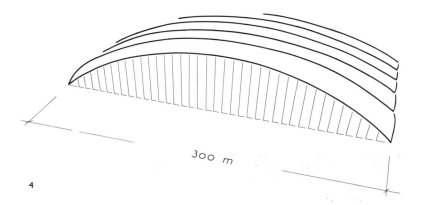

4

160. Two designs employing arched cylindrical shells:
      1 Hangar in Marignane, France [89].
      2 View of interior with stiffeners and suspended ties.
      3 The ends of the shells would reflect the structural principle more clearly
        if they were more emphatically expressed.
      4 Proposed convention hall with a span of about 300 m [90].

The new C.N.I.T. exhibition hall in Paris [91] represents a further development, in which the doubly curved segmental shell is modified to suit the requirements of a centrally oriented plan. It is one of the first structures of the hollow-shell type. It roofs the area enclosed by an equilateral triangle with sides 205 m long. Three sprays of curved and conically broadening segmental shells fan out from the supports and converge to form a dome. Here the idea of taking cylindrical segments and arching them in the direction of the longitudinal axis, as in the hangars at Marignane, has been applied to dome construction. The fanning of the shell elements represents a further modification. Given the enormous span of 205 m from one pier to the next, the line of pressure of the arch becomes the dominant structural theme. It determines the parabolic form characteristic of the three side elevations. The stability of this extraordinary structure is ensured by using a hollow shell. In fact, this shell consists of two parallel surfaces lying about two meters apart. They are kept at the right distance, held in shape and welded into a single unit by means of vertical diaphragms running in both longitudinal and transverse directions. These diaphragms are only 6 cm thick. The maximum thickness of the shells is 6.5 cm. This is only about 1/3,150 of the span. If we took both shells together and threw in the material used in the diaphragms, the equivalent layer of concrete per square meter of roof area would be about 18 cm thick. This corresponds to less than one thousandth of the span. Assuming that it is 0.4 mm thick in the middle, an egg shell has a thickness to diameter ratio of 1/100. Thus, the amount of material used in building the roof of the new exhibition hall in Paris is, in relative terms, ten times less than that which nature requires to build an egg. However, even if we base our calculations on the total thickness of the hollow slab, about two meters, the thickness to span ratio still works out at only 1/100, or exactly the same as in the case of the egg.

Whether the design of the three supports is appropriate to a building conceived with such extraordinary boldness is a different matter. Regrettably, it seems to us that they are just as structurally insipid as the edges of the roofs of the Marignane hangars (Fig. 160). Yet reducing these supports to a state of refinement comparable with that of the rest of the structure ought to have been such a challenge!

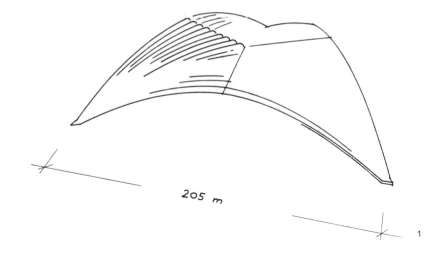

205 m

1

2

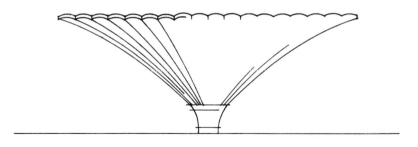

6,5 cm
180 cm
6,5 cm

3

161.   The new C.N.I.T. exhibition hall in Paris [91].
    1 Arched segmental shells fan out to form a dome supported at three points.
    2 The roof consists of two parallel thin shells connected by means of diaphragms.
    3 Detail of the double shell.

Among the projects sponsored by the UACC we intend to single out another shell structure, a stadium designed by the engineers Weidlinger and Salvadori [92]. The arena bowl is capped by a mushroom dome composed of segmental shells tapering upwards and inwards in a gentle curve to thrust against a central compression ring. Photographs of the model indicate that around the periphery the ends of the shells are stiffened not with the usual solid diaphragms but with slender reinforcing ribs. If this is possible over such a span, it is surely because the shells are curved not just in one direction but in two, that is, about both the longitudinal and transverse axes.

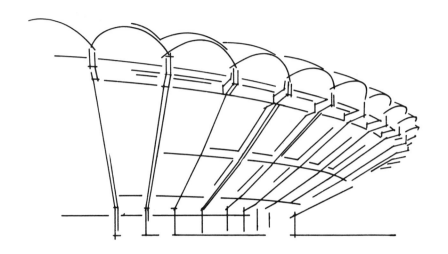

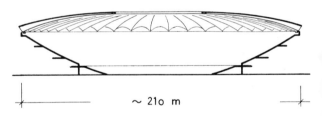

~ 21o m

162.   Proposed sports arena [92]. Arch: Raymond and Rado; Eng: Weidlinger and Salvadori. A circle of arched cylindrical shells converges on a central compression ring.

If the transverse curvature of the arched segmental shells we have been discussing is inverted, the resulting forms are characterized by two sets of curves running counter to each other. One such form is the hyperboloid of revolution of one sheet. The hyperboloid of revolution of one sheet is an important building form, because its doubly curved surface can be generated wholly with straight lines. This means, for example, that the cables in prestressed construction can be conveniently laid out (Fig. 163.2) and that formwork can be constructed relatively simply out of straight timbers and planks. This remarkable property of the hyperboloid of revolution is easy to explain:

If the walls of a short circular cylinder are replaced with threads parallel to the axis and the two ends of the cylinder are twisted in opposite directions, the system of threads will form a three-dimensionally curved surface with a hyperbolic cross section. A number of shell roofs have been designed on this principle. They are not, it is true, arched segmental shells, in the sense defined, but they are so similar in form that we have thought it fit to introduce them at the end of this section.

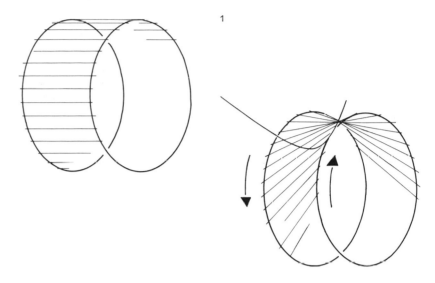

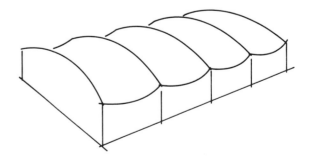

163. The doubly curved surfaces of certain hyperboloids of revolution give the impression of cylindrical shells that have been turned upside down and then arched in the direction of the span.
1 Two rings connected by parallel threads are twisted in opposite directions. The taut threads form the anticlastic surface of a hyperboloid of revolution. The cross section is a hyperbola.
2 In shape, a segment of such a hyperboloid of revolution is closely related to an arched cylindrical shell with its transverse curvature inverted.
3 A series of such segments forms a roof similar to that formed by a series of arched cylindrical shells (cf. Fig. 160).

We shall now summarize the most important characteristics of the cylindrical or segmental shell.

1. The curvature of the shell is *at right angles* to the direction in which it spans.

2. The transverse curvature may take any form; it need not necessarily follow the line of pressure. A parabolic cross section is *not* typical of the cylindrical shell. (The parabolic line of pressure only has the power to determine the form where true arch action is involved, for example, in short shells and in segmental shells with secondary curvature in the direction of the span.)

3. The transverse curvature of the shell should be sufficiently emphatic, not flat or feebly expressed as in Fig. 164.1.

4. The curve of the shell should be bold and harmonious. A succession of ill-matched arcs (Fig. 164.2) will never satisfy the eye.

5. The shell should be a closed unit. Skylights, openings and bands of glazing disrupt the form (Fig. 164.3).

6. The shell should be thin. A clumsy slab is structurally wrong and spoils the effect of the end elevations (Fig. 164.4).

7. The shell should end decisively. It should not simply peter out. Its form should be expressed at the edges. A curve that dies out feebly is incompatible with the inner tension characteristic of shell construction (Fig. 164.5).

8. If it is to retain its shape the cylindrical shell must be stiffened. The stiffeners belong at the supports. It is wrong to attempt to replace the stiffeners by thickening the whole shell. The resulting form is one determined by bending, not by true shell action (cf. Fig. 154). Unstiffened edges must be cantilevered (the only alternative is a doubly curved form).

1

2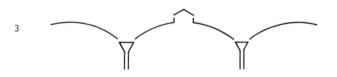

3

4

5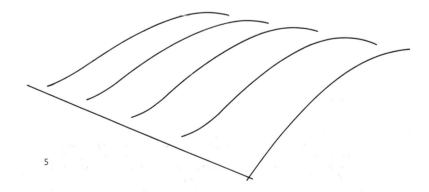

164. Some forms that contradict the principles of shell design:
1 Curve too flat.
2 Curves ill-matched.
3 Curve discontinuous.
4 Edges too thick.
5 Indecisive termination.

Shells of Revolution

In its elementary form, the cylindrical shell is curved in one direction only. It has a simple geometry and is easy to build. Accordingly, it received a great deal of attention from the early shell designers. Any attempt to modify the basic form (Figs. 148-150) leads inevitably to the abandonment of simple curvature, but the really decisive step in the direction of compound curvature was taken when shells of revolution were first introduced. With two exceptions they are all doubly curved. Only the cylinder and the cone can be unrolled into a plane sheet and hence lack double curvature. We shall not have any occasion to discuss them here. All other shells of revolution have doubly curved surfaces. Their elementary, wholly symmetrical prototype is the sphere. The sphere is a form found everywhere in nature, in the planets, in soap bubbles, fish roes, many fruits and, approximately, in the eye.

We propose to use the hemisphere to illustrate the action of doubly curved shells. Imagine a narrow strip cut out of a hemisphere (Fig. 165.1). In isolation this strip will tend to act like an arch. We know that under its own weight alone it will remain free of bending as long as its form follows the line of pressure, in this case a catenary, that is, approximately a parabola (cf. Chapter 2, page 164). Being part of a hemisphere, however, the strip has the shape of a semicircle and therefore deviates from the line of pressure quite sharply (Fig. 165.2). It ought to be strong enough to resist the bending thus introduced, but since it is merely a narrow band cut from a very thin shell, its resistance to bending is not very great. Consequently, it tends to sag

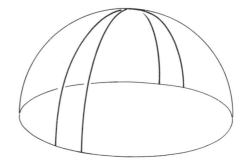

1

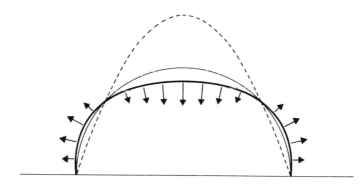

2

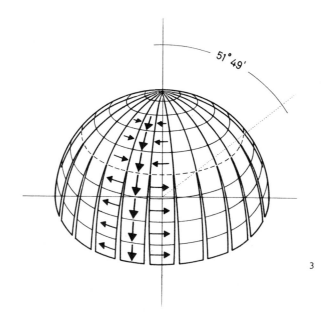

3

165. A hemisphere acting as a doubly curved shell.
   1 Arch formed by two narrow strips cut from opposite sides of the hemisphere.
   2 A narrow semicircular arch has a tendency to sag at the crown and bulge at the sides, the amount and direction of deflection depending on the deviation of the arch from the line of pressure.
   3 In a continuous hemisphere the parts of the elementary arches that tend to sag are squeezed together in compression, while the parts that tend to bulge hang together in tension.

at the crown and bulge at the sides, its behavior at any point corresponding to the degree of deviation from the parabolic line of pressure. The same tendency to deform will be characteristic of any number of similar, adjacent, arch-like strips. When continuity is restored, however, the three-dimensional action of the shell begins to make itself felt. The elements in the upper zone of the hemisphere, which tend to sag inwards, thrust against each other to form a solid cap, in which all the forces are compressive and act tangentially to the shell. In the lower zone the elements are tied together horizontally and form an annular band, which restrains their individual tendencies to bulge. In this zone the meridional stresses are compressive and the horizontal stresses tensile. Thus, all the forces are tangential, that is, they all act in the direction of the shell itself. The conditions for building a very thin shell with little or no resistance to bending, and hence the conditions for applying the "membrane theory" are satisfied. In principle, this theory of shell action, based exclusively on tangential forces, holds true not only for the hemisphere but for any doubly curved shell.

In order that the actual behavior of the shell may correspond as closely as possible with that postulated by the theory, shell designers try to satisfy a number of special conditions.

1. The curvature of the shell should be continuous.
2. The thickness of the shell should be constant, or at least it should not change abruptly.
3. The shell should be very thin in relation to the span.
4. The load should be distributed as uniformly as possible; concentrated loads should be avoided.
5. The supports at the edges of the shell should be designed to compensate as fully as possible for the lack of continuity at these points.
6. The nature of the supports should not be such that the shell is prevented from deforming freely, and so on.

Failure to satisfy these conditions results in the introduction of transverse bending stresses, which the shell, because of its extreme thinness, is ill-equipped to resist. This means that the shell has to be thickened and this, in turn, means violating condition 3, which requires it to be thin. Local concentrations of forces, for example at the supports, necessarily require a thickening of the shell, which, as explained, upsets the "membrane" assumptions by introducing bending. The usual technical word for these phenomena is "disturbance." If we ask ourselves, quite impartially, just what is "disturbed," in the last analysis it is only the designer's assumptions, namely membrane stresses and no bending. Unwanted bending stresses are always creeping in, although, to justify the thinness of the shell, they are assumed to be absent. A thin shell is essential, if the membrane theory is to apply, and but for the latter there would scarcely be a practicable way of determining the stresses. It is always bending moments that cause "disturbances." This phenomenon, which no doubt causes the shell designer a great deal of irritation, has led writers on the subject to reject the possibility of tolerating bending moments altogether. We do not intend to go as far as this; on the contrary, we shall deliberately confine ourselves to a discussion of structural form, irrespective of

methods of computation and the difficulty or impossibility of mastering shell analysis. This, of course, does not imply that we question the great pioneering work or the merits of the mathematicians and engineers who made shell construction possible. It is merely that we question whether today, when a variety of analytical, empirical and even experimental methods of designing shells are available, form—and it is with form that we are exclusively concerned—should be influenced in any way by assumptions based not on the idea of shell action itself but on the limitations which still surround our methods of computation. Is it not possible that the forms we build are victims of an assumption which, although necessary under certain conditions if the mathematical problem of designing a shell was to be tackled at all, has nothing to do with the natural principles by which the shell is governed? What right have we to insist that shells must be uniformly thin, that they must not suddenly change thickness, in short, that they must not admit any bending stresses? A glance at the structure of a nut or the shell of a snail is enough to reveal the presumptuousness of any such attempt to dictate to nature. Yet—to avoid giving any wrong impressions—this, too, is rather a lame comparison. Wherever bending stresses are involved, the scale of the structure plays an important part (cf. Chapter 1, page 76). Whereas in the case of the nut and the snail shell, the severest stresses are produced by the concentrated loads due to shock and impact, the typical building load is uniformly distributed. Nevertheless, wherever the loads become concentrated, at the supports for example, discontinuities and variations in thickness will be inevitable, even in buildings; in fact they will be essential, if the structural form is to be properly expressed. Even so, because of the difference in scale, not to mention the difference in function, they will be quite dissimilar from those characteristic of, say, the nut. The parallel with the snail shell and the nut exists only in principle; it should not be allowed to conjure up false associations.

To sum up, we consider this a timely moment to separate the search for structural form from problems of statical analysis, wherever analysis loses touch with natural laws, of which the elementary principle of the lever is a graphic example, and becomes exclusively mathematical. Not one of the design conditions mentioned above seems to us to flow necessarily from the intrinsic nature of a shell. Such dogmatic restrictions seem likely to carry us as far away from good structural form in one direction as an arbitrarily formalistic treatment of the problem would in the other.

The following discussion of a number of examples of symmetrical shells of revolution will therefore be free of references to the preconceived, seemingly inflexible "rules" of shell theory. Our efforts to evaluate forms and relate them to structure will be governed by the comparatively few principles, enunciated at the beginning of this section, which express the essence of the structural idea in terms of "natural laws."

Depending on the way they are stressed, shells are curved and, as we have just seen, preferably doubly curved; the material of which they are made is "rigid." This elementary definition is all that we require (cf. page 213).

The first dome to be designed as a hemispherical shell was that of the Zeiss Planetarium in Jena [63], built in 1925 (Fig. 166). It was followed by similar structures in Leipzig, Berlin and Dresden. Geometrically these domes are perfect hemispheres, since they were intended to form a surface for the projection of three-dimensional images. The way they act can best be understood by referring to Fig. 165. The horizontal tensile stresses are resisted by the shell reinforcement itself. The meridional compression is resisted by the substructure. This compression is tangential to the lower edge of the hemisphere, that is to say it acts vertically. Theoretically these are the ideal conditions at the supports of a spherical shell. All the reactions are vertical and there are no residual thrusts.

In this lies the essential difference between a hemispherical shell and old stone domes like those of St. Peter's in Rome, the Duomo in Florence or the Frauenkirche in Dresden, destroyed in the last war. All these old stone domes develop radial thrusts. The masonry, which has little strength in tension, is incapable of resisting the horizontal tensile forces in the lower part of the dome, even when strengthened with wrought-iron chains (cf. Fig. 165). It cracks at the weak points between openings and equilibrium is restored only by the initiation of a sort of arch action, in which opposite sectors of the cracked dome form pairs of independent vault ribs (Fig. 167). Each pair of ribs forms an arch, which, since it stands alone, ought to follow the curve of the line of pressure. Bending due to deviations from the line of pressure must be resisted by the material of the arch itself. Hence the thickness and massiveness of the old stone domes and the

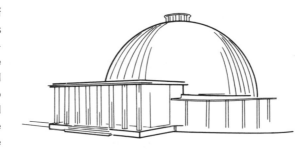

1

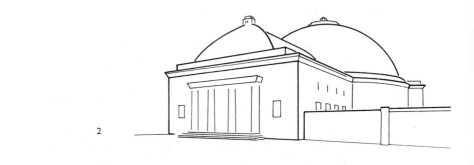

2

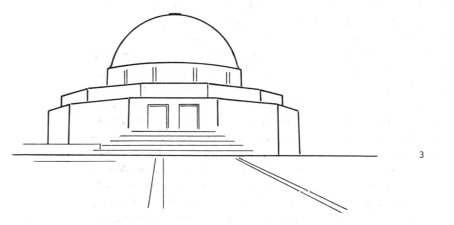

3

166. Some hemispherical planetarium shells.
    1 The first planetarium dome in Jena, Germany [63], became the prototype for all subsequent structures of this kind. At the bottom edge of the dome the meridional forces act tangentially to the shell, i.e. vertically. There are no horizontal thrusts.
    2 Berlin planetarium.
    3 Chicago planetarium.

impossibility of building them with anything like the thinness of a shell; hence, too, the great horizontal thrusts which the separate sectors of the dome, acting like the limbs of a true arch, exert on the substructure, which they not infrequently force out of place. In the mid-Thirties this interpretation of the statics of old stone domes was confiirmed by precise measurements of the cracks in the Frauenkirche, Dresden [93], and corresponding computations. The author himself took part in this work in collaboration with Prof. Georg Rüth. They proved conclusively that the old stone dome acted not as a space structure but as pairs of independent arch ribs, each of which had to be treated as a plane system.

To return to the hemispherical shell in Jena. It rests upon a continuous, drum-like substructure without transmitting any thrust. These conditions are not conducive to structural form. In general the shape is a purely geometrical one that tells us very little about the internal play of forces. The impressive thinness of shell construction is nowhere in evidence. The forces that the dome exerts upon the substructure are uniformly distributed, vertical loads. There are no concentrations of stress. There is no thickening or differentiation of the masses to suggest inner structural vitality. The hemispherical form is mathematically precise but no more pleasing than, for example, a billiard ball. As a structural form it is sterile and expressionless. We are impressed only by the fact that we know the shell to be so thin. The following table gives some idea of the savings in material made possible by shell construction, compared with old stone domes and a natural form, the egg:

	Span	Thickness of shell or dome	
	L	d	d/L
1. St. Peter's, Rome	40 m	3.00 m	1/13
2. Frauenkirche, Dresden	24 m	1.25 m	1/19
3. Hen's egg	4 cm	0.4 mm	1/100
4. Zeiss Planetarium, Jena	40 m	6 cm	1/666
5. Central Market, Basle	60 m	8.5 cm	1/700
6. Exhibition Hall, Paris	205 m	13* cm	1/1570

* 13 cm is the total thickness of the double shell, each part of which is 6.5 cm thick.

The sterility of the form is probably the reason why the closed hemisphere, in spite of being an interesting structural concept, has scarcely been used for buildings other than planetaria, where its shape is truly functional. It has played no part in the architecture of the last twenty years.

167.   The Frauenkirche in Dresden, Germany (18th century) [93], was a good example of a double massive stone dome which, like most other old stone domes, was not a true space structure. The pattern formed by the cracks shows that, instead of being continuous, the dome was fractured into segments which acted like independent arches.

The stadium in Porto [95] and the market in Sidi-Bel-Abbes [94] are also based on the geometry of the sphere (Fig. 168). In both cases, however, the hemisphere has been abandoned in favor of a spherical segment. Hence the problem of the supports becomes much more interesting. The continuous drum carrying only vertical loads dissolves into a series of independent buttresses. In sympathy with the distribution of forces within the shell they are inclined roughly tangentially to its lower edge. Of course, the forces must first be transferred to the tops of the supports. The normal thickness of the shell would be insufficient for this purpose. A reinforced zone is needed to collect the forces and convey them to the buttresses. The result is a ring beam which must be capable of resisting both bending and torsion. In Porto it forms an explicit design motif. In Sidi-Bel-Abbes it is visible from inside the building only; from the outside it is hidden behind a ring of lean-to roofs. The thinness of the shell is emphasized by numerous perforations. Whether the ribbed and perforated precast elements really express the thinness of the shell statically possible is a question of detail, which in this connection is of only secondary importance. It is worth noting, however, that both these prefabricated structures were erected without interior scaffolding.

We have already had occasion to discuss the Olympic stadium in Rome [41] in connection with its forked columns (Chapter 2). It deserves a second mention at this point because of the unequivocal manner in which these columns are inclined at a tangent to the edge of the dome. Special ribs, sprouting from the inside of the dome, pick up the forces and transfer them to the tops of the columns. The shell itself is lightly corrugated between supports to resist transverse bending. The ribwork inside the dome is attributable to the method used to fabricate the precast rhombic elements (Fig. 168.3), over which a continuous shell 2.5 cm thick was cast in place. This very thin shell derives its stiffness from the precast ribs. To what extent these ribs modify the action of the shell it is difficult to say. It is even possible that theirs is the dominating influence.

As a rule, a shell is continuous and smooth and the underside is free of ribs. The resulting form is hollow and not particularly expressive, especially on the inside where there are no shadows to enliven it. Thus, where the soffit of the shell remains visible, there is a good design reason for brightening it with ribs. Since over long spans there is a possibility of local buckling in thin membranes, this modification is equally desirable from the point of view of increasing the buckling strength. However, the author knows no examples of ribs, intended as reinforcement against buckling, being given a true structural form consonant with the actual distribution of forces.

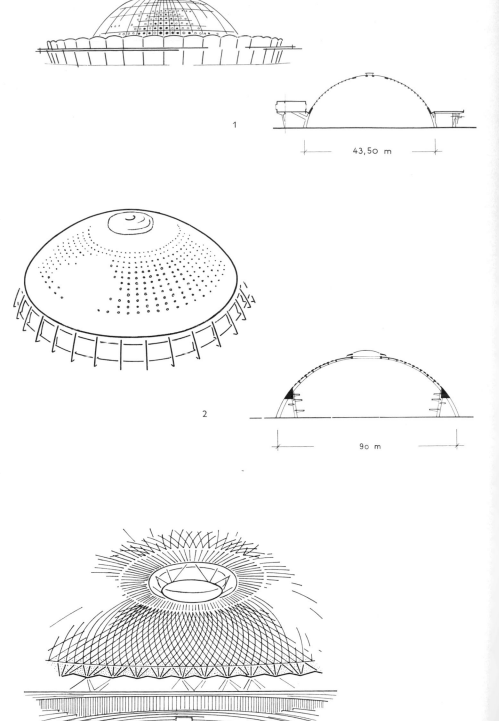

1

43,50 m

2

90 m

3

168.   Some applications of the spherical shell:
1 Market in Sidi bel Abbes, Algeria [94].
2 Sports stadium in Porto, Portugal [95].
3 Interior of the Oympic sports palace in Rome. Eng: Nervi [41].

Olympic sports palace in Rome [41] ▶
Eng: Pier Luigi Nervi

A convention hall built in Tokyo [96] has a roof in the form of a very flat spherical segment (Fig. 169). The flatness of the dome is reflected in the treatment of the supports. In this case the edge of the roof is carried on columns that are almost vertical and, in fact, have a slight outward tilt. Their axes are no longer aligned with the meridional forces which must now be balanced inside the shell itself. For this purpose a heavy belt of special ring reinforcing is required. Ordinary reinforcement would stretch so far that the structural continuity of the shell would be endangered. Like an old stone dome, it would crack in the direction of the meridians. Accordingly, this solution is dependent on the use of prestressed concrete. Prestressed concrete makes it possible to control the deformation of the edge of the dome by post-tensioning. Apart from this, the vertical components of the meridional forces must be transferred from the shell to the columns. This introduces bending into the edge of the shell, and torsion as well, since it follows a curve between supports. These stresses, which according to the assumptions usually made are inappropriate in shells, cannot be avoided, if such a system of supports is used. The necessary consequence is an edge member with a correspondingly heavy section capable of resisting tension, bending and torsion. The design of such a member and the gradual transition back to the normal thickness of the shell is by no means simple. It also presents mathematical difficulties. Our ideas about the actual play of forces in a shell are still rather vague and so far there have been no systematic investigations into the interaction between the form and the way the forces are distributed. Thus, we are hardly in a position to draw final conclusions about the optimum structural solution for such systems. Only one thing is certain: the edge of so flat a dome, resting on independent vertical supports, must be specially shaped in accordance with rigorous structural principles. To evade the problem by introducing merely decorative effects is just as wrong as to use arbitrary forms. This opens up a broad and highly interesting field of activity for all those concerned with the problems lying at the boundary between engineering analysis and esthetics.

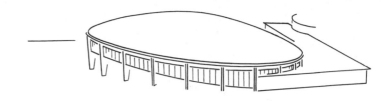

1

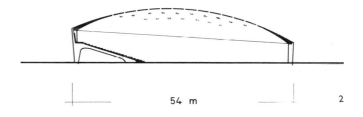

54 m

2

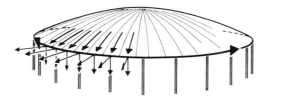

3

169.   Convention hall in Tokyo [96].
        1 View.
        2 Section.
        3 Distribution of forces.

The hyperboloid enjoys a special place among shells of revolution. It is an independent, expressive and yet strictly geometric form, which results from applying a twist to a family of straight lines drawn between two circles (cf. also Fig. 163). This form is frequently used for cooling towers (Fig. 170.2).

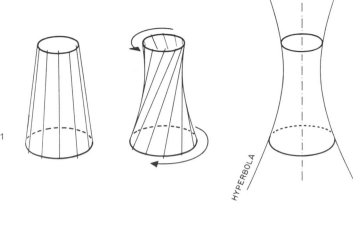

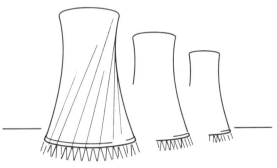

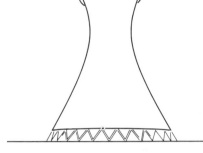

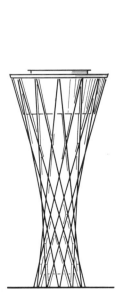

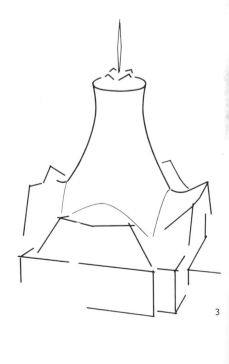

170.   Hyperboloids of revolution.
        1 If two rings connected by a series of taut threads are twisted in opposite directions, or if a hyperbola is rotated about some axis, a hyperboloid of revolution of a single sheet is formed (cf. Fig. 163).
        2 Cooling towers designed as hyperboloids of revolution.
        3 The new basilica in Algiers [97] has the form of a hyperboloid of revolution. Arch: P. Herbé and J. Le Couteur. Eng: Sarger.
        4 Proposed water tower constructed from straight generatrixes intersecting in a diamond pattern. (Although this is not a true shell, the geometry of the structure is relevant to our discussion).

The dome of the synagogue at the University of Jerusalem [99] is something quite different from the convention hall in Tokyo and the typical hyperboloid of revolution. Instead of ending in a sharp edge it is smoothly bent round into the vertical. Independent supports are formed by cutting a series of segments out of the vertical walls of the shell. It is to be assumed that, just as with the hemisphere, the meridional forces are gradually deflected into a vertical direction at the edge of the shell. They are then transferred to the individual supports by simple arch action. A certain thickening at the edges of the arches and at the foot of the supports will be both structurally necessary and formally desirable. There remains one question of detail—how to express the thinness of the shell at its lower edges. It is satisfying to learn that the ceiling, introduced above the crowns of the arches, is freely supported and is not in contact with the shell.

In shell construction deviations from the precise form of a body of revolution should not necessarily be considered mere capriciousness. In principle, it is perfectly compatible with shell design and in the Jerusalem synagogue (Fig. 171.1) is obviously part of the architect's conscious intention. This kind of modification has a powerful refining effect and at the same time raises the question of the design of shells as plastic masses. As yet these extraordinary possibilities have scarcely been grasped by the architect. Once more we hasten to emphasize that the shell is not bound to any definite form, so that the designer has the greatest freedom imaginable. The few really adventurous examples of new plastic invention, however, all come from the drawing boards of the engineers. Interestingly enough, they are not primarily artistic creations but direct expressions of natural laws. Particularly impressive are the sublime forms of certain storage tanks (Fig. 171.2) [100]. When these tanks are supported on level foundations, every part of the walls is subjected to the same stress. The mathematical definition of this form is to be found in textbooks on mathematics, not in volumes on art. Nature, however, creates it endlessly in every drop of water.

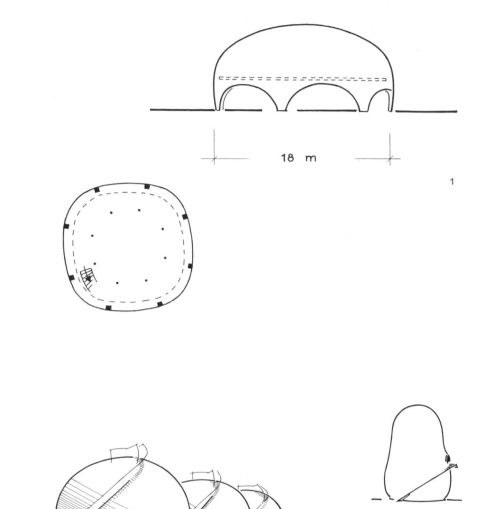

18 m

1

2

3

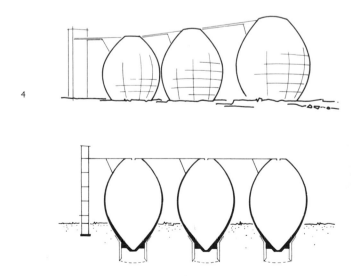

4

171.   Some shells of revolution of impressive plasticity.
  1 Synagogue in Jerusalem [99]. The plan is not perfectly circular but slightly distorted in the direction of a square. Arch: Ezra Rau.
  2 Liquidity tanks [100].
  3 A vertical wind tunnel [101].
  4 Settling tanks [102].

A water-drop.

Let us now summarize the discussion so far.

The closed shell of revolution has no free edges at which to express its curvature and thinness. Only in the design of the substructure can we recognize the influence of the forces characteristic of shell action. The undoubtedly interesting problem of designing shells to resist local buckling is still largely unexplored. The question of the general form of a shell of revolution has hardly been recognized as an architectural problem. We still know very little about the true distribution of stresses in the transition zone between shell and substructure or about the relationships between the proportions of edge members or stiffening ribs and the forces that act upon them. Every more important shell design, therefore, calls not only for a fresh analysis of the distribution of stresses, in order to determine the factor of safety for a shell of given dimensions, but also, and more particularly, for a systematic investigation into the interrelationships between statics and form, in order to establish what we have called the structural form.

Of course, the edge of a shell of revolution does not have to follow a parallel of latitude. The shell may be terminated in other ways as well. Thus, the range of possible forms is considerably broadened.

Dyckerhoff and Widmann's experimental shell [103], dating from 1924, may be regarded as the prototype of this series (Fig. 172). Although it is really a translational shell rather than a shell of revolution, we have introduced it at this point, because from the point of view of form this is clearly where it belongs. By slicing a spherical segment we can obtain edges of an expressiveness equal to that of simply curved shells. The design depends to a large extent on the nature of the supports. In the experimental shell (Fig. 172.1) the shape of the edges is preserved by means of solid diaphragms. At Brynmawr [104] and in Belgrade [105] the end walls are glazed. The solid diaphragms have been cut away to leave a tie at the bottom and a stiffening rib at the top.

1   7,30 m

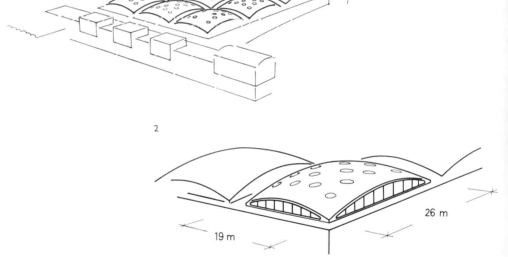

2

26 m

19 m

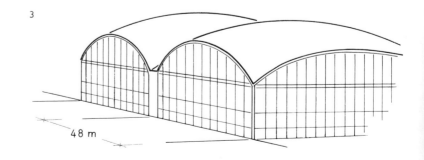

3

48 m

172.   Spherical shells on a square plan.
    1 The Dyckerhoff and Widmann experimental shell built in 1924 [103].
    2 Factory at Brynmawr, Wales [104].
    3 Exhibition halls in Belgrade, Yugoslavia [105]. Eng: Kostanievac.

The result is livelier if the sphere is cut away on three sides, as in the roof of the MIT auditorium [106]. The curved outside walls under the edge of the roof are glazed. Thus there are no diaphragms. The three feet of the dome are held together by ties located beneath the floor. The edges of the shell are only lightly reinforced, the doubly curved form being naturally stiff. However, the concentration of load at the points of support leads to the development of forces and corresponding stresses in the shell, which, as we infer from published descriptions of this notable structure, caused numerous design difficulties. The sharp corners of the shell had to be thickened, so the spherical form was lost. So far, however, there appears to be no clear idea of what the optimum shape for such details really is, at least not in relation to our main theme, the development of structural form. To us this slice of a sphere seems almost too abstract, smacks too much of geometry and models, and appears both insufficiently organic and ill-adapted to the loads; in short, it is not enough of a structural form. Surely the concentration of loads at the supports should have produced a different, more eloquent, more expressive and in the long run possibly more efficient detail. Although we recognize that in this special case the sphere and in other cases similar strictly geometrical forms determine the practicability of mathematical analysis and are often essential to facilitate construction (although building formwork for a spherical surface is difficult enough in itself), we suspect that there must be forms, not so rigorously geometrical, that come much closer to the actual concept of a "shell" and its concrete realization. Following normal usage, we shall call such forms "free forms," although, while freed of the restraints of geometry, they remain bound by structural principles. Their shape, in fact, is uncompromisingly structural. More about them in the last part of this section.

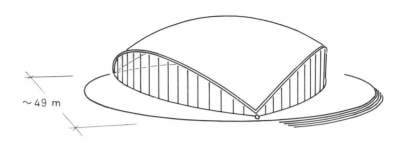

~49 m

1

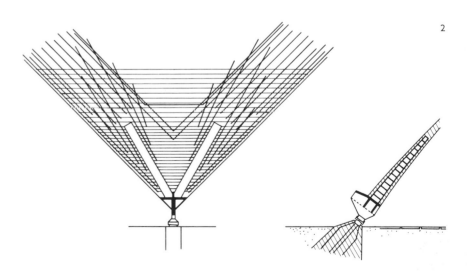

2

173. A triangular spherical segment with curved edges.
      1 M.I.T. auditorium, Cambridge, Mass. [106]. Arch: Saarinen.
      2 Detail at supports.

CONOIDS

The textbooks do not all define a conoid in the same way. We shall interpret the term broadly, since we are only interested in the form. Conoidal surfaces are obtained by movng a straight line over another straight line and a curve. So far the conoidal shell has not acquired very much importance. We mention it here partly for the sake of completeness, but partly because it may achieve greater popularity in the future. At any rate the fact that conoids are doubly curved and yet can be constructed wholly of straight lines makes them inherently suitable for shell design.

Northlight type roofs using conoidal shells have the advantage that one edge of the roof elements can be made straight. These elements span from the top chord of one bowstring truss to the bottom chord of the next. The trusses can be designed to follow the line of pressure or any other suitable curve. They stiffen the shells like diaphragms.

The engineer Mario Salvadori has designed a shell (Fig. 174.3) which can be regarded as two opposed conoids superimposed one upon the other [107]. Normally the disappearance of the conoidal curvature at the straight edge would leave the shell weak at this point. To counteract this, the engineer has corrugated the straight edge and allowed the corrugations to die away in the direction of the broad curve at the other end. In this way the general stability of the structure is ensured. Of course, both ends, the principal curve and the secondary corrugations, must be stiffened with diaphragms. There is a striking resemblance between this form, determined purely by engineering considerations, and an analogous natural form, the scallop shell.

If we define the term "conoid" broadly enough, we can also apply it to the canopy of the Unesco Building in Paris. This canopy is formed by two conoidal surfaces cantilevering from either side of a parabolic arch. The larger surface, projecting away from the building, is defined by two parabolas, curved in opposite directions, the curvature of the upper one being only faintly pronounced. The surface was generated by moving a straight line over these parabolas.

The conoid, in particular, leaves us with the feeling that a geometrical form is not necessarily a structural one. It needs further refinement. It is to be hoped that in the future the principal structural elements of these shells will be more sensitively designed, the stiffeners, ribs and edge members more subtly combined, the loads more visibly concentrated at the points of support and the supports themselves better expressed, even if this means abandoning the strictly geometrical form in favor of one that is structurally more efficient.

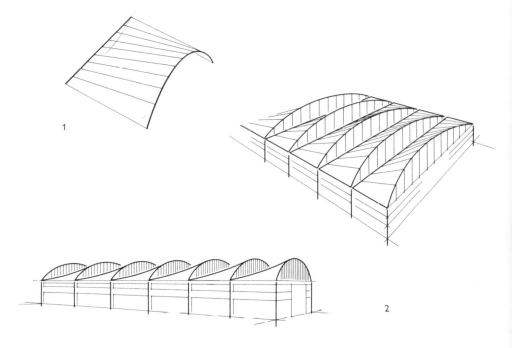

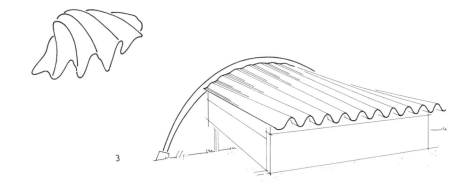

174. Conoids.
   1 A conoid is formed by moving a straight generatrix along a curve and a straight line.
   2 Factories with conoid shell roofs.
   3 House with roof resembling a sea-shell in the form of opposed conoids. Arch: Nakashima. Eng: Salvadori [107].

Canopy of the Unesco Building, Paris [18]. Arch: Breuer, Zehrfuss. Eng: Nervi ▶

Hyperbolic Paraboloids

In the search for surfaces suitable for shell construction that were
1. doubly curved,
2. mathematically analyzable,
3. easy to build, and
4. pleasing and expressive,

the hyperbolic paraboloid, henceforth abbreviated to h.p., had to be rediscovered. It was not a part of classical geometry. Its equations had been known only since the seventeenth century. For many years textbooks on mathematics and geometry had given it only the most cursory treatment. Who deserves the credit for designing the first h.p. it is impossible to say. As so often when uncertainty prevails, the discovery was probably made at the same time by several people working independently. Since the last war h.p.s have been built in increasing numbers all over the world. Extensive publicity no doubt contributed to the rapid acceptance of the form.

Just what is meant by a hyperbolic paraboloid and which of its characteristics most concern us?

Fig. 175 will make the geometry clearer. A family of identical parabolas is inverted and suspended between two other parabolas that arch upwards. The resulting surface is saddle-shaped. In the transverse direction it contains a second family of identical and parallel but upright parabolas. The saddle is curved in two mutually opposed directions (Fig. 175.1).

Horizontal sections, i.e. contour lines, form hyperbolas (Fig. 175.2). The same applies to oblique sections.

The surface of an h.p. contains two families of intersecting straight lines (Fig. 175.3). Thus, any opening in the saddle can be framed by four straight lines forming a warped quadrilateral. Or in other words: any warped quadrilateral can be cut out of a hyperbolic paraboloid. If two opposite straight edges are divided in the same ratio and the points thus marked off connected by straight lines, then these straight lines will be generatrixes lying in the doubly curved surface of the h.p.

The most important elementary and composite h.p. surfaces are:
1. the saddle, defined by vertical parabolas and horizontal hyperbolas;
2. the basic straight-edged form, defined by a warped quadrilateral;
3. combinations of several basic straight-edged forms;
4. sections wholly or partially defined by curves;
5. combinations of sections defined by curves.

We shall proceed to discuss the form and structure of a number of actual buildings and drawing-board projects grouped in accordance with this scheme of classification.

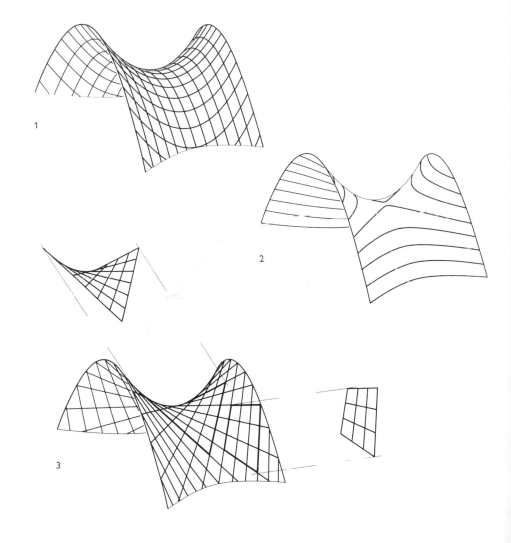

175.   The hyperbolic paraboloid.
     1 A family of identical parabolas is suspended between two upright parabolas. The result is a saddle-shaped hyperbolic paraboloid. At right-angles to the suspended parabolas the saddle surface contains a second family of identical but upright parabolas.
     2 Horizontal sections are hyperbolas.
     3 The saddle surface of the hyperbolic paraboloid contains two sets of straight lines. Thus any warped form that can be defined by four straight lines can be cut out of an h.p. surface.

Some years ago Candela designed a cosmic-ray pavilion for the University of Mexico [108]. The reinforced concrete membrane, though only about 1.5 cm thick, spans approximately 10 meters. The shell had to be made very thin in order to reduce its resistance to the penetration of cosmic rays. The roof is shaped like a saddle terminating in two parabolas, in the manner of Fig. 175. Since the generatrixes are straight lines, the formwork could easily be built from ordinary planks and scantlings. The gable walls are stiffened by means of corrugations. They support the shell at each end. In the center the shell is stiffened by means of a special rib, although the natural ridge formed along the line where the two h.p. surfaces meet would probably in itself have been sufficient for this purpose. The end cantilevers, the overhang at the eaves and the general tautness of the surface draw attention to the balance of forces that prevails in the thin reinforced concrete membrane. The suspended mesh of steel and the brittle concrete combine to give that high degree of three-dimensional rigidity characteristic only of doubly curved shells and expressed so powerfully in the warped surfaces of the hyperbolic paraboloid. This small pavilion is a particularly neat example of a saddle-shaped h.p.

~ 6 m

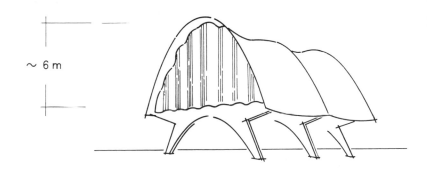

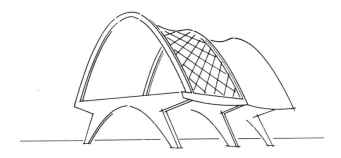

176.   The cosmic-ray pavilion at the University of Mexico. Eng; Candela [108]. The formwork was built to a warped surface using two layers of straight planks.

We shall now turn our attention to the basic straight-edged form taken from the middle of the saddle. The double counter-curvature dramatically emphasizes the interplay between tensile and compressive forces in which every stress is balanced with maximum economy. A properly reinforced shell can absorb tension and compression at any point and in any direction tangential to its curved surface. The two low points are obviously the best places to locate the supports. Then the dead weight of the structure, usually the most critical load in this kind of roof, can advantageously be carried by the hanging parabolas in tension and by the arched parabolas in compression. These parabolas, moreover, correspond very closely with the respective lines of pressure for uniform load. Thus, from the outset, the tendency for forces to deviate from the parabolic curvature of the shell is only slight.

If we begin by assuming that, first of all, the loads make their way to the straight edges along narrow parabolic arch elements, then at the end of these arches they will produce a resultant compression D acting at a tangent to the edge of the shell. This resultant can be imagined resolved into a compressive force Dr acting along the edge of the shell in the direction of the support and a tensile force Z tangential to one of the hanging parabolas. This tensile force tautens the roof and relieves the other arches (Fig. 177.1). On the other hand, we can assume that the loads are first transformed into tensile forces acting in the direction of the hanging parabolas and that, having reached one of the straight edges, they are again resolved into a compressive force Dr acting along the edge of the shell towards the support and a second compressive force D acting in the direction of the parabolic arch. By thrusting tangentially against the arch from below, the force D relieves the hanging parabolas. The two processes interact and supplement each other. Every tendency of an element to depart from the strict curve of the surface is opposed by a corresponding force acting in the direction of the counter-curvature. The only unbalanced forces are the resultant compressions Dr along the edges. They have to be collected in an edge member, connected with the shell by a joint capable of resisting shear, and transferred to the supports. There they combine with the forces delivered by the opposite edge member to produce a reaction R tangential to the surface of the shell. In this basic straight-edged form the edge members are stressed wholly in compression. Since the compressive forces resulting from the combined arch and catenary action of the shell accumulate in the direction of the supports, the dimensions of the edge member must increase in the same direction. In theory, the only bending stresses developed are inconsiderable ones introduced by the dead weight of the edge member itself. They do not determine its form. Unlike the stiffening ribs and diaphragms in simply curved shells, these members do not have the function of preserving the shape of the shell. The doubly curved surface is naturally stiff, provided that it is properly supported. Like an arch, the shell as a whole exerts a horizontal thrust. The supports must either be designed to resist lateral displacement or be held together by means of a tie. The vigor with which the play of forces in the shell is expressed depends a great deal on the design of the substructure.

254

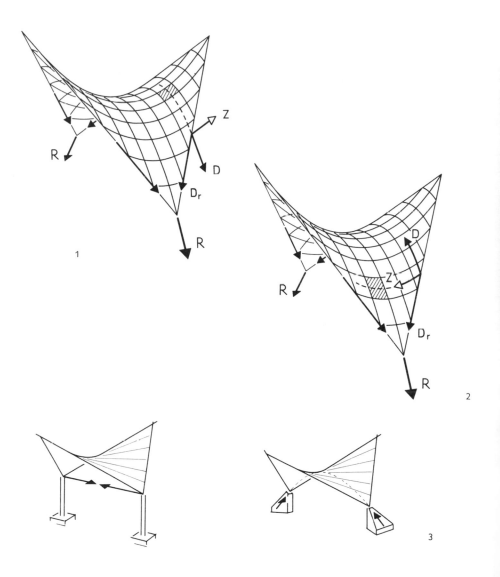

177. The structural principle of a straight-edged hyperbolic paraboloid supporting a uniformly distributed vertical load.
1 Arch action develops in the direction of the upright parabolas. At the edge of the shell the resultant thrust D can be resolved into a compressive force Dr parallel to the edge and a tensile force Z tangential to one of the suspended parabolas.
2 Conversely, the edge is stressed in the direction of the suspended parabolas by a tensile force Z. This force can likewise be resolved into a compressive force Dr parallel to the edge and another compressive force acting tangentially to the upright parabolas, i.e. against the direction of the arch thrusts.
3 At each support the edge forces Dr combine to form a resultant R which acts tangentially to the surface of the h.p. The oblique thrusts R must be resisted either by ties or by sloping buttresses. In the other direction the structure is initially unstable.

The geometry of h.p. surfaces strongly favors timber construction. It is just as easy to bend thin boards and planks in the direction of the parabolas as it is to use wood in the direction of the straight generatrixes. Catalano has chosen a symmetrical element out of the middle of an h.p. saddle for the wooden roof of his own residence [109]. This roof is composed of planks nailed together in three layers, two in the direction of the compressive forces and one in the direction of the hanging parabolas. The edge members are of steel. They thrust against concrete piers held together by a post-tensioned tie located beneath the floor.

Varying the basic form by cutting out sections away from the middle of the saddle does not affect the structural principle. The resulting shapes may well be perfectly adapted to their particular purpose and may even increase the expressiveness of the form. The church at Coyoacan, Mexico [110], is based on an eccentrically located saddle element. The asymmetry accentuates the site of the altar, which stands directly under the high point of the roof. The roof, which is made of reinforced concrete 4 cm thick, spans about 30 m along one diagonal and about 25 m along the other. The mullions have no load-bearing function, apart from helping to prevent the asymmetrical roof from tipping. We assume that the unbalanced thrust in the edge members is absorbed by the massive outside walls acting as ties. However, we can imagine a better material than random rubble for expressing this critical structural function. We are not conscious of the thrust of the roof, though it amounts to about 40 tons. The roof appears to rest unrelatedly on the walls without the manner in which its stresses are transferred to the substructure being made explicit.

The Congress Hall in Shizuoka [111] has an h.p. roof over a square plan with sides more than 50 m long. The large span and the tremendous dead loads (the reinforced concrete shell alone is 18 cm thick) mean that the edge members transmit a resultant thrust of about 1,400 tons. The concrete section needed to resist this thrust has an area of about 1.4 sq. m and weighs about 3.3 tons per running meter. An edge member of these proportions cannot be left to hang from the shell without additional support, as in Catalano's light wooden roof. Its own weight alone would produce bending moments too great to be absorbed by the shell. Hence, in this design the problem of supporting the edge member assumes critical importance. The architects chose to use a continuous folded wall on one side and a glazed concrete lamella wall on the other. The resultant diagonal thrusts amount to about 2,000 tons at each support. The horizontal com-

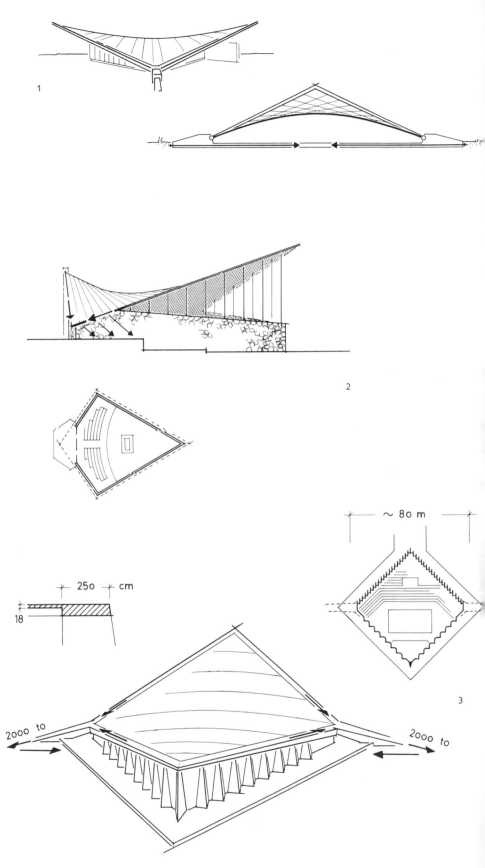

178. Straight-edged h.p. elements taken from the middle of the saddle.
    1 The residence of the architect Catalano [109] has a wooden roof built up of three layers of nailed boards. The h.p. form is symmetrical about both axes.
    2 Church in Coyoacan, Mexico [110], an h.p. in reinforced concrete. The shell is asymmetrical about one axis, i.e. it is kite-shaped in plan. Arch: De la Mora. Eng: Candela.
    3 Congress hall in Shizuoka, Japan [111]. The symmetrical shell is square in plan. Arch: Kenzo Tange and Y. Tsuboi.

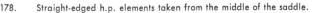

ponent is resisted by powerful ties underneath the floor. The geometry of the roof corresponds to the simplest bilaterally symmetrical shape that can be cut from the middle of an h.p. saddle to cover a square plan. One gets the impression that the architects have been successful in imposing a genuinely Japanese idiom on this self-willed geometry and thus have given further proof of the versatility of the hyperbolic paraboloid.

Straight-edged forms of the type described can also be used in various combinations. As long as each elementary shell remains free to behave in the way illustrated in Fig. 177, the full efficiency of h.p. action will be maintained. The simplest combination consists of two basic shapes butting one against the other. Each unit transmits its load to the foundations in the form of an oblique thrust. The two edge members are identically stressed, so at the point where they meet there are no unbalanced forces to contend with. Whereas, however, an independent unit, like the roof of Catalano's home (Fig. 178), is initially unstable and, if no special precautions are taken, will over-turn sideways, two h.p. surfaces in contact are stable automatically. The structure as a whole then rests not on two, but on three supports and any number of units can be added to the chain.

The roof of the Girls' Grammar School, London [113], shown in Fig. 179.2, is a composite form consisting of a radial arrangement of five asymetrical elementary h.p.s. Again, each unit behaves like the single shell illustrated in Fig. 177. The designer has emphasized their independence architecturally by introducing intermediate strips of glazing; the 5 cm thick shell was gunited from below against a layer of insulating board supported by a network of cables. The five supports are all vertical and resist only the vertical loads; the horizontal thrusts are resisted by a pentagonal tie incorporated in the thickness of a mezzanine floor. Unfortunately, the powerful restraint exerted by this important tension member is nowhere visibly expressed.

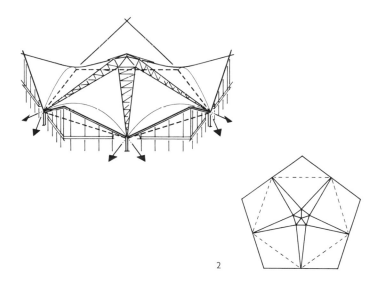

179.   Combinations of straight-edged h.p.s.
    1 Experimental timber roof (nailed board construction) at Kansas University [112].
    2 Girls' grammar school in London [113], a concentric arrangement of h.p. saddle elements. The five shells, kite-shaped in plan, are separated by bands of glazing and held in a pentagon by means of a common tie.

The entrance feature of a Denver shopping center [114] consists of four elementary h.p.s. combined in such a way that the thrusts meet in the middle and spread out diagonally at the four corners. Here they are resisted by inclined piers that transmit the forces to the foundations.

The same system has found numerous applications in factory construction, the horizontal thrusts being resisted by ties. The columns are left with only the vertical loads.

In his design for the Lederle laboratories in Mexico [116] Candela employed an extremely clever device to neutralize all the horizontal thrusts within the roof structure itself, so that neither external buttresses nor external ties were required (Fig. 180.4). The horizontal resultants of the thrusts meeting at each column balance out in pairs, tied together directly along the bottoms of the horizontal valleys. The four columns receive only vertical loads. The internal balance of horizontal forces gives the structure an air of exceptional lightness. A roof that exerts thrusts, on the other hand, is always solidly rooted in its substructure.

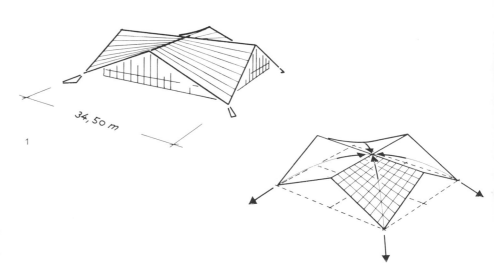

1

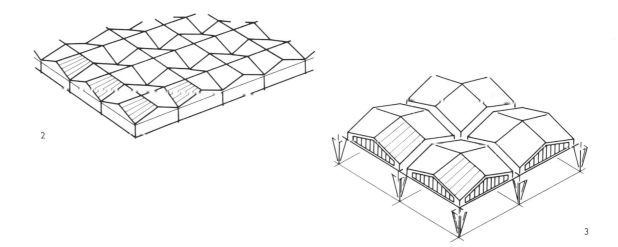

2

3

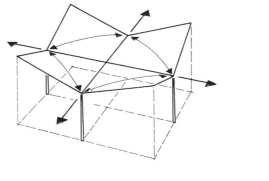

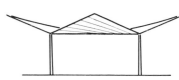

180.   H.p. elements, square in plan, arranged in groups of four, supported at four points.
    1 Entrance to a department store in Denver, Col. [114].
    2 Factory in Dallas, Texas [115].
    3 The Herdez plant in Mexico [38].
    4 Lederle laboratories, Mexico. Eng: Candela [116]. Four elements combined in such a way that all the thrusts are balanced within the shell itself. The four columns carry only vertical loads.

4

If the four elements are swiveled round so that the outside corners fall and the middle rises, we get an "umbrella" roof perched on a single column (Fig. 181.1). The thrusts from each pair of adjacent elements produce a resultant in the direction of the common edge member, through which a tensile force is transmitted to the apex of the roof. Here the four horizontal components cancel each other out and there remains a resultant vertical force to be taken by the column. This force is equivalent to the total weight of the roof.

Baroni has used reinforced concrete to build roofs of this kind for the market in Caserta [117]. He is also occupied in designing them in aluminum. Since, given a square plan, all the sectors are the same, an aluminum umbrella roof consisting of four prefabricated elements could be transported in a stack only one quarter as large as the roof itself.

Inverting the umbrella gives a saucer. On the outside the diagonal thrusts are resisted by tension developed in the edge members. In the center the horizontal components cancel out, while the vertical resultant is transferred to the column and again equals the total weight of the roof. Candela has combined a number of elements of this kind to form a northlight roof for a shopping center in Mexico [118] (Fig. 181.2).

These examples constitute only a small selection from the many possible combinations of h.p. elements. When we recall that any unsymmetrical warped quadrilateral defines a shape that can be cut from a hyperbolic paraboloid, with all the prerequisites for a doubly curved structure, we can judge what an absolute profusion of forms must be producible by combining them in different ways. At the same time the straight-edged, warped quadrilateral is a relatively simple and uncomplicated figure. Later we shall see that by using h.p. surfaces with curved edges the range of possible forms can be multiplied still further.

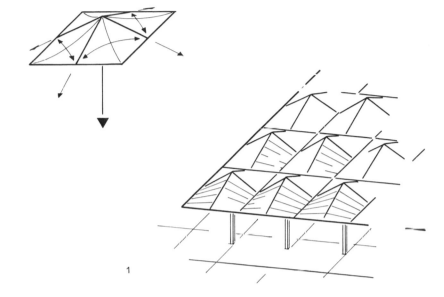

1

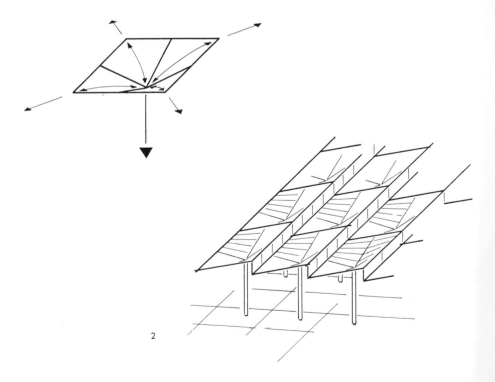

2

181. Umbrella shells.
1 Market in Caserta, Italy. Eng: Baroni [117].
2 Shopping center in Mexico. Eng: Candela [118].

Although in architectural circles hyperbolic paraboloids have now been a subject for discussion for many years, so far few architects have ventured to go beyond the purely engineering applications of these forms. Candela and De la Mora have built a church in Mexico [119], the entire structure of which—roofs, walls and columns—is composed of straight-edged h.p. elements. Anyone who takes the trouble (and few do) simply to try and understand this complicated but inspired design, that is, to determine just what geometrical relations have been brought into play, will be astonished at the wealth of forms and the abundance of opportunities for dramatic expression that such geometries enfold. Whether the design itself appeals to him or not is another matter. Candela, who is absorbed in these problems, claims that shell construction is the beginning of architecture. He makes the point that if architecture is the shaping of space, then, compared with the potentialities of shell construction, the works of antiquity are plastic art, not architecture at all [120]. Let us refrain from examining Candela's words too critically, and treat them instead as just as symptomatic of the modern situation as the seriously intended criticism of his church designs [121] that draws its arguments from a parallel with the futuristic German stage designers of the year 1930. This is not enough for us to pass judgment on so important an experiment. The formal relationship with futuristic motifs, in fact, is only one of many possible relationships, and, moreover, one which can scarcely be based on any causal connection. Thus, these problems cannot be judged purely from externals. At any rate, it is quite certain that this is not just a game with forms that one day will produce stage decor and the next advertising art; on the contrary, we are dealing with a genuine structural order. In this building a single one of the numerous possibilities inherent in the construction of h.p. shells has been carried consistently to its unique conclusion.

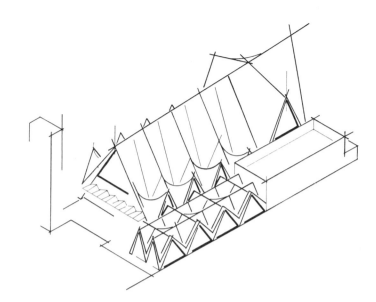

1

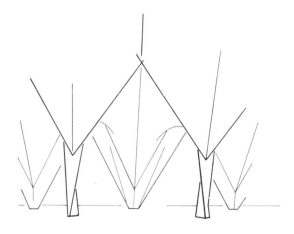

2

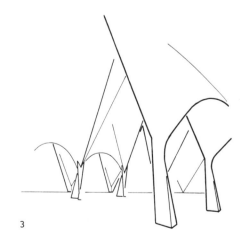

3

182. Church of the Virgin Milagrosa, Mexico [119]. Arch: De la Mora. Eng: Candela.
1 The roof surfaces are all composed of straight-edged h.p. elements.
2 and 3 Inside the church, too, only straight-edged h.p. surfaces are to be seen. Even the columns are formed of h.p.s. The visible curves are not edges but the silhouettes of saddle surfaces.

Another example that belongs here is the Philips Pavilion designed by Le Corbusier for the 1958 World Fair in Brussels [122]. This structure, too, has led to sharp differences of opinion. Here Le Corbusier, one of the most celebrated architects of our age, has made use of the rigorous laws of h.p. geometry to realize what was originally conceived as a perfectly free form. In one sense the shapes are the reverse of those that characterize the Mexican church. In the latter the elaborate wall and roof surfaces wind in sharp ribs and ridges from a slender base high into the nave. The complex interpenetration of the individual h.p. elements is thus subordinated to a system that is broadly axial, symmetrical and repetitive. The Philips pavilion, on the other hand, is a tent that sweeps right down to the ground in broad, membrane-like folds. Sharp peaks, like those formed over tent poles, generate ridges running in different directions. The asymmetry is carried to the extreme. Yet in both cases the structural principles are the same. It makes no difference that one building is poured in place while the other is assembled from precast parts. These are minor problems solved one way today and another way tomorrow. The general form, however, which in the one case is more expressive from the inside and in the other from the out, obeys exactly the same laws. Both buildings are consistent combinations of mainly straight-edged h.p. elements. In both form and structure are inseparable. They must be counted among the most interesting excursions into the unexplored fringe of modern architecture. Their geometry, unlike that of the sphere, cylinder and cone, is so various that it is not experienced as a constraint, from which the structural form must be liberated. On the contrary, in this case it seems almost as if the geometry were breathing life into the structure.

So far the discussion has been all of straight-edged h.p. surfaces. As long as our attention is confined to the superstructure of the Philips pavilion, it is clear that it too belongs in this class. Without exception, all the surfaces that rise above ground level, and thus determine the general appearance of the structure, have straight edges. If we turn our attention to the plan, however, we find that it consists entirely of curves. Thus, it is also possible to give h.p. surfaces curved edges. The effect this has on the elevation is discussed in the following pages.

1

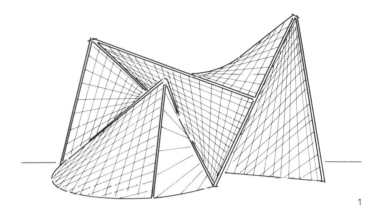

2

183.   The Philips pavilion at the 1958 Brussels exhibition, designed by Le Corbusier [122].
       1 The entire structure is built up out of straight-edged h.p. elements.
       2 Plan. The same h.p. surfaces that have straight edges in elevation meet the ground in curves.

Philips pavilion at the 1958 Brussels exhibition [122]
Arch: Le Corbusier

One of the striking things about the hyperbolic paraboloid is the generation of surfaces curved in two mutually opposed directions by the movement of straight lines along predetermined paths. This impresses every one who uses and understands this geometry. It is not surprising, therefore, if the straight line, the generatrix of the form, should have been emphasized so strongly in most of the h.p.s. built so far. The straight edge is the dominating feature in shells constructed of h.p. surfaces. Curved edges, on the other hand, have been chosen relatively seldom, although there are no geometrical or structural reasons why they should not be employed. However, in the suspended roofs, discussed in the next section, the curved compression arch is often used to provide support (see page 284 ff.).

The architectural effect produced by any building is heavily dependent on the view from the side, determined by eye level and the angle of observation. Both the frog's and the bird's eye view are of secondary importance. The horizontal contours and the plan are often overestimated when judgments are based on models viewed unrealistically from above. The predominantly horizontal angle of observation remains the most important. The geometry of the h.p. is remarkably well-adapted to this state of affairs.

If we modify the basic form by pivoting one edge while keeping it straight in horizontal projection, in elevation we see a curve. This curve can be made to sag or arch depending on the way the pivoting is carried out. The result is that h.p. roofs can have curved edges though the plan remains bounded by straight lines. The true shape of these curves is a parabola.

The expressiveness of the edges can be varied by adjusting the sharpness of the curve and the direction in which it runs. The designer's imagination can be given full rein. He is free to explore other sections with other curves at the edges and combine them as he will (Fig. 184). Curving the edges of h.p. shells opens up a broad new field of application with still untapped powers of expression.

184.　H.p. elements with curved edges.
　　1 A straight-edged element taken from the middle of an h.p. saddle (A-b-C-d) is symmetrical about the two principal axes. Its plan projection is a rhomb (A-B-C-D). If A-B is pivoted to A-B' and A-D to A-D', the edges (A-b', A-d') vertically above are curved.
　　2 Above edges 1 and 2 of the plan, which are straight, we get the curved edges 1' and 2' of the roof. The curves rise or fall (arch or sag) depending on whether the original edges are pivoted in or out.

An information pavilion built in the form of an h.p. with curved edges has been standing in the middle of Brussels since the World Fair in June 1958 [123]. Thanks to a clever system of prestressing by means of mullions acting in tension, this wooden roof, for such it is, should, in accordance with the definition of the engineer Sarger himself, be classed as a stressed or suspended roof. We mention it in this section, since it could just as easily have been built, in exactly the same form, as a reinforced concrete or timber shell. At this point we are chiefly interested in the curved edges. As the plan reveals, they are produced by pivoting towards the straight generatrixes in horizontal projection. The gentle curves (see sketch in Fig. 185.1) are just sharp enough to lend a more ingratiating air to edges otherwise austerely straight. If the curvature is made more pronounced, it takes on an additional, statical function by assisting the edge members to carry their own weight, to some extent without bending, by means of arch action.

The same fundamental idea of a composite h.p. form with edges straight in plan and curved in elevation underlies a triple h.p. roof designed by the engineers Weidlinger and Salvadori. The building was to serve as a smart restaurant in Long Beach [124]. Though only a proposal, this scheme has already attracted worldwide attention. The individual sectors are cut, slightly asymmetrically, from the middle of an h.p. saddle in such a way that the central crown of the structure lies somewhat higher than the freely projecting lateral peaks. On top of the roof the gently curving lines along which the three shells meet are expressed as prominent ribs. Their curvature, like that of the outside edges, is chosen so as to convey the forces to the supports along, as it were, the line of pressure. Over a span as large as 60 m the dead weight of straight edge members would unavoidably have produced undesirable bending stresses (cf. the Shizuoka Congress Hall, Fig. 178). Curved edges, however, can carry their own weight with maximum economy and without introducing bending. Moreover, curved edges tend to enrich the design. They raise geometry to the level of structural form. The engineer himself comments: "It's beautiful shape . . . is not cosmetic, but actual. The form is itself almost a diagram of the stresses it must meet, not a sculptural shape selected by the architect, then made to stand up by the engineer. . . . The shell reveals its conceptual grace to the observer because its outside edges are thin. The stiffening ribs are not run around the shell edges, but instead have been set back" [125].

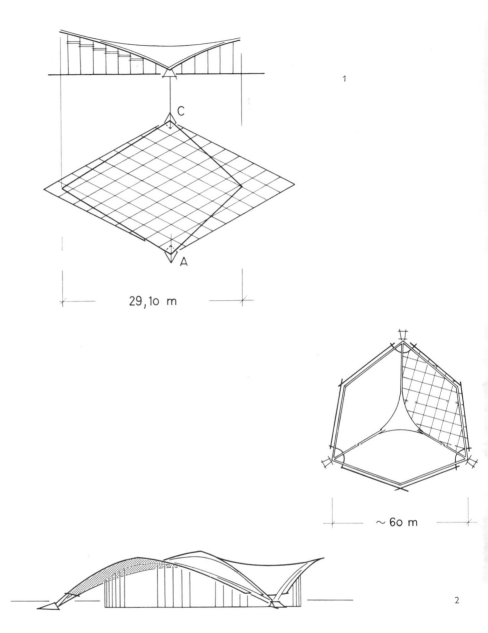

185. Some applications of h.p.s. with curved edges:
   1 Information pavilion, Brussels [123]. The plan shows how the edges have been pivoted inwards about points A and C. Thus, the edges of the roof appear arched.
   2 In their design for a large beach restaurant at Long Beach. Cal. [124], the engineers Weidlinger and Salvadori have combined three h.p. shells with curved edges. The arch action assists the edge members to carry part of their own weight.

Combining h.p. elements of various kinds has long been a favorite student project. Elegant models have been constructed and photographs of some of these have been attractively reproduced in the architectural magazines. The value of these studies is incontestable. They develop the student's powers of three-dimensional visualization, they excite his imagination and familiarize the young architect with the geometrical and statical principles he must master, if he is to have full control over this new world of forms. We must not forget, however, that it is a long way from wood and paper models and geometrical exercises to the realization of a full-scale shell. At this point, while concerned mainly with form and only secondarily with statical analysis, we must emphasize that although geometry counts for a great deal in building h.p. shells, it is by no means the only important factor. The investigation of the specific properties of the materials, possible methods of construction and, finally, the mechanics of the forces and their vital interaction with the form is more than a routine check on the safety of the structure. It is not merely the necessary evil, that the artistically gifted architect all too frequently tends to consider it; it is something with which the designer must inevitably grapple, if he is to pass from the abstract world of models to the reality of shell construction. From this he will derive the impulse to advance beyond sterile geometry to genuine structural form.

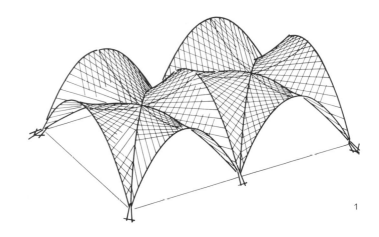

1

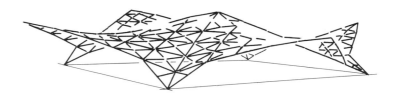

2

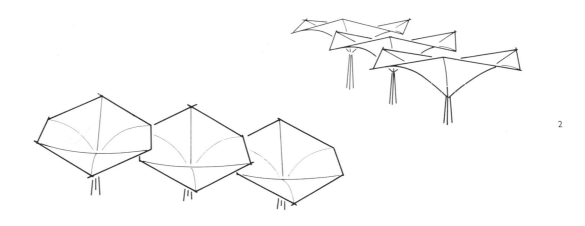

3

186.   Studies in shell geometry.
        1 A proposal of Candela's [126].
        2 A student design.
        3 A sketch by one of the Catalano school [127].

Nightclub in Acapulco, Mexico [128].
Eng: Felix Candela ▶

Really mature projects or, even better, finished buildings naturally excite our interest more than the most handsome models. Again and again we come back to Candela's pioneering work. His night club in Acapulco [128] and his restaurant in Xochimilco [129] consist of concentric arrangements of h.p. elements with curved edges. One structure has three and the other eight elements selected from an h.p. saddle in such a way that the tapered ends converge on the center, while the curved edges form the outer self-supporting termination of the roof. Where adjacent elements meet, highly rigid gullies are formed." These gullies collect the loads, which reach them as arch thrusts along parabolic sections or else, as Candela suspects, as strictly longitudinal forces along the straight generatrixes of the shell. For reasons of symmetry the resultants of these forces are in the direction of the gullies. Since the latter vanish at the ridge, this area forms a zone weak in bending which acts like a hinge. Accordingly, opposite pairs of gullies behave like three-hinged arches. The curved contour in the bottom of the individual gullies approximates quite closely to the line of pressure of the three-hinged arch and thus favors the elimination of bending. The most interesting feature, however, is the free edge of the shell, which rises and falls without any special reinforcement. This possibility has already been hinted at in connection with our discussion of the St. Louis Priory (Fig. 150). We infer from Candela's writings that he looks upon the elimination of edge members in favor of free edges as a refinement of the form. In his opinion this simplification is made possible by the presence of stiffening elements (in this case gullies) *in the actual fabric* of the structure itself, by the symmetry of the plan and by the double curvature of the shells [130].

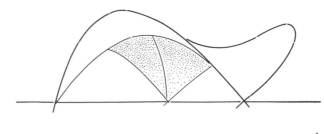

1

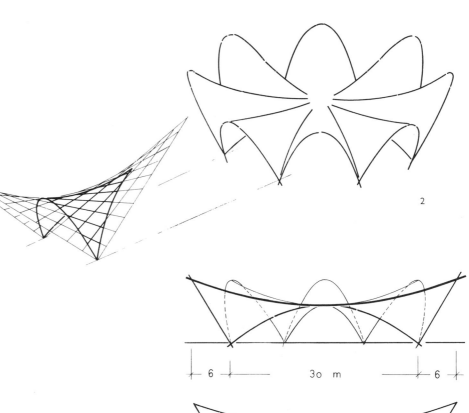

2

6 ⊢ 3o m ⊣ 6

187. Two buildings by Candela:
1 Nightclub in Acapulco, Mexico [128]. Three h.p. elements (cf. detail 187.2) meet in a point at the center and turn parabolically curved edges towards the outside.
2 Restaurant in Xochimilco, Mexico [129]. Eight elements, shaped like paper bags, form a dome. The gullies have the same stiffening effect as folds. The edges of the doubly curved h.p. surfaces are not braced (cf. Fig. 150).

Restaurant in Xochimilco, Mexico [129]
Eng: Felix Candela ▶

The author has designed a roof of unusual form for a foundry at Lohr am Main [131]. This roof, which incorporates a series of h.p. elements with certain edges curved, has a rather special function, namely to avoid the accumulation of fumes by providing a highly efficient, but natural updraft. To this end two mirror-image h.p. elements each with two curved and three straight edges were selected and fitted together so as to provide a to some extent freely formed, but continuous transition to a circular ventilating shaft. The pyramidal shells thus formed, each consisting of two large h.p. surfaces and a ventilating shaft, roof an area measuring 13.5 x 15.0 meters. One side is glazed to admit light to the foundry floor beneath. It is clear that h.p. elements can easily be adapted even to shapes as specific as these. It is true that these surfaces could not be based on an element taken from the middle of the saddle, nor on elements with exclusively straight edges. Fig. 188.2 shows how the final form was cut out of an irregular h.p. element, defined by a warped quadrilateral.

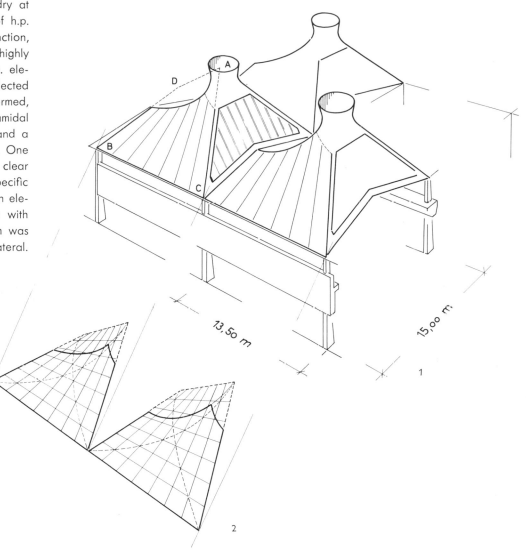

188.   Reinforced concrete roof of a foundry at Lohr-am-Main, Germany [131].
        1 and 3 Each roof shell consists of two symmetrical h.p. elements, a glazed surface and a ventilating hood. The form is designed to provide good natural ventilation.
        2 Schematic representation of the h.p. element employed.

Shell roof of a foundry at Lohr-am-Main [131].   ▶

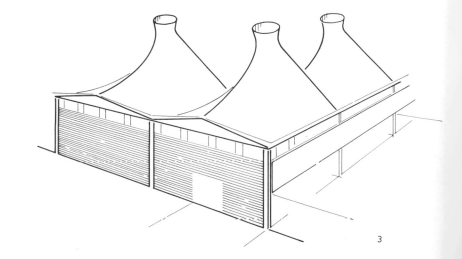

Free Forms

Free form bound by structure sounds almost like a paradox. Yet the free forms we shall discuss are in every respect structurally determined. Free forms that were unrelated to structure, mere expressions of a designer's whim, would, of course, be a crass contradiction of the views advanced in this book. In what sense, then, are free forms "free," if they are completely determined by mechanical laws?

At the beginning of this chapter we decided that a shell need satisfy only two elementary conditions. It had to be "curved" and "rigid." The critical discussion of various shell forms that followed did not encourage us to add any geometrical riders to these two elementary requirements. On the contrary, the geometry was often found irksome. The laws governing structural form are far more subtle. The line of pressure, to which we have so often referred, is not really a parabola. It resembles a parabola, it is true, but the two curves are only rarely identical. The line of pressure varies with the load—it is, as it were, alive. The elementary geometry of circle, cylinder and sphere is important from the point of view of facilitating construction and mathematical analysis, but it is not intrinsically related to the carrying capacity of the shell. We quickly recognized that the sphere had a tendency to be unexpressive and was no better suited for the specific purposes of shell construction than many other forms. Its severe geometry was experienced as a constraint and the much greater flexibility of, for example, the hyperbolic paraboloid was welcomed with relief. There is no doubt that the introduction of the h.p. has considerably broadened the scope of practical shell design. At least it has made all concern about stagnation in the development of forms groundless. Even here, however, we must recognize that, in the last analysis, shells, by their very nature, cannot be tied down to specific geometrical forms, whatever these may be. Interpreted in this way a free form is nothing but a form that has been delivered from geometrical constraint. There is nothing arbitrary about this deliverance. On the contrary. The natural laws of structure continue to determine the form and liberation from the constraint of a non-structural geometry means only that the structural form is freed from extraneous influences so that the nature of the shell can be expressed with even greater purity.

In order to exclude any possibility of misunderstanding, it should be stressed that, as defined here, "free form" must be looked upon as a very distant goal. It has nothing in common with the "oblique" effects and wilful fantasies of a fashionable, publicity-conscious architecture. It is, in fact, a goal achievable only to the extent that our most talented designers consent to concern themselves with structural problems.

"Free form" does not mean the abandonment of all geometrical discipline. A geometrical order is found in all, even the freest natural forms. Accordingly, we shall also apply the concept of free form where certain geometrical rules are still obeyed, provided that the form as a whole is not dictated by a mere geometrical principle.

The roof of the market at Royan [132] is shaped like a sea-shell with undulating edges. We consider it a free form, since the general conception is free invention, guided only by laws of mechanics. Here the geometry has an auxiliary, rather than a dominating function. The plan is circular; it might equally well have been oval or elliptical.

The engineer has made the peripheral sections through the corrugations a combination of parabolic and sine curves. He could have chosen differently. However, he had to have a rule of some sort before he could start designing. The same rule simplifies the actual construction of the shell. Conceptually, the form is perfectly "free." It is bound only by the corrugations as such, by its double curvature, by its undulation subordinated to a concentric arrangement and by its vaulted form, which, in a cross section through the dome, suggests a line of pressure. The form is "free" of the shackles of geometry, yet firmly bound to a precise structural order. There is no trace of freedom in the sense of caprice or juggling with forms.

The shell designed by Weidlinger and Salvadori for a beach restaurant in Puerto Rico [133] is based on geometrical principles different from those of the shell in Royan. The plan and cross section are elliptical. The elliptical ring section through the corrugations is composed of parabolas that are mutually tangential, not combined with sine curves, as in Royan. Yet the analogy between the two shells is unmistakable. Despite the freedom of the general composition, the form is determined not by chance or caprice, but by an unequivocal structural order.

Earlier in this chapter we described a number of other projects strikingly reminiscent of the market in Royan and the Puerto Rican restaurant. Candela's pavilion (Fig. 187) and the proposed St. Louis Priory, in fact, have the same sea-shell type of structure. The only difference is in the modification of the geometrical dimensions. Even Candela's form-determining hyperbolic paraboloids submit to this comprehensive order.

The ultimate refinement flows only from the skilled hand of an artist with a knowledge of structures or from that of an engineer with an artist's feeling for form. Hence the range, and at the same time the difficulty of the design problems of our time. Sheer engineering ability is rarely accompanied by plastic inspiration. Without structural substance talent for design remains hollow. It fails to get to the heart of the matter. Our hopes of a positive outcome depend entirely on the extent to which born architects and experts in structures will devote themselves to this, perhaps the greatest of the problems facing modern design. So far this all sounds like a utopian dream, and there are many who doubt whether "free form" will become anything more than a new architectural fad.

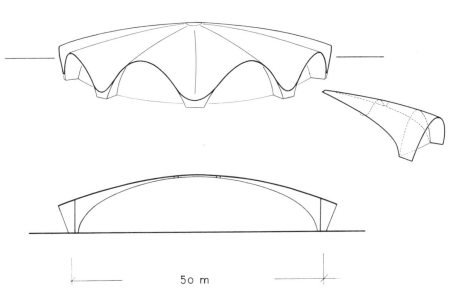

50 m

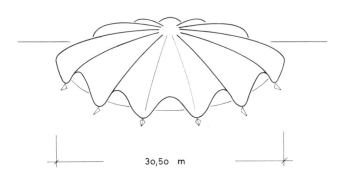

30,50 m

189.   Shapes resembling sea-shells.
       1 Market in Royan, France. Eng: Sarger [132].
       2 Restaurant in Puerto Rico. Eng: Weidlinger and Salvadori [133].

Accordingly, we should rejoice all the more that Saarinen, for example, has ventured to take a stride in the direction of "free" structural form. His design for the TWA terminal building at Idlewild [134], produced in collaboration with the engineers Ammann and Whitney, is one that has grown out of the very nature of shell construction. None of the forms is crippled by a harsh geometry. There is not a circle, right angle or parabola in sight. New forms and novel proportions unfold before us in uninhibited patterns, and yet every curve and every detail suggests a general sense of direction and order. We see the laws of gravity, strength of materials and, in particular, shell design combined in an harmonious and original fashion. The roof consists of sweeping, doubly curved surfaces. The ribs that sprout from its edges broaden out in the direction of the supports to meet the increasing load, while simultaneously stiffening the shells against deformation. These ribs, however, are not mere appendages added to the edges of the roof, but develop organically out of the totality of the structural function. They form the transition between roof and substructure and thus round off the great, closed form that soars from the foundation right up to its lofty peak. The four shells are distinctly separated from each other by strips of glazing. Nevertheless, they constitute an organic unit that bears comparison with the works of nature.

We are quite prepared to believe the architect, when he writes: "We may say that it is a question of structural forms, derived from the laws of curved shells. It is a matter of plastic inspiration, directed towards the spatial continuity of all the architectural elements. . . . The way these elements flow makes design from drawings impossible. . . . The experiments on models continued right up to the moment the final solution was found" [135].

The description of the method of designing the supports makes interesting reading. They were modeled "freely" around a wire armature, after the engineers had fixed the position and direction of the resultants and estimated the size of the concrete sections required (Fig. 190.3). Saarinen writes: "One of the happiest moments was when we finished the models of the supports. When we subsequently prepared drawings from them, we found that (in plan, for example) they were marvellous forms that we would never have arrived at by drawing alone."

The finished building is a manifestation of structural form that only a combination of artistic feeling and engineering knowledge could produce.

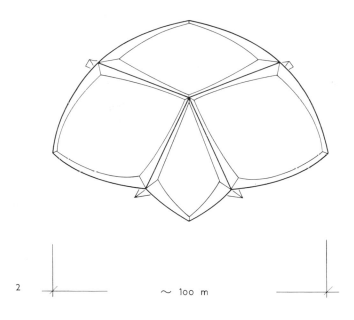

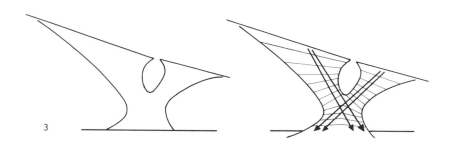

190.   The free shell forms of the new T.W.A. terminal building at Idlewild, New York. Arch: Saarinen. Eng: Ammann and Whitney [134].
        1 View from the road.
        2 Roof plan. The four shells, separated by bands of glazing, are supported at altogether only four points.
        3 The supports are freely modelled to correspond with the directions of thrust.

Model of the T.W.A. terminal building, Idlewild, New York [134]
Arch: Eero Saarinen ▶

At this point we ought also to mention the Ronchamp chapel [136], perhaps Le Corbusier's most important work. To put it bluntly, Ronchamp is not a structural form. Neither the heavy wall with its tiny perforations, nor the suspended roof, nor the details have the least structural logic. Ronchamp is inspired sculpture, full of charm and poetry, and no richer or more beautiful solution of the problem is imaginable. Its appeal, however resides entirely in the form, not in the structure and in this case the significance of the form is not derived from structural laws. It would therefore be pointless to criticize the wall for not being really massive or the roof for not being really hung. In fact, it would be just as pointless as making a structural analysis of one of those splendid Baroque churches, whose "dressing" of stucco, marble and gold we know to be one of their most important means of expression. Good theater can also be good art. On the other hand we know that in all ages great works of architecture have been closely bound up with structure. And the more important the technical component the closer the bond. The forms of the Parthenon are appropriate to marble. What would be the effect if they were rebuilt in gypsum? What would be the point of a Chartres Cathedral in reinforced concrete, or a Stuttgart TV tower as a huge cylinder with a steel mast hidden at its core? These examples can be multiplied indefinitely; they are of almost painful absurdity. The more technical their content, the more painful they become. From this we derive our justification for advocating the overriding importance of structural form in modern architecture in particular.

Ronchamp is the unique achievement of a genius, standing far above the average. It is beyond rules and the conclusion that it is not a structural form in no way detracts from its value. Structural form, however, does not lose in importance, simply because works of art can exist without it. Many areas of art have nothing to do with structure or with building.

On other occasions Corbusier himself has created structural forms of remarkable power. In the Philips pavilion in Brussels, for example, he displays a consistent mastery of the hyperbolic paraboloid far in advance of his times.

Let us return to forms that are "free" but bound by structure. Opinion is divided about the prospects for this kind of design. Candela very definitely takes the stand that the ties with geometry cannot be entirely dissolved. He even recommends using only perfectly definite, simple forms, he himself preferring h.p. surfaces. He justifies this preference on the rather ingenuous grounds that the computations are easy to understand. He also professes absolute loyalty to analytical methods. He writes: "The hyperbolic paraboloid is the easiest to build . . . it is the only warped surface with an equation simple enough to allow the calculation of its membrane stresses by plain, elementary mathematics. . . . In view of the actual existing methods of practical analysis we can employ, I am very pessimistic about the use of entirely free forms in architecture, and I believe architects should consider them a little more soberly, if only to spare themselves much distress and disappointment. Free surfaces defy simple analysis. . . .

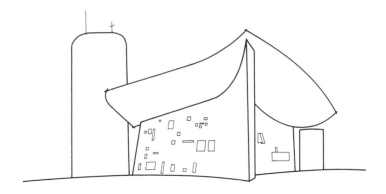

191.   Though Le Corbusier's chapel at Ronchamp, France [136], is a great work of art, it is not a structural form. It is sculpture on an architectural scale.

Some people claim that if the mathematics are too hard we can always revert to the testing of scale models. I have never resorted to such means myself, because the problem is never to discover the internal stresses in a structure (which are normally very low) but to find the forces at the edges. . . . I cannot see how this can be done by means of small-scale models. . . . The only way is to calculate the stresses. But we must employ methods on which we can rely, not the vague hypotheses about the deformability of materials. So I personally only believe in statics and geometry. And in order to disregard the deformation of a structure, we must use compound surfaces. . . . But the h.p. is the only compound surface which can be analyzed by simple statics. This is its real justification and a far more valid one than the beauty of its form" [137].

So much for Candela. Quite different opinions are held by Torroja, who in his institute in Madrid relies heavily on models. He writes: "As regards roofs, present-day architecture tends progressively to more varied surfaces, without regard to the difficulties of calculation involved . . . " [139]. As an example he cites his scheme for the Tachira Club [138] in South America: "The impossibility of handling the differential equations which would be involved in a methodical analysis of this surface forced us to limit our calculations to a provisional rough estimate." On the basis of such estimates Torroja proceeds to build models and tests them to arrive at the final design. In his opinion it is always possible to determine the stresses and conditions of stability for an unusual form of shell by means of an experimental-analytical technique developed from investigating models.

Many engineers have no confidence in such methods. They take the stand that the mathematical approach is the only one that is really serious and worthy of a good engineer. At the Symposium on Shell Structures held in Oslo in 1957, on the other hand, Torroja concluded his report with the words: "Summarizing, I would like to say how important I think it is to improve the analysis of the classical shapes, i.e., cylinders and other standard surfaces. But I think that we should *also* try new developments; . . . So we have to be prepared to face, every day, new and more complex problems, and to exploit all our resources, materials, techniques and so on" [139]. From the purely experimental method practiced in his institute in Madrid [140] we must conclude that by this he means experimental statics in the broadest sense, as used increasingly throughout the world.

Apart from Candela's method which, though analytical, is restricted to elementary geometries, in particular that of the hyperbolic paraboloid, and simple statical systems, and the more experimental method favored by Torroja, a more abstract and mathematical technique is often employed. This technique is based on the state of stress and deformation of the differential shell element and aims at general solutions for particular geometrical forms. To some extent it involves dealing with difficult mathematical problems. It is obvious that this method does not encourage the development of new forms. Once a general solution for a particular form has been laboriously obtained, the engineer naturally prefers to repeat the same procedure as often as possible. Every departure from it seems to him like wilful frivolity. Many engineers refuse to recognize that form is not something superficial, that it may even be of greater significance than a method of calculation. This is the reason why in Germany, where shell construction began, the development of new forms is progressing so slowly and may even be said to stagnate.

As far as the search for form is concerned, the creative designer is relatively indifferent to the choice of a method of statical analysis. A purely mathematical treatment always involves the risk of solving the problem piecemeal and thus losing sight of the over-all idea. The need to make simplifying assumptions and carry out complicated computations in a series of independent steps easily leads to the debasement of form to the status of a necessary consequence of the analytical principle or the method of computation. The decisive theo-

192.   The Tachira Club project for South America. Eng: Torroja [138]. A very free design which, nevertheless, has all the prerequisites of a structural form.

retical separation of the edge member from the actual shell (cf. Fig. 146), by which the designer hopes to eliminate bending and obtain simple membrane conditions, is certainly wrong in terms of structural form. Seen from the point of view of the unity of the structure, edge member and shell ought to merge into a single whole. The only question is how. So far the analytical method has been unable to produce any answers to questions about how the right form is to be achieved. In fact, it has not even posed the question with precision. We are hopeful, however, that, in future, systematic experiments on models will carry us further along this path. No doubt, in the end, one technique will supplement the other. There is room for every approach and every method, whether experimental or analytical. The area to be explored is so vast that suitable tasks can be found for every mentality and every point of view.

If we disregard fashionable styles of architecture with their profusion of twists and curves and confine ourselves to "free forms" in which the elements of structural form are apparent, the number of examples from which to choose is extremely small. The structural aspects of Castiglioni's extraordinary design for the Naples railroad station have already been discussed in Chapter 2 (Fig. 113). In the present context we will allow the free form of the shell roof to speak for itself in the photograph on the facing page. The Nervi-Carminos design for Tucuman [141] also deserves mention (Fig. 193), and possibly the design for the new Sidney Opera House [142]. So far all we know about the latter is what is conveyed by photographs of a very small-scale preliminary model. Whether this idea can be expanded to encompass a large structural form we shall discover in due course.

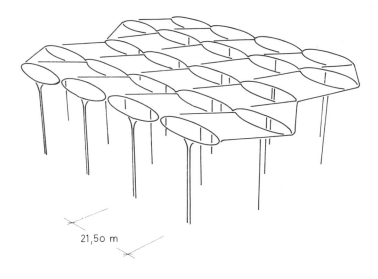

21,5o m

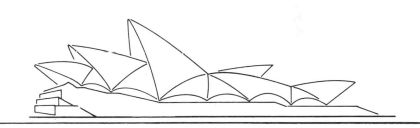

193.   Free forms for different purposes:
        1 Design for a hall for the University of Tucuman, Argentine. Arch: Carminos.
          Eng: Nervi and Bartoli [141].
        2 Design for a new opera house in Sydney [142].

Design for Naples railroad station [51]. Arch: Enrico Castiglioni

A great deal of good work is done in the studios of our schools of architecture. Many excellent ideas are conceived there, only to be abandoned at the paper model stage. One such student project [143], which originated in Torroja's laboratory in Madrid, may serve as an example (Fig. 194). The three shells which converge to form a cup have no associations with known geometrical forms. At the same time, however, their structural origin is clearly expressed. The shells, obviously doubly curved saddle surfaces, cantilever far beyond the three outward sloping masts between which they are suspended. The curved edges point to a conscious attempt to escape from the constraints of conventional geometry and approach a shape more closely related to natural forms. The difficulty of forming and building such a shape is another matter. Our main object here is to draw attention to the contribution made by this design to the development of free, yet structurally determined form.

As a contrast to what we mean when we talk about forms that are "free" as well as structural, we have included the group of sketches shown in Fig. 195. Free forms based on wild caprice and undisciplined invention are to be found in plenty. Our object in closing this section with a few sketches of structures of this kind is to enable the reader to recognize them and distinguish them from genuine structural form, as we have defined it.

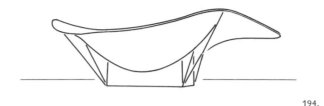

194.

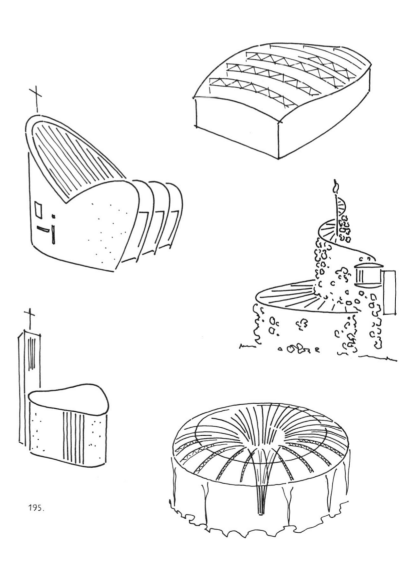

194.   Design for an air terminal building by a student of Torroja's school in Madrid [143].

195.   When structural principles are disregarded, the result is an arbitrary form which may have some meaning as sculpture but can hardly be considered architecture.

195.

The idea of building with cables gave us the suspension bridge. The suspension bridge is a "plane system" in the sense of our original definition. Although it is many years now since the first such bridge was built, the idea of building with cables has only recently been extended to roof construction and the term "suspended roof" coined to describe the result. Apart from a few exceptional cases, however, "suspended roof" is not an accurate description of the cable roof, as we understand it. This new form of construction is chiefly characterized not by "suspension" but by the stressing of orthogonal families of cables into surfaces curved in mutually opposed directions so as to produce systems with three-dimensional stability.

In striking contrast with the shell, three-dimensional cable structures have few parallels in nature. There is, perhaps, a certain analogy with the wing of a bat or the webbed feet of waterfowl. The spider's web, on the other hand, is a "plane system" and its action depends far too heavily on its elastic deformability for it to be comparable with a cable roof. Among human artefacts the tent and the sail bear the closest resemblance to a three-dimensional cable structure. We can distinguish the following groups:

1. Simply curved roofs, the stability of which is derived entirely from their own weight or from auxiliary stiffeners. These can only be classed as space structures with certain reservations.
2. Doubly curved cable systems, the stability of which is derived from prestressing.
3. Systems in which cables and compression members are combined.
4. Tents.

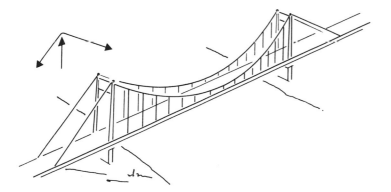

Simply Curved Suspended Roofs

Suspended roofs with simple curvature behave like a group of cables suspended in parallel. Each cable deforms under its own load, independently of its neighbors (Fig. 196.1). The cables can only be made to act as a unit if a series of rigid transverse members is laid across them (Fig. 196.2). In the presence of vibration or asymmetrical loading, however, the structure will not be rigid even then (Fig. 196.3). Flutter due to wind loads can be counteracted by increasing the dead weight of the structure, but this is not exactly an economical solution. Distortion of the form under asymmetrical loading can only be avoided by applying vertical tension at the ends of the transverse members (Fig. 196.4). This, however, means sacrificing the clarity of the original conception. Instead of being carried by the suspended cables the unsymmetrical portion of the load is transferred to the rigid transverse members that stiffen them.

Simply curved roofs of this kind have also been cast in concrete (Fig. 197). The result is a simply curved suspended shell following a catenary; this shell is equivalent to the short shell described on page 224 (Fig. 151) with all the signs reversed. The loads are transferred as tensile (compressive) forces along the catenary (line of pressure) to the continuous supports at either end of the structure. All the unsymmetrical components of the load, which might cause flutter or distort the shape of the roof, are dispersed to the edges by the stiffening action of the curved shell; here again, for purposes of comparison, one might think in terms of a series of plane elements meeting in folds (Fig. 197.1). The curved edges of the roof perform the same function as the stiffening ribs of the short shell. They must therefore be either very stiff or effectively supported. In structures with suspended roofs it is convenient to punctuate the outside walls with columns, since columns are usually needed anyway as mullions or wall framing (Fig. 197.4).

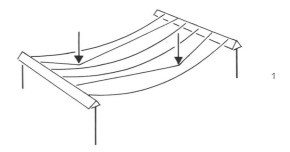

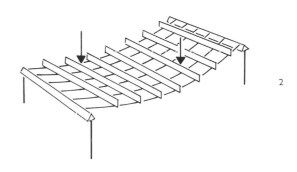

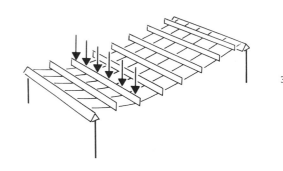

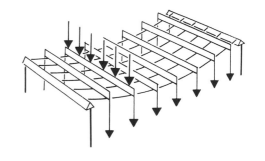

196.   Simply suspended cable roofs.
      1 Under load each cable deforms independently.
      2 In order to make all the cables act together transverse stiffeners must be introduced.
      3 Under asymmetrical loading the structure will be unstable, even if stiffeners are employed.
      4 Complete stability can only be ensured by tying down the ends of the transverse stiffeners.

Such simply curved concrete shells, for this is how they act rather than as suspended roofs, are relatively heavy, whereas the chance of achieving lightness is the most attractive thing about a genuine cable structure. Moreover, the loads are transferred to the foundations by a very circuitous route. In the arched short shell (Fig. 151) most of the load flows directly into the foundations along the line of pressure, but the loads from simply suspended shells, though carried clear of the area covered by the roof, instead of being conveyed directly to the foundations are concentrated at the high points at each end. Here either ties (Fig. 197.2) or rigid fins (Fig. 197.3) must be provided to resist the horizontal forces that develop or the loads must be absorbed by stiff trusses, lying in the plane of the roof, and transmitted to the edges, where they are balanced by suitable edge members stressed in compression (Fig. 197.4). These edge members act like inverted arches and introduce additional vertical compression into the exterior columns. The path followed by the forces is rather complicated and hence difficult to express architecturally. The simple catenary surface is a structural form closely related to the long-familiar plane system of the suspension bridge. It can only be counted as a space structure with certain reservations.

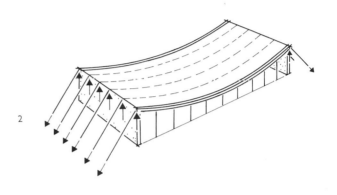

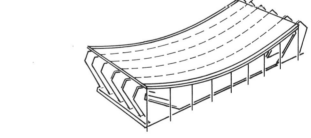

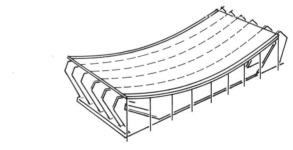

197.   Simply suspended concrete shells can be regarded as inverted short shells (Fig. 151).

    1 Symmetrical loads are transferred to the high points of the structure as pure tensile forces. Asymmetrical loads are transferred to the sides by the curvature of the shell (cf. the action of the folded plate).

    2 The forces are concentrated at the high points of the structure and must be resisted either by ties (which develop vertical components along the edges of the roof), as in a suspension bridge (page 279), or

    3 by concrete fins cable of resisting bending or

    4 by a large truss in the plane of the roof. In this case the truss reactions A and B tangential to the shell are absorbed by the lateral stiffeners acting in compression. The latter act like inverted arches and exert compressive forces on the exterior walls.

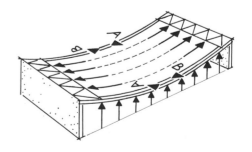

The design of the Wuppertal swimming pool [144] is based on a decision to protect the cables from corrosion by embedding them in concrete (in the light of our definition it would be better to call this structure a suspended shell) (Fig. 198.1). As depicted diagrammatically in Fig. 197, it behaves like an inverted short shell.

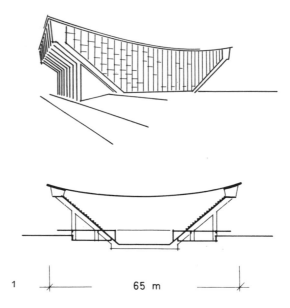

198.   Examples of suspended shells.
    1 Swimming pool in Wuppertal, Germany [144]. The structural principle is roughly the same as that illustrated in Fig. 197.3.
    2 An aircraft hangar based on the principle illustrated in Fig. 197.2 [145].

We have had to suffer various unenlightened imitations of this clear and unambiguous structure. A number of these are illustrated in Fig. 199.

As distinct from a simply suspended shell, a series of parallel cables strung between two supports makes little sense. Because of the ever-present threat of asymmetrical loading due to snow and wind and the risk of flutter, such structures always need to be stiffened, as illustrated in Fig. 196, in ways that contradict their real nature. Any saddle surface, on the other hand, reveals at a glance the true significance of a network of cables curved in two mutually opposed directions.

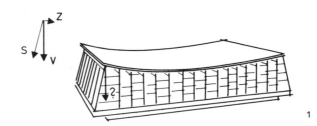

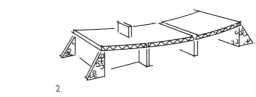

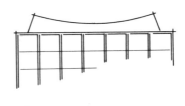

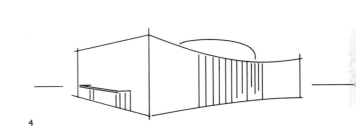

199.   A number of formalistic designs in which the outward appearance of the suspended roof has been imitated but the structural principle has been misunderstood.

1 The dishonesty of the structure is evident from the lack of effective means of resisting the normal reactions from a suspended roof. Tensile forces S cannot act in the direction of the sloping end walls, since there are no means of resisting the vertical components V. The roof, in fact, is of conventional beam and slab construction. The short sides of the building are sloped in misconceived imitation of forms of the type illustrated in Figs. 197.2 and 198.2.

2 In this case the random-rubble buttresses (introduced where the forces should be tensile) represent formalism carried to ridiculous extremes. Clearly the roof must be supported by trusses resting on transverse bearing walls. Supporting a suspended roof is just as absurd as suspending a vault.

3 A pseudo suspended roof crowning a skeleton frame. The outward form has been used in the wrong place and the structural content ignored.

4 If a suspended roof is interrupted by the superstructure of an auditorium, the form cannot be a genuine one.

Cable Systems Curved in Two Mutually Opposed Directions

This idea has been consistently applied in the Rio Grande do Sul exhibition hall in Brasilia [146] (Fig. 200). The main longitudinal suspension cables are draped over two transverse circular arches to form catenaries, the ends of which are anchored in the ground in clusters. Between the arches, instead of running parallel, the main cables are concentrically gathered in towards the central axis of the building by means of a series of transverse bracing cables. These transverse cables are all arcs of circles. The end result is a segment of a perfectly definite body of revolution. Owing to the vertical arrangement of the transverse bracing cables the tangential component of the reaction at the points of intersection with the suspension cables remains unbalanced. Consequently, the bracing cable has a tendency to slide down the main cable (Fig. 200.3). In order to prevent this, the engineers designed a special clamp which was used to lock the cables together wherever they crossed. In this way the predetermined geometrical shape was preserved. This simplified the computations and construction details. The form accords perfectly with the principle of a prestressed roof. Apart from the circular compression arches at each end, the structure consists entirely of cables acting in tension.

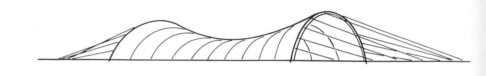

1

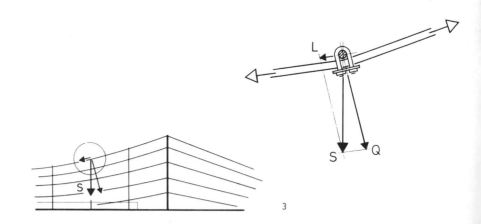

catenary line

102,80 m

2

59,40

circle

3

200. The Rio Grande do Sul exhibition hall, Brasilia [146], consists of two sets of cables stretched in opposite directions. The main cables are catenaries, the transverse bracing cables arcs of circles. Apart from the compression arches at each end, the structure is composed entirely of cables.
  1 View.
  2 Geometry of the form.
  3 Diagram of forces at the points where the cables intersect. The bracing cable, acting in the vertical plane, exerts a force S on the main cable. This is resolved into a force Q at right-angles to the main cable and a force L along it. Under the action of force L the bracing cable tends to slide down the main cable, but is restrained from doing so by a clamp.

Raleigh arena, North Carolina [147]
Arch: Matthew Novicki ▶

Whereas the precise geometry of Rio Grande do Sul, like that of the shells of revolution discussed in the last section, is characterized by a certain lifelessness, saddle shapes, which are not cut from a surface of revolution, are considerably more expressive. Nowicki has recognized this fact and all its consequences for structure and form in his design for an arena in Raleigh, N. C. [147], which has thus come to be regarded as a sort of prototype of the cable roof (Fig. 201). One set of cables is suspended between two compression arches; a second set, stretched at right angles to the first, gives the resulting network three-dimensional rigidity. The two intersecting sets of cables together support the roof deck. This idea of a doubly curved roof surface, which, though without members capable of resisting compression and bending and consisting only of stressed cables, is still sufficiently rigid, means that the dead weight of the roof structure can be reduced to a fraction of the usual figure.

A reinforced concrete shell only 6 cm thick would weigh, including roofing, not less than 160-170 kg/m². The roof of the Raleigh arena weighs only 30 kg/m². Of course, a roof that weighs so little, less than the load due to snow and wind, is seriously exposed to the risk of flutter. Nowicki's roof is able to resist this tendency thanks to the three-dimensional rigidity imparted by its network of stressed cables. This rigidity is the greater, the sharper the curve of the roof. The unusually light weight of the roof reduces the load on the substructure and foundations, and hence the cost. The cables were installed without scaffolding, which significantly simplified the construction. All this, however, is of less immediate interest to us than the form. The path followed by the loads through the compression arches is as clear and economical as it is rational and expressive. (The path followed by the forces in the simply suspended roof shown in Fig. 196 is tortuous in comparison.) The suspension and bracing cables are in equilibrium with the forces in the arches and with each other. Part of the dead weight of the arches serves to stress the cables and part is resolved into a compressive component in the direction of the arch itself. The network of cables and the arches together form a closed unit which, when symmetrically loaded, does not even require the arches to be supported by columns in the exterior walls.

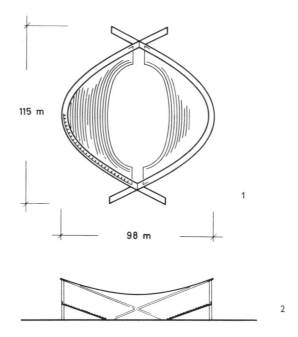

115 m

98 m

1

2

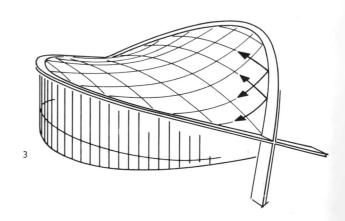

3

201.   The Raleigh arena, North Carolina. Arch: Novicki. Eng; Severud, Elstad and Krueger [147]. Sets of cables curved in two mutually opposed directions are stretched between two inclined parabolic compression arches.
     1 and 2 The plan and section show how both the tiers of seats and the roof itself rise towards the crowns of the arches.
     3 Under symmetrical loading the compression arches are in equilibrium with the stressed roof. Load-bearing outside walls are only needed to resist asymmetrical loads.

Nowicki's preliminary design (Fig. 201.4) acknowledged this fact by tilting the columns inwards. This would have helped to prevent anyone getting the false impression that the columns actually carried the loads from the roof. Unfortunately, after the architect's premature death, this scheme was abandoned in favor of a solution with vertical columns and parallel strips of glazing. The tendency of the exterior columns to escape the loads would have been even more strikingly expressed by giving them an outward kink or else by replacing them with stressed cables and gathering in the wall surface by means of a horizontal tie.

4

The Raleigh arena saddle, stretched between its two tilted arches, thus became the prototype of the "suspended roof," or more correctly the "stressed cable roof," curved in two mutually opposed directions. The latter description tends to draw attention to the shape of the roof surface, which is more important in this type of construction than the shape of the arches. If we set ourselves to find the saddle surface with the maximum over-all rigidity, we shall inevitably arrive at the hyperbolic paraboloid. The roof of the Raleigh arena, however, is not an h.p. surface. The choice of parabolic arches (for an h.p. surface they ought to have been hyperbolas, cf. Fig. 175) and the almost tangential attachment of the suspension cables led, in the upper part of the roof, to the development of a surface that, instead of being an h.p. is very flat indeed (Fig. 201.5). At first this flatness was responsible for a certain amount of flutter, which was subsequently eliminated by allowing the cables to sag. These remarks are not intended to detract from the pioneering achievement which the Raleigh arena represents. Their only object is to draw attention to the structural significance of the form.

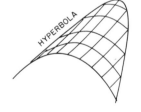

PARABOLA   HYPERBOLA

5   6

201. 4 One of Novicki's preliminary designs shows how the impression that the roof is supported by the perimeter wall can be softened by making the latter inclined rather than vertical. The same effect can also be obtained by introducing a kink in the exterior columns.
5 The saddle-shaped roof is not an h.p. and accordingly the upper parts are rather too flat.
6 If the arches had been hyperbolic, it would have been possible to make the roof a true h.p., and increase the curvature and hence the overall rigidity.

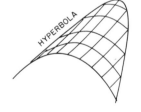

287

The Berlin Congress Hall [148] has a form somewhat resembling that of the Raleigh arena. One assumes that the structural principle is the same and that a network of cables has been stretched between the two arches (Fig. 202.1). There is no doubt that this was, in fact, the original intention. The architect's idea was that the hall should nestle under a light, sheltering roof, which was to project freely beyond the line of the outside walls. A cable roof stretched between two compression arches suggested itself. The free projection of the eaves, however, forbade the use of peripheral columns, like those of the Raleigh arena, and hence such a structure would not have been stable under asymmetrical loading (Fig. 202.2). The problem was solved by stiffening the center. The walls of the hall were crowned with a heavy ring beam, rigidly anchored to the springings of the arches (Fig. 202.3). This skeleton was then covered with a suspended reinforced concrete shell.

The architect was reluctant to abandon his original idea of a roof suspended between compression arches. These arches were actually built, but they carry only the static load from the roof. In order to counteract the asymmetrical loads due to wind and snow, the critical loads in this design, they are tied to the stiff ring beam described above. This is their only source of stability. To make sure that the deliberate tying back of the arches was really effective, the concrete roof between them and the main body of the hall had to be divided into narrow strips separated by joints. Otherwise the roof would have behaved like a shell, and arch action might have developed at the expense of the suspension effect. In order to induce, at least partially, a similar suspension effect in the area directly above the hall, the shell roof was split by another joint which divides it into two halves along the ridge. In this way it was prevented from behaving like an arch in the transverse direction and obliged, to some extent at least, to hang from the arches. A continuous shell would have behaved differently. This whole series of complicated and confusing modifications obscures the principle and prejudices the unity of an otherwise impressive structural form. We imagine we see a powerful suspended roof stretched between two great arches. This we assume to be the essence of the design. The real situation is just the opposite. The roof is actually a concrete shell, the center of which is stiffened by means of a heavy ring beam. The arches are tied back to this beam which is their only source of stability.

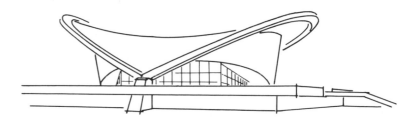

1

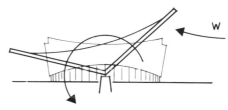

2

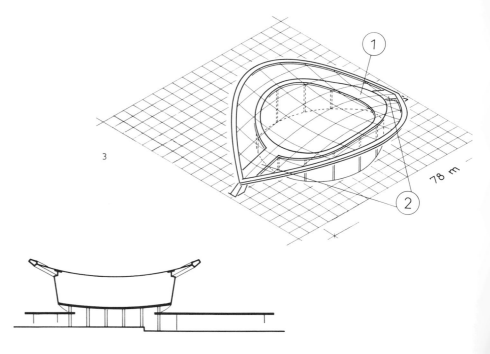

3

4

202. Although the roof of the Congress Hall in Berlin [148] gives the impression of being a network of cables stretched between compression arches, it is in fact a concrete shell.
1 Elevation.
2 A stressed cable roof supported at only two points would have been unstable under asymmetrical loading.
3 A concrete shell is suspended over the hall from a heavy ring beam (1), rigidly connected with the springings of the arches (2).
4 The arches are tied back to the ring beam which ensures their stability.

It would have been more consistent to have stabilized the structure against asymmetrical loading in one of the following ways: either by separating the roof from the body of the hall and giving it an intrinsically stable form (Figs. 202.5-202.7), or by fusing roof and hall together, i.e. by utilizing the three-dimensional stability of the outside walls and the ring beam they support, while omitting the then superfluous arches. The place of the latter might well have been taken by a cantilevered shell projecting freely beyond the perimeter of the hall (Fig. 202.8).

We can only regret that so splendid an idea was prevented from coming to full maturity by the rush to meet a completion date, an enemy of all sound design. Our regret is all the greater, since in every other respect this structure is one of the best built in Germany since the war.

These two examples, the Raleigh arena and the Berlin Congress Hall, have shown how difficult it is to give such novel construction a consistent form. We saw how easily the basic structural principle can be abandoned in the face of technical difficulties. The inevitable result is a chain reaction of structural and formal inconsistencies. Inflexible logic in design and puritanical simplicity in form offer the only hope of a further advance.

5

6

7

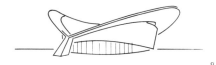

8

202.   5, 6 and 7 As originally conceived the roof could only have been built if the arches had been made self-supporting under asymmetrical loading or 8 if the idea of arches had been scrapped. The body of the hall might then have been used to provide the necessary stiffness and the overhang of the roof could have been cantilevered from the walls.

A sports arena, the design of which has been entrusted to Sarger [149], is to be built in Paris, not far from the exhibition hall (Fig. 161) in St. Ouen. A doubly curved network of cables spans between two compression arches which run in the longitudinal direction of the arena. The floor plans of both the Raleigh arena and the Berlin Congress Hall suggest that it would be better for the arches to be oriented in the longitudinal rather than in the transverse direction. In Sarger's project this idea has actually been adopted. Here again the plan is not to support the arches on columns or tie them back to a massive central core, but, in the true spirit of cable construction, to stabilize them with tension members running from arch to arch and from the arches to the ground. The two arches transmit the resultant compressions to common foundations, tied together under the floor along the length of the arena. We trust that no intellectual reservations and no insuperable practical difficulties will prevent the uncompromising realization of this bold concept.

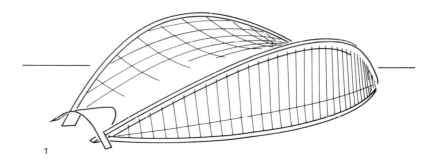

1

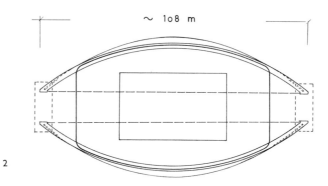

2

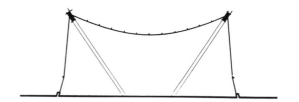

3

203. Design for a sports stadium in Paris [149].
   1 The saddle-shaped roof, spanning between two longitudinal compression arches, and the side walls consist of networks of cables. Apart from the concrete arches, cables are the only structural elements employed.
   2 and 3 The plan and section show how the arch thrusts are transferred to common foundations tied together beneath the stadium floor.

At present Sarger is designing an indoor swimming pool for Monaco [150], a structure of unrivalled lightness and grace. Only the network of stressed cables is intended to remain permanently in place; during the summer months the roofing, a plastic skin, will be removed. The cables will then be left to support lighting fixtures and, during festivals, objects such as flowers and garlands.

The main suspension cables, across which a set of bracing cables is laid, span longitudinally between two transverse arches made of steel. At each end of the building the tensile forces in the suspension cables are transmitted through the arch into another system of cables that forms the outside wall. These cables are tied to the foundations. High-grade prestressing steel is to be used. The structure will be stressed by the combined weight of the arches and the foundations. Thanks to hinged bearings at the springings, the arches will be able to absorb the resulting displacements without suffering distortion. The lateral lean-tos meet the saddle surface of the main roof in a decided valley. In this valley, stretched between the feet of the arches, runs a main cable that stiffens the structure by acting as a "tension arch." The lean-to roofs are curved in two mutually opposed directions, but, in contrast to the main roof, sag in the transverse and arch in the longitudinal direction. They end in edge cables which are carried across a series of inclined struts to the feet of the steel arches. These struts are tied back to the foundations by means of vertical tension members. Apart from wires and cables the only structural elements employed are the two arches and the two rows of short, inclined struts.

The roof is intended to have a plastic skin, weighing about 1 kg/m² and made up of sections each about 500 m² in area. These sections are divided into bands, the shape of which is determined exactly by the geometry of the doubly curved surface. The different bands are sewn and sealed together and the larger units thus formed are made watertight by overlapping them at right angles to the pitch of the roof.

To many this "architecture" may seem utopian or simply wrong, but no one who is free of preconceived opinions will be able to close his eyes to the fact that these novel forms are based on perfectly definite structural considerations, by which in the long run they are justified.

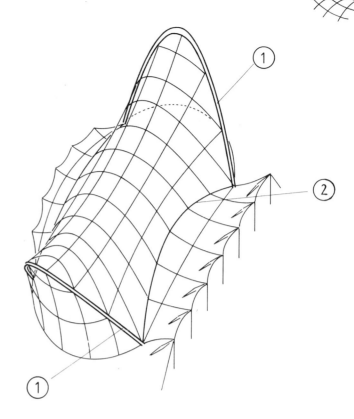

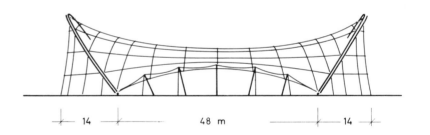

204.   Covered swimming pool, Monaco [150].
        A doubly curved network of cables is stretched between two compression arches (1). The only roof covering is a transparent plastic membrane which is removed during the summer months. The long sides of the building are opened up by stretching one of the main cables between the springings of the arches, forming a valley (2) where the lateral lean-tos (also composed of cables) meet the main roof.

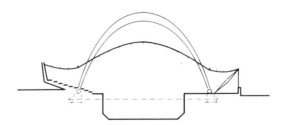

It was inevitable that the suspended roof should be added to the list of attractions offered by the fashionable architect. The Brussels exhibition of 1958 was a show window for misconceived structures and spiritless imitations. Among the wares on display were suspended roofs (not shells) which, through failure to understand the elementary function of the form, were doubly curved in the same rather than in two mutually opposed directions (Figs. 205.1 and 205.2). It is impossible to stiffen such roofs by tensioning the cables. They hang as limply as a wet sack. Structures of this kind can only be prevented from fluttering in the wind or overturning in a hurricane by adding useless ballast. This pseudo structure often pervades the entire design. The report of Rene Sarger, the engineer responsible for the French pavilion, is very much to the point [151]:

"But where the mendacity of the new formalism becomes really flagrant is in the astonishing structure of the . . . . (Fig. 205.3). Its roof is shaped like a saddle stretched between two inclined parabolic arches, which intersect about two meters above the ground to form an unmistakable forked abutment." (The analogy with the Raleigh arena is obvious. Author.) "The designer genuinely believed that this was an architectural fantasy that also demanded a cable roof. He failed to understand that the inclined arches were true structural elements and treated them like a decorative fringe. He must have persuaded the architect to accept this, since the building was erected before the abutments of the arches were poured. Doubtless to give an impression of solidity, the elevations have been larded with rigidly anchored piers, which contribute absolutely nothing to the stability of a saddle-shaped suspended roof, if the arches rest on continuous perimeter walls." As Sarger suggests the false abutments were added as an afterthought to make the structure correspond with the architect's design.

And what is one to make of a roof oval in plan and composed of two surfaces that are mutually inclined and perfectly flat? Such a structure is neither a shell nor a suspension system; it can only act in bending (Fig. 205.4). Forms of this kind are inspired only by a desire to keep up to date and have no structural basis at all.

Shells, which can resist both tension and compression, may be simply or doubly curved and the curvature may be in the same or in two mutually opposed directions. They always form a closed, rigid system, which transmits its loads directly, either as a vertical reaction or as an oblique thrust. The true cable roof, on the other hand, can only consist of two intersecting sets of cables curved in two mutually opposed directions. The loads are transmitted through the suspended cables up to the high points of the roof. The stressed cables induce upward tensile forces in the substructure. The form of the substructure and the auxiliary supports should therefore express the forces developed in the roof. The latter are never vertical or transverse forces, but always act tangentially to the roof surface.

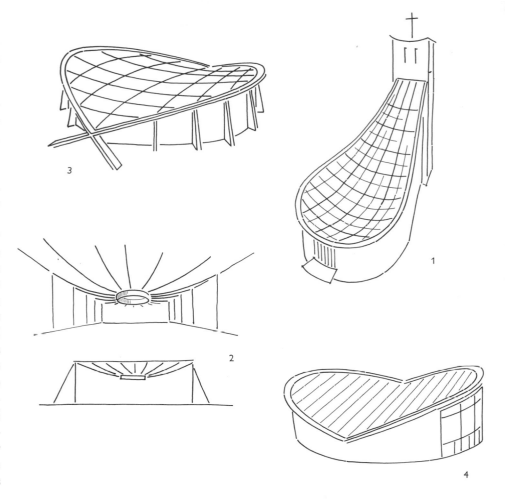

205. In these examples the idea of the suspended roof has not been properly understood. Technical formalism consists in using external forms simply for effect, without regard for function and logic.

1 and 2 Surfaces doubly curved in the same direction are quite unsuitable for suspended roofs. Flutter can only be prevented by adding dead weight.

3 Superfluous buttresses, used to decorate the structure at points where neither tensile nor compressive forces are developed.

4 Flat roof surfaces indicate conventional beam and slab construction. The inclined arch form of the eaves has been blindly borrowed from suspended roof design.

If a tensioned cable system is stretched across a frame to form a straight-edged warped square (Fig. 206), it is immediately obvious that the prestress in the cables will cause bending at the straight edges. If these edges are made stiff enough to resist bending, the roof will be stressed by the dead weight of the edge members alone, acting just like the weight of the arches in Fig. 201.

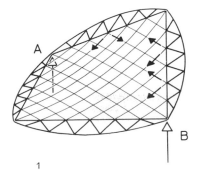

1

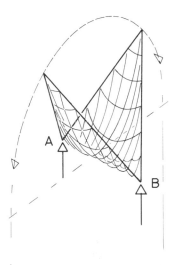

2

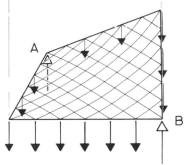

3

206.   Networks of cables stretched between the sides of a warped square (cut from an h.p.).
     1 If a network of cables is stretched over a warped square, the straight edges are stressed in bending.
     2 and 3 The cables are tensioned by loading and depressing the edges of the square. The loads are all concentrated in supports A and B.

In the French pavilion at the 1958 Brussels exhibition [152] the engineer Sarger has put these ideas to good use (Fig. 207). Two sets of oppositely curved cables are stretched across each of a pair of warped rhomboids. The basic form is an h.p. cut from the middle of the saddle (cf. Fig. 175.3). The cables are prestressed by the weight of the stiff edge members and the walls. The vertical reactions of the two rhomboids are concentrated at points A and B. Along the edges A-E and E-B the roof is tied down by a deep lattice girder, which projects above its surface, and by the outside walls. Here then, after being stressed, the cables exert forces directed vertically upwards. Or in other words, under the final loading the walls B-E are stressed in tension and the lattice girder A-E in upward bending. At first the edges F-A and F-B float freely. The stressing of the roof is complete when these edges deflect under the dead weight of the edge members and the stressing force in the exterior walls, acting together. The deflection at the point F due to stressing the cables was calculated to be about 50 cm. The network of cables weighs about 18 kg/m² including insulation and roofing. It spans a column-free area of about 12,000 m².

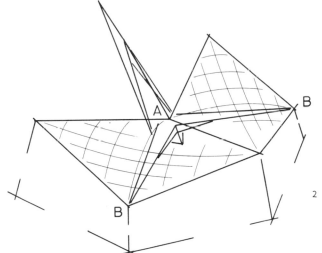

The forms which interest us here are primarily those of the doubly curved roof surfaces. Curves with large radii, however, find formal expression only at the edges, not within the surface itself. The edges are straight, but the important thing is that they are twisted into warped rhomboids. This leads to a seemingly arbitrary rise and fall of the rim of the roof, an irregular elevation, confused proportions and a general impression of wilfulness. The composition as a whole, determined as it is by h.p. surfaces with warped edges, strikes a very characteristic, structurally modulated note. Only a small minority of the visitors to the exhibition understood this. Moreover, as so often happens, in the rush to complete the work in time many details did not turn out as successfully as had been hoped and, measured against the gigantic scale of the building as a whole, these defects impressed themselves on the visitor more readily than the general form. The framework of the outside walls, for example, is structurally quite unnecessary. According to the original plan the outside walls functioned not as supports but as tensile elements. They were retained unchanged partly because of the rush to finish in time and partly to control the overturning tendency of the great lattice edge members. Viewed as the first attempt to erect a system of stressed cables over a rhombic h.p., this building is a notable, sweeping and consistent solution, which will doubtless exert a strong influence on the future development of structure and form.

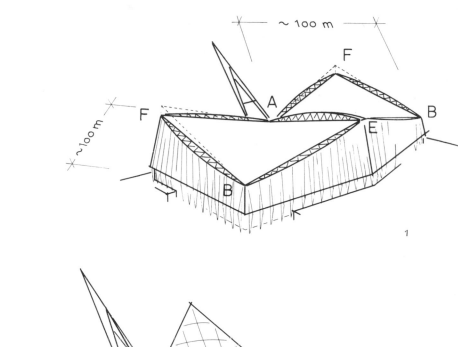

207.   The French Pavilion at the 1958 Brussels exhibition. Arch: Gillet. Eng: Sarger [152].
    1 Two h.p. rhomboids A-B-E-F are supported at points A and B only. The rigid edge members are subjected to vertical loads consisting of their own weight and the weight of the walls. Under the action of these loads the points marked F deflect about 50 cm.
    2 The cut-away view shows how the two h.p. rhomboids are supported at points A and B. The members A-B are designed to resist the horizontal tensile forces developed by the cable roof.

Sarger employed the same basic idea in his information pavilion in Brussels [123], to which we have already referred. In this case the "cable system" consists, rather interestingly, of several layers of wooden planks stressed in tension. The stressing force is derived from the load imposed by the foundations which are suspended from the edge of the roof by means of slender mullions. Thus, this structure too, though built of wood, must be regarded as a stressed roof. The slight deviation of the edges from the plane of the straight generatrixes of the h.p. makes the eaves appear gently curved. This both gives the structure a friendly and inviting air and at the same time, by introducing a certain amount of arch action, relieves the bending stresses in the edge members.

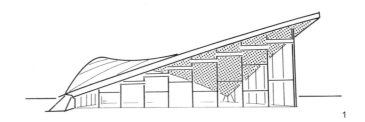

1

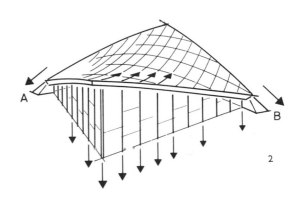

2

208. This information pavilion in Brussels [123] (cf. Fig. 185) may be regarded as a cable roof, since the material (glued boards) is subjected to tensile stresses in two directions like interlacing cables. Eng: Sarger.
      1 The mullions, acting in tension, transfer the weight of the foundations to the edge of the roof, where it exerts a prestressing force.
      2 Diagram showing the tensile forces in the mullions and the diagonal thrusts at points A and B, which determine the shape of the buttresses.

Combinations of Cables and Struts

A recent development is the appearance of various combinations of cables and struts, in which the tension in the cables is diverted through a series of intermediate compression members in such a way that the interplay of tensile and compressive forces produces three-dimensional rigidity. The physical results still lack coherence and it is not yet possible to identify this type of construction with a particular structural form. Accordingly, we shall do no more than briefly mention one or two of the more interesting known examples, and leave open the question whether a characteristic group of structural forms, though not yet recognizable, will eventually emerge.

The roof of the American pavilion at the 1958 Brussels exhibition [153] was nothing other than a great bicycle wheel 104 m in diameter, the steel rim of which rested on a circle of columns. In the center floated a drum-shaped "hub," supported by two sets of radially stressed cables, the "spokes." A surprising feature was the large opening in the middle—a direct consequence of the solution adopted—through which daylight entered. The shape was determined by elementary geometry. There was no sense of progress towards a structural form. The statical principle was obscured by the decorative treatment, especially by the unusual design of the exterior walls.

Elsewhere in the same exhibition stood an impressive mast [154], again a combination of cables and struts. This structure owed its stability to the interplay between the compression and bending in the rigid members, on the one hand, and the tension in the stressed cables, on the other. The work of Buckminster Fuller includes numerous compositions of a similar type [155]. Today the possible uses of such structures are still limited. It may be, however, that in the future conditions will be different. The more important flexibility, lightness and demountability become, the better the chances for systems employing stressed cables. Tensile stresses are always the most economical in material, and hence can be resisted by members of minimum weight.

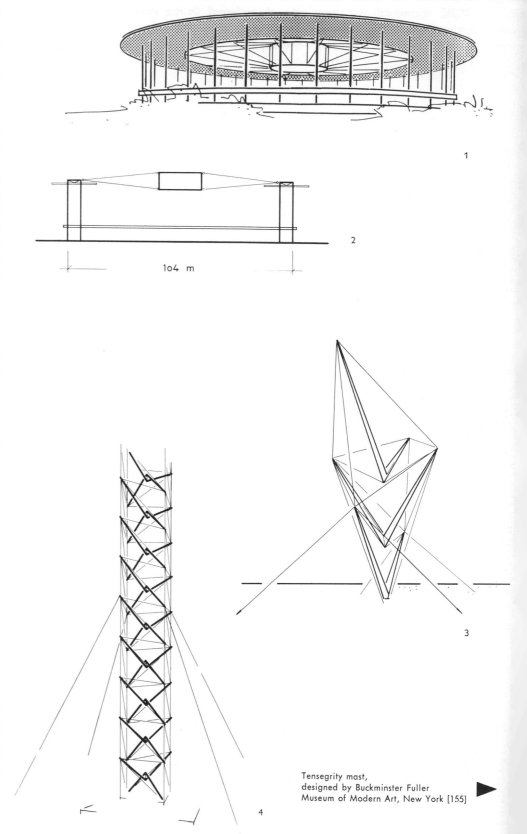

1

2

104 m

3

209.   Combinations of cables and struts:
   1 and 2 The American Pavilion at the 1958 Brussels exhibition is a huge bicycle wheel. A hollow drum, consisting of two tension rings separated by compression members, floats over the middle of the building, supported by cables stressed in tension. These cables connect the central drum with an outer compression ring, thus giving the structure three-dimensional stability.
   3 A rigid mast composed of V-shaped compression members and stressed cables (Brussels exhibition).
   4 A similar combination of struts and wires designed by Buckminster Fuller. In this case the components are prefabricated [155].

Tensegrity mast,
designed by Buckminster Fuller
Museum of Modern Art, New York [155]   ►

4

Tents

This brings us to the question of tents, the last of our groups of suspended or stressed roofs. First made from the skins of animals and later from woven fabrics, tents have been used by men since the earliest times. It is only recently, however, that they were rediscovered by the architect. In Germany Frei Otto [156] deserves the credit for drawing attention to the geometrical and technical problems of tent construction and to the attractive and elegant forms that can be achieved. Tent design is by no means just a game. It demands to be taken with the utmost seriousness and its problems are highly topical. There is no doubt that tent forms will be used increasingly in more ambitious architectural compositions. Tents are of special importance to a discussion of structural form, since the form of a tent is itself the structure. In no other type of construction does the form flow so spontaneously from the structural principle. Whereas we have previously concerned ourselves entirely with stressed or suspended cables and nets, we must now think in terms of woven fabric. Actually this means no more than a modification of the central idea, since woven fabric is really only a net with a very fine mesh. At the end of this section we shall again return to stressed cable construction, simply to pursue an association of forms. Since Frei Otto has himself written extensively on this subject [156] and given a comprehensive account of its architectural, structural and purely technical aspects, the author feels that it would serve no purpose to repeat here what is readily available at the source. He will merely attempt to summarize the main principles of tent construction and explain what they signify in terms of form.

Tents consist of stressed fabric. If they are not to flutter, that is, if they are to be as rigid as it is possible for them to be, the tent panels, when stressed, must be curved in two mutually opposed directions, i.e. they must obey the same laws as the doubly curved cable systems already discussed. Since doubly curved surfaces cannot be developed, the panels must be cut in such a way that they assume a double curvature after stressing. For example, the basic h.p. element, a convenient form for tent construction, has to be made up by joining strips that, rather than being parallel, taper from the edges towards the center.

Tents need to be supported by compression masts, arches or ribs, otherwise they cannot be properly stressed.

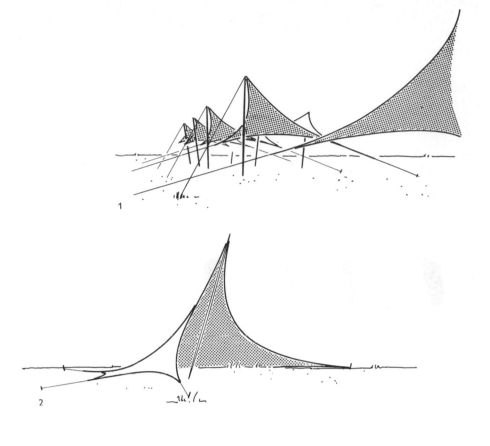

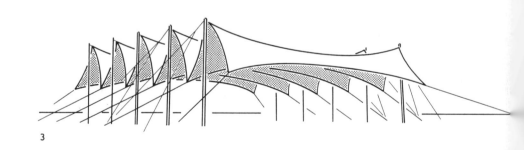

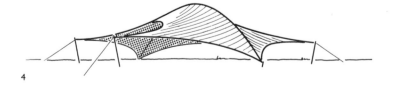

210.   Tents designed by Frei Otto [156]. In tent construction warped surfaces are indispensable.
   1 and 2 Masts and guy wires or
   3 counterstressed cables forming rigid gullies (cf. Fig. 204) or
   4 compression arches, over which tent-cloth is stretched, are the most effective means of stressing and stiffening canvas or plastic tent panels, which can only act in tension.

Tent over a dance floor, Cologne [156]
Arch: Frei Otto

There is an unlimited abundance of possible shapes. Designing them is more a job for an artist with a good sense of form than for a mathematician. In developing new forms, experiments on models can be extremely fruitful, while "exact" mathematical techniques are virtually useless. Fig. 210 gives a glimpse of a variety of forms typical of tent construction. There is no need for a specific discussion of structure in connection with tents, since form and structure are identical. Non-structural form is impossible as far as tents are concerned. Such tents would either flutter or lack stability.

Tent construction has already produced a very strong reaction among American architects. Saarinen's hockey stadium at Yale [157] is built on tent principles. A great reinforced concrete spine arches the entire length of the building to span about 85 m. The tent-like roof, suspended from this spine, assumes a form that is not geometrically pre-

Yale University hockey stadium, New Haven [157]
Arch: Saarinen ▶

determined. The initially slack roof cables are braced and stressed by superimposing a second set of cables running longitudinally. The stability of the roof depends on the state of stress thus induced. The resulting surface is curved in two mutually opposed directions. All the curves in the structure are "free" in the sense of our definition of "free forms" in the section on shells. They are neither severely geometrical nor purely arbitrary. They have the same natural beauty as the folds of a simple tent. We must, however, permit ourselves one critical observation: at the ends of the building the longitudinal cables develop a countercurvature without the curvature of the transverse cables being similarly reversed. This is an impossible arrangement for a system of stressed cables. In actual fact, at these points the longitudinal cables are attached to steel trusses concealed within the thickness of the roof. Without these trusses the countercurvature in the longitudinal direction would be a technical impossibility. Curvature in one direction without countercurvature in the other is incompatible with the principles of stressed cable construction. Since we are mainly concerned with structural form, this local discrepancy between external form and structure cannot be overlooked. In all other respects, however, the unusual shape of this building has been developed very consistently from the novel structural principle. The boldness of the treatment deserves the highest praise. The result is a structural form of great intrinsic worth.

It is not to be judged, as occasionally happens, simply on the basis of considerations of taste. The form and the structural content are one. This must be so and cannot be otherwise.

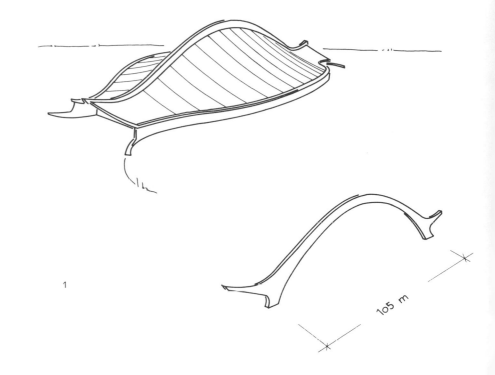

1

105 m

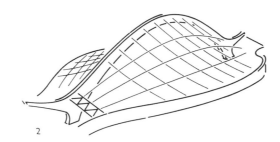

2

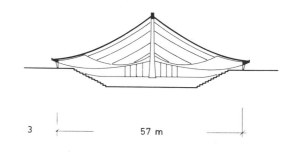

3   57 m

211.   Yale University hockey stadium, New Haven [157]. Arch: Saarinen. Eng: Severud, Elstad and Krueger.

   1 Like the tent in Fig. 210.4, a network of cables is stretched over a large reinforced concrete compression arch. The structural and formal analogy with tent construction is unmistakable.

   2 In cable construction it is not possible to end the main cables in a reversed curve without reversing the curvature of the transverse cables as well. Therefore auxiliary steel trusses have had to be added at the low points of the structure.

   3 The cross section shows that this forceful structural form is well adapted to the practical requirements of a stadium.

Let us again leaf through the pages of this book and allow images of the various forms to pass once more before our eyes. Suppose we fix our attention on the forms that seem especially typical and representative of a broad group of related structures. Perhaps we shall recall most vividly the severe rectangularity of skeleton construction (page 12), Candela's shells (pages 253-266), Maillart's bridges (pages 160-167) or the folded plates of the Unesco Congress Hall (pages 204-205). If we then try to merge these visual impressions into a unified image of structural form, we shall soon have to confess our inability to do so. The resources of the modern builder are far too great and the themes of the modern, international architect far too diversified. In fact, contemporary building forms do not suggest a unified image of the kind we associate with historical styles of architecture.

What we do find is a gay variety of structural forms, characterized by complex interrelationships. Sometimes, indeed, a form of perfectly definite origin will suddenly reappear in a different place and in an entirely different context. Consider, for example, the V-support, a form derived from the tapered leg of a rigid frame, which turns up again, inverted, as a three-pronged forked column in Castiglioni's design for the Naples railroad station (page 172) or, combined with cantilevers in the Caracas stadium (page 130). Similarly, the elementary principle of the simple cylindrical shell, long confined exclusively to roof construction, has suddenly, thanks to a stroke of genius, been applied to the design of a skyscraper, decisively influencing the entire architectural concept (page 220).

Of course, a trained observer, who knows what he is about, can detect a definite order in this seeming confusion. For him all structural forms, no matter how disparate they may appear, have the same rational origin. For him they are all evidence of the logic and necessity of good technical design that respects the nature of the materials with which we build. He finds them all conceived in the same spirit.

The untrained, however, who rely primarily on immediate visual impressions, will not be able to perceive relationships between structural forms directly. Approaching the problem by way of the outward image, they remain ignorant of the inner structural analogies linking seemingly unrelated forms. How are they to impose any unity on such profusion?

This question brings us to one of the most important points about structure:

> Modern structural form cannot be fully appreciated without some "technical knowledge."

These unequivocal demands on the intellect, though they do not prevent structural form from being raised to the level of art, point emphatically to its place in a technological world.

> Another important characteristic of structural form is its independence of all "trends" and "new directions" in architecture.

These "new directions," as the "school" of Mies van der Rohe, on the one hand, and so-called "organic architecture," on the other, are so eagerly labeled, have no claim to a monopoly of structural form, though, in principle, it cannot be denied that they sometimes make use of it. It is quite wrong and short-sighted to think of a "structural" architecture as one in which the right-angle predominates, while dismissing an architecture of free forms as "non-structural." The repetition of certain formal relationships (pitched or flat roofs, angular or rounded forms), which so impresses the observer, especially the layman, as a "new direction" or the expression of a novel architectural approach (to avoid the use of both "style" and "fashion"), really has nothing to do with the presence or absence of structural form. Every architectural trend is characterized by numerous examples of structural form, both genuine and spurious.

These two points are of vital importance in evaluating the role of structural form in modern architecture. They can be formulated more concisely as follows.

Structural form is not born of simple intuition alone. To discover and shape it, even for a mere observer to understand it, technical knowledge is required.

Structural form is not tied to any narrow trend in modern architecture. Its principles lie deeper; they are discernible in the architecture of the past and have now spread throughout the world, without being confined to any particular "school."

The fact that structural form has an indispensable intellectual component and is independent of the humanistic currents, with which certain "movements" in modern architecture are (not always rightly) identified, leads too easily to the conclusion that, in the last analysis, structural form is "just" a rationally evolved, utilitarian affair, properly the business of the engineer and lying somewhere outside the domain of art, while architecture, as an art, is exalted above structural form, which it should, indeed must surpass.

It is impossible to argue away the fact that structural form is an essential element of modern architecture, but the kind of attitude described above does lead to the sort of pseudo structure [pages 72-75, 119, 278 (Fig. 195), 292] that not infrequently shows modern architecture in a rather dubious light.

It would be wrong to rush to the other extreme and confuse structural form with the architectural statement itself. Nothing could be more foolish than to maintain that good construction alone is enough to constitute architecture, and nothing could be more misconceived than to try to make structural form a sort of fashion or architectural trend. Structural form is a means of architectural expression typical of our times. It springs from a perfectly definite conception of the design process that recognizes natural order as the supreme law. As a means of expression it is comparable with language. Like the latter, it can swamp even the best ideas, leaving them misunderstood and neglected. At the same time, however, it can elevate an essentially modest statement to the level of a work of art with ultimate clarity and distinction.

If this goal is to be achieved, if structural form is to become a purifying, ordering and constructive principle of modern architecture, we shall need to improve our understanding of its technical basis and achieve a profounder insight into its essential nature. Since structural form is a product of the region where the activities of the architect and the engineer touch and overlap, good will and studious endeavor will be required of both. Otherwise, as we well know, the result will be either mere form or mere structure. Only by restoring lost contact, embracing a common goal and collaborating in the solution of common problems shall we arrive at what is truly meant by structural form.

[1] *Kunstgewerbliche Laienpredigten*, see Henry van de Velde: *Zum neuen Stil*. Selected from his writings by Hans Curjel (Piper-Verlag) p. 125.

[2] *Baukunst und Werkform* 1953, No. 6, p. 276.

[3] Gio Ponti: *Espressione dell' edificio Pirelli in costruzione a Milano*, published in *Domus*, No. 316, p. 1 ff.

[4] Office building in Rome. Arch: Luccichenti. From information supplied by the architect.

[5] Corner of the Alumni Memorial Hall, Illinois Institute of Technology, Chicago. Arch: Mies v. d. Rohe. In P. Johnson: *Mies van der Rohe* (Verlag Hatje, Stuttgart), p. 154.

[6] Volkswagen repair shop, Brunswick. Arch: F. W. Kraemer, in *Bauen und Wohnen* 1956, No. 5, p. 165.

[7] Lever Building, New York. Arch: Skidmore, Owings and Merrill, Bunshaft. Eng: Weiskopf and Pickworth. In *Architectural Forum* 1952, No. 6, p. 101; *l'architecture d'aujourd'hui*, No. 50-51, p. 34; *Bauen und Wohnen* 1952; No. 7, p. 306; *Werk* 1954, No. 2, p. 49; *Bauingenieur* 1952, No. 10, p. 371; J. Joedicke: *Office Buildings*, p. 110 (Crosby Lockwood & Son Ltd., London)

[8] German Pavilion at the 1958 Brussels exhibition. Arch: Eiermann, Ruf. *Bauwelt* 1958, No. 31, p. 757; *l'architecture d'aujourd'hui*, No. 78, p. 16.

[9] General Motors Technical Center, Warren/Detroit. Arch: Eero Saarinen and Assoc., Smith, Hinchman and Grills. Published in Joedicke: *Office Buildings*, pp. 58, 96, 204 (Crosby Lockwood & Son Ltd., London); *l'architecture d'aujourd'hui* No. 50-51, p. 49 and No. 69, p. 88; *Architectural Forum* 1956, No. 5, p. 123; 1956, No. 7, p. 49; 1956, No. 11, p. 51 and 1956, No. 12, p. 56; *Architectural Record* 1956, No. 5, p. 151; *Bauen und Wohnen* 1956, No. 5, p. 145.

[10] Office building in London. Arch: Gollins, Melvin, Ward and Partners. In *Architectural Review*, No. 728, Sept. 1957, p. 175; *Architectural Design* 1958, No. 7; Dennatt: *Modern Architecture in Britain* (Batsford Ltd.), p. 63.

[11] Inland Steel Co. Building, Chicago. Arch: Skidmore, Owings and Merrill, New York. In *Architectural Forum* 1955, No. 5, p. 155 and 1958, No. 4, p. 88; *Engineering News Record* Jan. 1957, p. 42; *Baukunst und Werkform* 1957, No. 4, p. 206; *Architectural Record* 1958, No. 4, p. 169.

[12] Hart: *Skelettbauten* (Callwey-Verlag), p. 36.

[13] Olivetti Building, Milan. Arch: Bernasconi, Fiocchi, Nizzoli. In *l'architecture d'aujourd'hui*, No. 58, p. 52; *Bauen und Wohnen* 1956, No. 1, p. 11; *Domus*, No. 305, p. 53.

[14] Technical school in Berne. Arch: H. Brechbuhler. In Volkart: *Schweizer Architektur* (Otto Maier Verlag, Ravensburg), p. 110. Bill: *Moderner Schweizer Architektur 1925-1945* (Karl Werner Verlag, Zurich).

[15] Ruins of the Cistercian Abbey, Heisterbach. Founded 1202, choir and transept consecrated 1227, general consecration 1237, architect unknown. Secularized in 1803 and sold for demolition. The choir is still standing, because the demolition shots failed. In *Reclam's Kunstführer, Baudenkmäler in Rheinland und Westfalen*, Vol. 3, Stuttgart 1959. Egid Beitz: *Kloster Heisterbach* (1926).

[16] The Pilgrims' Basilica in Lourdes. Arch: P. Vago. In *l'architecture d'aujourd'hui*, No. 81, pp. 46-55.

[17] Platform underpass, Duisburg, Germany. From the drawings of the contractors, Johannes Dörnen, Dortmund-Derne. Prewar riveted structure destroyed. Welded structure: 1950-51. Bridges of similar design: Helmstedter Strasse underpass, Brunswick; Hamburg-Harburg railroad bridge. See *Bauingenieur* 1956, No. 11, p. 397.

[18] Unesco Building, Paris. Arch: Zehrfuss, Breuer, Nervi. Reviewed in *Baukunst und Werkform* 1956, No. 10, p. 556; *Bauwelt* 1956, No. 48, p. 1132; *l'architecture d'aujourd'hui*, No. 47, p. 77 and No. 58, p. 26; *Architectural Forum* 1958, No. 12, p. 81; *Architectural Record* 1958, No. 11, p. 14; Rogers: *P. L. Nervi—Bauten und Projekte* (Verlag Hatje, Stuttgart), p. 110.

[19] Unité d'Habitation, Marseilles. Arch: Le Corbusier, A. Wogensky. Eng: V. Bodiansky. In *l'architecture d'aujourd'hui*, No. 46, p. 12; *Architectural Forum* 1954, No. 3, p. 156; *Werk* 1954, No. 1, p. 20; *l'Homme et l'Architecture*, special number 11-14, 1947.

[20] Stuttgart TV-Tower. Eng: F. Leonhardt. In Leonhardt: *Der Stuttgarter Fernsehturm*; *Beton und Stahlbetonbau* 1956, No. 4, p. 73 and No. 5, p. 104.

[21] Pierelli Building, Milan. Arch: Ponti, Fornaroli, Rosselli. Eng: Nervi. In Ponti: *Espressione dell' edificio Pirelli in costruzione a Milano*, in *Domus*, No. 316, p. 1 ff.; *Baukunst und Werkform* 1957, No. 4, p. 204; Joedicke: *Office Buildings* (Crosby Lockwood Ltd., London), p. 73.

[22] School in Cataguazes, Brazil, canopy. Arch: O. Niemeyer. Eng: A. Froufe. In Papadaki: *The Work of Oscar Niemeyer* (Reinhold Publishing Corporation, New York), p. 153.

[23] Unité d'Habitation, Nantes-Rezé, France. Arch: Le Corbusier. In *Bauen und Wohnen* 1957, No. 1, p. 1; *l'architecture d'aujourd'hui*, No. 66, p. 2.
Unité d'Habitation, Berlin. Arch: Le Corbusier. See Hermann: *Über die Konstruktion und Ausführung des Wohnhochhauses Le Carbusier in Berlin*, in *Beton und Stahlbetonbau* 1958, No. 8, p. 202; *Le Corbusiers Wohneinheit Typ Berlin*, published by F. Muller-Reppen (Verlag fur Fachliteratur, Berlin-Grunewald).

[24] Florence stadium, grandstand. Eng: Nervi. In Rogers: *P. L. Nervi—Bauten und Projekte* (Verlag Hatje, Stuttgart), p. 4; P. L. Nervi: *Costruire Correttamente* (Hoepli-Verlag, Milan), plates I-VI.

[25] Rosenau stadium, Augsburg. Designed by the Augsburg City Planning Board. In *Bauen und Wohnen* 1952, No. 9, p. 425.

[26] St. Jakob football stadium in Basle. Arch: J. Gass and W. Boos. Eng: E. B. Geering. In *Werk* 1954, No. 10, p. 389.

[27] University stadium Caracas, Venezuela. Arch: C. Villanueva. Contractors: Christiani and Nielsen. In *Architectural Forum* 1954, No. 11, p. 155; H. R. Hitchcock: *Latin American Architecture Since 1945* (Museum of Modern Art, New York), p. 94.

[28] Municipal stadium, Rabat, Morocco. Arch: J. Foccoll, J. Chemineau. In *l'architecture d'aujourd'hui*, No. 47, p. XV and No. 55, p. 68.

[29] The Rohrdamm Bridge, Berlin. See Heusel: *Die Spannbetonbrücken Berlins*, in *Beton und Stahlbetonbau* 1958, No. 5, p. 97.

[30] M. Viollet-le-Duc: *Entretiens sur l'architecture*. Atlas, plate XXI, Paris 1864.

[31] Filling station in Sesto San Giovanni, Milan. Arch: Favini. From information supplied by the architect.

[32] Dome of Discovery, London. Arch: Ketchum, Gina, Sharp. Eng: Tubbs, Freeman, Fox. In *Architectural Forum* 1952, No. 9, p. 156; *l'architecture d'aujourd'hui*, No. 29, p. 65 and No. 39, p. 16.

[33] Sul America hospital, Rio de Janeiro. Arch: Niemeyer and Uchoa. In *l'architecture d'aujourd'hui*, No. 62, p. 76.

[34] Apartment house in the Hansa district of Berlin. Arch: O. Niemeyer. See Georg Zahel: *Das Verhalten der Fundamente beim Niemeyer-Bau*, in *Bauwelt* 1958, No. 6, p. 132; G. Biermann: *Der statische Gedanke des Niemeyer-Hauses—*

Entwicklung und Ausführung, in Bauwelt 1958, No. 10, p. 230; C. Siegel: Die Gabelstützen am Niemeyer-Haus in Berlin, in Bauwelt 1959, No. 1, p. 9

[35] Apartment building in Belo Horizonte, Brasil. Arch: O. Niemeyer. In l'architecture d'aujourd'hui, No. 52, p. 26.

[36] Apartment house development, "Groupe Queliverzan", in Brest, France. Arch: Graveraux, Lopez. In l'architecture d'aujourd'hui, No. 46, p. 25.

[37] Rubber factory in Brynmawr, Wales. Arch: Architects' Cooperative Partnership. Eng: O. Arup and Partners. In Architectural Forum 1952, No. 5, p. 142; Bauen und Wohnen 1952, No. 5, p. 254; l'architecture d'aujourd'hui, No. 39, p. 64.

[38] Herdez factory, Mexico City. Eng: Felix Candela. In l'architecture d'aujourd'hui, No. 64, p. 42.

[39] Prestressed concrete railroad bridge over the Rhône near La Voulte, France. In Beton und Stahlbetonbau 1958, No. 1, p. 16.

[40] Birsfelden power station, Switzerland. Arch: H. Hofman. Eng: A. Aegerter and O. Bosshard. In Werk 1953, No. 2, p. 65; l'architecture d'aujourd'hui, No. 75, p. 82.

[41] Olympic sports palace (Palazetto), Rome. Arch: Vitellozzi. Eng: P. L. Nervi. In Architectural Forum 1958, No. 3, p. 83; l'architecture d'aujourd'hui, No. 76, p. 28; Bauingenieur 1959, No. 4, p. 165; Architectural Record 1958, No. 5, pp. 207-209.

[42] Central Garage, St. Gallen, Switzerland. Arch: Brantschen. Eng: Scheitlin, Hotz und Zahner. In Werk 1955, No. 10, p. 308.

[43] Road bridge at Baden-Baden. See Lämmlein: Hochbrücke über das Oostal bei Baden-Baden, in Beton-und Stahlbetonbau 1959, No. 7, p. 161, and No. 8, p. 197.

[44] Road bridge over the Arve, Champel-Vessy, near Geneva. Eng: Robert Maillart. See Bill: Robert Maillart (Verlag fur Architektur, Zurich), p. 118 ff.

[45] Aircraft hangars at Orbetello, Orvieto and Torre del Lago, Italy (1938-1942). Eng: Nervi. In Rogers: Pier Luigi Nervi—Bauten und Projekte (Verlag Hatje, Stuttgart), p. 36; P. L. Nervi: Costruire Correttamente (Hoepli-Verlag, Milan), plates VII-IX, XVIII-XXI; P. L. Nervi: L'architecture du béton armé et le problème des coffrages, in l'architecture d'aujourd'hui, No. 48, p. 68; Architectural Forum 1953, No. 11, p. 146; J. Joedicke: Pier Luigi Nervi, Ein Gestalter des Stahlbetons, in Baukunst und Werkform 1956, No. 10, p. 550.

[46] Proposal for a church in Montecatini, Italy. Arch: E. Castiglioni. See G. C. Ortelli: Opere di Enrico Castiglioni, in l'architettura 1955, No. 11-12.

[47] Robert Maillart, Swiss engineer, 1872-1940. A thorough appraisal of his work can be found in Bill: Robert Maillart (Verlag für Architektur, Erlenbach-Zürich) and "Robert Maillart", a special publication of the Schweizer Verband für Materialprüfungen der Technik, Zurich 1940.

[48] See "Robert Maillart", Schweizer Verband für Materialprüfungen der Technik, Zurich 1940, p. 6.

[49] War memorial, Milwaukee, Wis. Arch: Eero Saarinen. Eng: Ammann and Whitney, in l'architecture d'aujourd'hui, No. 85, p. 26; Architectural Forum 1957, No. 12, p. 144.

[50] See Architectural Record 1948, No. 7, p. 88.

[51] Naples railroad station competition, design entered by E. Castiglioni, in l'architecture d'aujourd'hui, No. 64, p. 10.

[52] Mannheim National Theater competition, design entered by Mies van der Rohe, in l'architecture d'aujourd'hui, No. 52, p. 94 and No. 79, p. 66; Architectural Forum 1953, No. 7, p. 129.

[53] Human hip bone. See Kummer: Bauprinzipien des Säugerskeletts (Thieme Verlag, Stuttgart). For further references see ibid.

[54] Steel and aluminum scaffolding. From information supplied by the Mannesmann-Leichtbau-G.m.b.H., Munich.

[55] Mero system, steel scaffolding. From information supplied by the Dr.-Ing. Mengeringhausen Co., Würzburg.

[56] Exhibition "The City of Tomorrow", Berlin INTERBAU 1957. Arch: Karl Otto. In Bauwelt 1957, No. 30, p. 762.

[57] Unistrut system. From information supplied by the Unistrut Corp., Wayne, Mich. Articles in Architectural Forum 1955, No. 7, p. 141; l'architecture d'aujourd'hui, No. 64, p. 84.

[58] Jay-Cee public recreation pavilion, Wayne, Mich. From information supplied by the Unistrut Corp., Wayne, Mich.

[59] Convention Hall, Chicago (proposal). Arch: Mies van der Rohe. In Architectural Forum 1953, No. 12, p. 43; l'architecture d'aujourd'hui, No. 55, p. 10.

[60] Aircraft hangar (proposal), designed by K. Wachsmann. See K. Wachsmann: The Turning Point of Building (Reinhold Publishing Corporation, New York); Hans Curjel: Ein Beispiel dreidimensionaler Architektur, in Werk 1954, No. 10, p. 377; Baukunst und Werkform 1954, No. 9, p. 549.

[61] Fence around the Casa della Cultura, Busto Arsizio, Italy. From information supplied by the architect, Enrico Castiglioni, illustrated in G. C. Ortelli: Opere di Enrico Castiglioni, in l'architettura 1955, No. 11-12, and R. Castiglioni: Il significato dell' architettura (Milan).

[62] Central markets in Frankfurt-am-Main and Budapest. See Dischinger: Die weitere

Entwicklung der Schalenbauweise "Zeiss-Dywidag", in Beton und Eisen 1932, No. 7-14.

[63] The Jena planetarium. See Dischinger: Fortschritte im Bau von Massivkuppeln, in Bauingenieur 1925, No. 10, p. 362.

[64] For information on R. Buckminster Fuller's domes see—R. W. Marks: The Dymaxion World of Buckminster Fuller (Reinhold, New York); Mc. Hall: Buckminster Fuller, in Architectural Review, No. 714, 1956, 7, p. 13; l'architecture d'aujourd'hui, No. 50-51, p. 122; Architectural Forum 1956, No. 1, p. 149 and No. 11, p. 158; Bauwelt 1958, No. 52, p. 1266; Baukunst und Werkform 1960, No. 1, p. 23; l'architecture d'aujourd'hui, No. 83, p. 58.
Ford rotunda dome, Detroit. Arch: Buckminster Fuller and Sanborn Brown. Eng: Lancomer and Mauser. In R. W. Marks: The Dymaxion World of Buckminster Fuller (Reinhold, New York), pp. 165-169; Architectural Forum 1953, No. 5, p. 109.

[65] Hydrotechnical Institute, Haifa, Israel. Arch: Weinraub and Mansfield. In l'architecture d'aujourd'hui, No. 77, p. 81.

[66] St. John's Abbey, Collegeville. Arch: M. Breuer. Eng: Nervi, Farkas, Barron. In Bauen und Wohnen 1958, No. 11, p. 370; Architectural Forum 1954, No. 7, p. 148; prospectus of the Universal Atlas Cement Co., New York.

[67] Sports arena in Pavia, Italy (proposal). Arch: A. Belloni. Eng: F. Breva. In Domus, No. 296, p. 12.

[68] The McGregor Memorial Conference Center, Detroit. Arch: M. Yamasaki and Assoc. Eng: Ammann and Whitney. In Architectural Record 1957, No. 5, p. 178; l'architecture d'aujourd'hui, No. 89, p. 60.
Sarger. In l'architecture d'aujourd'hui, No. 64, p. 20. Further details from the engineers' drawings.

[69] Church in Royan, France. Arch: G. Gillet and M. Hebrard. Eng: B. Laffaille, R. Sarger. In l'architecture d'aujourd'hui, No. 64, p. 20. Further details from the engineers' drawings.

[70] Sears Tampa store, Tampa, Florida. Arch: Weed, Russell, Johnson and Assoc. Eng: Ammann and Whitney. See Raafat: Reinforced Concrete in Architecture (Reinhold, New York), p. 154 and Architectural Forum 1958, No. 7, p. 90.

[71] See Girkmann: Flächentragwerke, 5th ed. (Springer Verlag), ch. 179, p. 419.

[72] Lower Saxony stadium, Hanover. Arch: Building Department of the City of Hanover. Eng: Goemann. See Bay: Vorgespanntes Tribünendach im Stadion Hanover, in Beton und Stahlbetonbau 1955, No. 4, p. 118; l'architecture d'aujourd'hui, No. 76, p. 3.

[73] Baseball stadium, Cartagena, Colombia. Arch: Solano, Gaitán, Ortega, Burbano. Eng: González. In Architectural Record 1948, No. 7, p. 88; H. R. Hitchcock: Latin American Architecture Since 1945 (Museum of Modern Art, New York), p. 98.

[74] Bus station, Bogota, Columbia. Arch: Ortega and Solano. Eng: González. In l'architecture d'aujourd'hui, No. 64, p. 28; Architectural Forum 1954, No. 8; H. R. Hitchcock: Latin American Architecture Since 1945 (Museum of Modern Art, New York), p .102.

[75] Toronto City Hall (proposal). Arch: V. Revell. In Bauen und Wohnen 1959, No. 3, p. 95.

[76] Water tank in Egypt. See Mortada: Der Stahlbetonbau in Ägypten, in Beton und Stahlbetonbau 1952, No. 12, 282.

[77] Water tank in Caen, France. Arch: Gillet. Eng: Sarger. In l'architecture d'aujourd'hui, No. 66, p. XXXVII, supplemented by the engineers' drawings.

[78] Design for "Tomorrow's Auditorium". Arch. The Architects' Collaborative, Cambridge, Mass. Eng: Weidlinger and Salvadori. In Baukunst und Werkform 1957, No. 12, p. 709; prospectus of the Universal Atlas Cement Co., New York.

[79] Priory of St. Louis and St. Mary, St. Louis (proposal). Arch: Hellmuth, Obata and Kassabaum. Eng: Weidlinger. Consultant: Nervi. In Progressive Architecture 1958, No. 1 and No. 10, p. 129.

[80] Central market, Cologne. See Dischinger: Die weitere Entwicklung der Schalenbauweise "Zeiss-Dywidag", in Beton und Eisen 1932, No. 7-14.

[81] Textile mill, Gossau, Switzerland. Arch: Danzeisen and Voser. Eng: Hossdorf. In Werk 1954, No. 7, p. 288; l'architecture d'aujourd'hui, No. 64, p. 35.

[82] Cement hall at the 1939 Zurich exhibition. Arch: H. Lenzinger. Eng: R. Maillart. See Max Bill: Robert Maillart (Verlag für Architektur, Erlenbach-Zürich), p. 170; "Robert Maillart", a special publication of the Schweizer Verband für Materialprüfungen der Technik, Zurich 1940.

[83] Flower market, Pescia, Italy. Arch: Gorri, Ricci and Savidi. Eng: Brizzi. In Architectural Forum 1953, No. 2, p. 156; l'architecture d'aujourd'hui, No. 70, p. 78.

[84] St. Louis airport. Arch: Hellmuth, Yamasaki, Leinweber. Eng: W. C. E. Becker, E. Contini. In Architectural Forum 1952, No. 11, p. 134 and 1956, No. 5, p. 107; l'architecture d'aujourd'hui, No. 55, p. 18; Bauingenieur 1958, No. 2, p. 73; Architectural Record 1956, No. 4, p. 195.

[85] Parke-Davis store, Menlo Park, Cal. Arch: Yamasaki, Leinweber and Assoc. Eng: Ammann and Whitney. In Architectural Forum 1957, No. 12, p. 38; Architectural Record 1958, No. 6, p. 17.

[86] Central markets in Basle and Leipzig. See Dischinger: *Die Theorie der Vieleck-kuppeln und die Zusammenhänge mit den einbeschriebenen Rotationsschalen*, in *Beton und Eisen* 1929, No. 5-9.

[87] Covered market in Tressanti, Italy (proposal). Arch: G. Vaccaro. In *Domus*, No. 306, p. 2.

[88] Design for "Tomorrow's Airport". Arch: Victor Gruen Assoc. In *Progressive Architecture* 1957, No. 12, p. 108; prospectus of the Universal Atlas Cement Co., New York.

[89] Hangar at Marignane, France. Eng: N. Esquillan. In *l'architecture d'aujourd'hui*, No. 47, p. 14; *Beton und Stahlbetonbau* 1952, No. 7, p. 172.

[90] Design for "Tomorrow's Multi-Purpose Building". Eng: K. P. Billner, B. A. Anderson. Prospectus of the Universal Atlas Cement Co., New York.

[91] Centre National des Industries et des Techniques, Paris. Arch: Camelot, de Mailly, Zehrfuss. Eng: Nervi, Prouvé. See Esquillan: "*Palais des Expositions au Centre National des Industries et des Techniques à Paris*", International Colloquium on Construction Processes of Shell Structures, Madrid 1959, No. a-16. Esquillan: "*Palais des Expositions au Centre National des Industries et des Techniques à Paris*", special publication of the Association Scientifique de la Précontrainte, 6, rue Paul Valéry, Paris. Other articles in *l'architecture d'aujourd'hui*, No. 64, p. 54 and No. 83, p. 8; *Beton und Stahlbetonbau* 1958, No. 9, p. 231.

[92] Design for a stadium. Arch: Raymond and Rado. Eng: Weidlinger and Salvadori. See *Architectural Forum* 1956, No. 11; Raafat: *Reinforced Concrete in Architecture* (Reinhold, New York), p. 166; prospectus of the Universal Atlas Cement Co., New York.

[93] Frauenkirche, Dresden, built by G. Bahr. Built 1726-1743, burned out 1945.

[94] Market, Sidi Bel Abbes, Algeria. Arch: M. J. Mauri. Eng: Considéré and Caquot. In *l'architecture d'aujourd'hui*, No. 60, p. 28 and No. 64, p. 49.

[95] Gymnasium in Porto, Portugal. Arch: J. Loureiro. Eng: A. dos Santos Soares. In *l'architecture d'aujourd'hui*, No. 58, p. XVI; *Architectural Forum* 1956, No. 5, p. 159.

[96] Convention hall in Tokyo. Arch: K. Tange. Eng: Y. Tsuboi. In *Architectural Forum* 1955, No. 7, p. 159.

[97] Basilica in Algiers. Arch: Le Couteur and P. Herbé. Eng: Sarger. In *l'architecture d'aujourd'hui*, No. 64, p. XIII; supplemented by information provided by the engineer.

[98] Water tower in Livorno, Italy (proposal). Arch. and eng.: R. Morandi. See Piccinato: *Strutture di Calce struzzo armato e di Calce struzzo precompresso de Ricardo Morandi* (Rome 1954), reviewed in *l'architecture d'aujourd'hui*, No. 55, p. XIII.

[99] Synagogue of the University of Jerusalem. Arch: Ezra Rau. In *l'architecture d'aujourd'hui*, No. 77, p. 77; *Architectural Forum* 1958, No. 7, p. 167; *Baukunst und Werkform* 1960, No. 1, p. 14.

[100] Liquidity tanks. Built by Chicago Bridge and Iron Co. In Torroja: *Philosophy of Structures* (Univ. of California Press), p. 291; see also Flügge: *Statik und Dinamik der Schalen*, 2nd ed. (Springer-Verlag), p. 39.

[101] Wind tunnel, Berlin-Adlershof. Arch: W. Deutschmann, H. Brenner. See Joedicke: *Geshichte der modernen Architektur* (Verlag Hatje, Stuttgart), p. 144.

[102] Settling tanks, Frankfurt-am-Main. See Lücking: *Neue Gesichtspunkte für die konstruktive Ausbildung von Faulbehältern*, in *Der Bau* 1957, No. 19, p. 583.

[103] Dyckerhoff and Widmann experimental shell. See Dischinger: *Weitgespannte Tragwerke*, in *Bauingenieur* 1949, No. 7, p. 193.

[104] Rubber factory, Brynmawr, Wales. Arch: Architect's Cooperative Partnership. Eng. O. Arup and Partners. In *Architectural Forum* 1952, No. 5, p. 142; *Bauen und Wohnen* 1952, No. 5, p. 254; *l'architecture d'aujourd'hui*, No. 39, p. 64.

[105] Exhibition halls, Belgrade, Jugoslavia. Arch: M. Pantovic. Eng: Kostanievac. In *l'architecture d'aujourd'hui*, No. 78, p. XVIII. *Bauingenieur* 1958, No. 8, p. 299.

[106] M.I.T. auditorium, Cambridge, Mass. Arch: Saarinen and Assoc. See *l'architecture d'aujourd'hui*, No. 50-51, p. 48 and No. 64, p. 50; *Architectural Forum* 1953, No. 1, p. 127.

[107] Nakashima residence, New Hope, Penn. Arch: G. Nakashima. Eng: Weidlinger and Salvadori. In *Architectural Record* 1957, No. 11, p. 183; *Engineering News Record* 1957, No. 5 Dec., p. 46.

[108] University cosmic-ray pavilion, Mexico City. Arch: G. Reyna. Eng: F. Candela. In *Architectural Forum* 1952, No. 9, p. 104; *Baukunst und Werkform* 1954, No. 11, p. 693 and 1958, No. 8, p. 439; *l'architecture d'aujourd'hui*, No. 59, p. 15.

[109] Catalano residence, Raleigh, N.C. Arch: E. F. Catalano. In *l'architecture d'aujourd'hui*, No. 64, p. XXIII.

[110] Church in Coyoacan, Mexico. Arch: E. de la Mora. Eng: F. Candela. In *l'architecture d'aujourd'hui*, No. 64, p. 25.

[111] Congress hall in Shizuoka, Japan. Arch: K. Tange and Y. Tsuboi. In *l'architecture d'aujourd'hui*, No. 76, p. 23; *Bauwelt* 1958, No. 23, p. 541.

[112] Experimental roof of the School of Engineering and Architecture, Kansas University, Lawrence. See W. Strode and D. L. Dean: *Design, Construction and Testing of a Plywood Hyperbolic Paraboloid Lattice Structure* (Univ. of Kansas Publications, The Bulletin of Engineering and Architecture, No. 41).

[113] Girls Grammar School, London. Arch: Chamberlin, Powell and Bon. See A. R. Flint and A. E. Low: *The construction of hyperbolic paraboloid type shells without temporary formwork*. International Colloquium on Construction Processes of Shell Structures, Madrid 1959, No. a-15; *Bauen und Wohnen* 1958, No. 10, p. 349.

[114] "Mid-City" shopping center, Denver, Col. Arch: M. I. Pei and Assoc. Consulting Eng: Roberts and Schafer. In *Architectural Forum* 1958, No. 7, p. 110; *Architectural Record* 1958, No. 2, p. 229; *l'architecture d'aujourd'hui*, No. 83, p. 43.

[115] Texas Instruments, Inc., Dallas, Texas. Arch: O'Neil Ford and R. Colley. Eng: Wilkerson. Shell design. Candela. In *Architectural Forum* 1956, No. 12 and 1958, No. 9, p. 132; *Architectural Record* 1958, No. 9, p. 238.

[116] Lederle Laboratories, Mexico. Eng: F. Candela. In *l'architecture d'aujourd'hui*, No. 64, p. 42.

[117] Market in Caserta, Italy. Eng: Baroni. In *Architectural Forum* 1953, No. 1, p. 151.

[118] Shopping center in Mexico. Eng: F. Candela. In *l'architecture d'adjourd'hui*, No. 64, p. 43; Raafat: *Reinforced Concrete in Architecture* (Reinhold, New York), p. 142.

[119] Church de la Virgin Milagrosa, Mexico. Arch: De la Mora. Eng. F. Candela. In *l'architecture d'aujourd'hui*, No. 64, p. 22; *Architectural Forum* 1954, No. 8; *Architectural Record* 1958, No. 7, p. 191; *l'architettura* Nos. 19 and 20.

[120] See Candela: *Les voutes minces et l'espace architectural*, in *l'architecture d'aujourd'hui*, No. 64, p. 22.

[121] See *l'architecture d'aujourd'hui*, No. 64, p. 22.

[122] Philips pavilion at the 1958 Brussels exhibition. Arch: Le Corbusier and Xenakis. In *l'architecture d'aujourd'hui*, No. 78, p. 14; *Bauwelt* 1958, No. 1, p. 3; detailed structural information in *Philips Technische Rundschau*, 20, No. 2, pp. 33-68 and No. 3/4, pp. 69-82, extracts in *Bauen und Wohnen* 1959, No. 8, p. VIII and No. 9, p. IX.

[123] Information center in Brussels. Arch: Baucher, Blondel, Filippone. Eng: Sarger. In *l'architecture d'aujourd'hui*, No. 78, p. XI; R. Sarger: *Conceptions, calculs et essais de la couverture du pavilion francais a l'Exposition de Bruxelles*, in *Études et Réalisations* 1959, No. 59, p. 7; R. Sarger: *La technique des voiles prétendues et leurs développements futurs*, in *Études et Réalisations* 1959, No. 67.

[124] Restaurant in Long Beach, Cal. Arch: Raymond and Rado. Eng: Weidlinger and Salvadori. In *Architectural Forum* 1956, No. 2, p. 152 and 1956, No. 8, p. 155.

[125] See *Architectural Forum* 1956, No. 8, p. 155.

[126] Study by Candela. In *Dimension*, student publication, College of Art and Design, Univ. of Michigan, Ann Arbor, Mich.

[127] Study by one of the Catalano school. In *Architectural Forum* 1953, No. 2, p. 159.

[128] Nightclub in Acapulco. Arch: Sordo. Eng: Candela. In *Bauwelt* 1959, No. 42, p. 1247.

[129] Restaurant in Xochimilco, Mexico. Eng: Candela. In *Baukunst und Werkform* 1958, No. 8, p. 438 and 1960, No. 1, pp. 27-28; *Progressive Architecture* 1959, No. 2, pp. 137-139.

[130] See *Progressive Architecture* 1959, No. 2, p. 141.

[131] Foundry at Lohr-am-Main, Germany. Arch: C. Siegel. Eng: H. Gall. Not yet published.

[132] Market in Royan, France. Arch: L. Simon, M. Merisseau. Eng: R. Sarger. In *l'architecture d'aujourd'hui*, No. 64, p. 48; *Architectural Forum* 1957, No. 11, p. 267; *Baukunst und Werkform* 1960, No. 4, p. 190.

[133] Restaurant in San Juan, Puerto Rico. Arch: Toro, Ferrer. Eng: Weidlinger and Salvadori. In *Architectural Forum* 1956, No. 11, p. 126; *Progressive Architecture* 1959, No. 8, p. 103.

[134] TWA terminal building, New York-Idlewild. Arch: Eero Saarinen and Assoc. Eng: Ammann and Whitney. In *l'architecture d'aujourd'hui*, No. 77, p. 10; *Architectural Forum* 1958, No. 1, p. 78; Borcherdt: *Planung des Flughafengebäudes in New York*, in *Baukunst und Werkform* 1960, No. 5, p. 259.

[135] See *l'architecture d'aujourd'hui*, No. 77, p. 10.

[136] Ronchamp chapel, Belfort, France. Arch: Le Corbusier. See Conrads: *Ronchamp oder die "Travestie der Unschuld"*, in *Baukunst und Werkform* 1956, No. 1, p. 9; *Werk* 1955, No. 12, p. 375; *Architectural Forum* 1955, No. 9, p. 120.

[137] See Candela: *Understanding the Hyperbolic Paraboloid*, in *Architectural Record* 1958, No. 7, p. 191 and No. 8, p. 205.

[138] Tachira Club, Caracas, Venezuela. Eng: E. Torroja. See Torroja: *The structures of Eduardo Torroja* (Dodge Co., New York), p. 43 ff.; Torroja: *New Developments in Shell Structures*, Proc. of the 2nd Symposium of Concrete Shell Roof Construction, Oslo 1957, p. 97.

[139] See Torroja: *New Developments in Shell Structures*, Proc. of the 2nd Symposium of Concrete Shell Roof Construction, Oslo 1957, p. 95.

[140] Instituto Tecnico de la Construccion y del Cemento, Laboratorio Central de Ensayo de Materiales de Construccion—Costillares, Madrid, Spain.

[141] Design for the University of Tucuman, Argentine. Arch: Carminos. Eng: Aracibia, Nervi and Bartoli. In *Architectural Forum* 1953, No. 2, p. 156.

[142] Sidney Opera House, competition design. Arch: J. Utzon. See Kultermann: *Une Architecture Autre*, in *Baukunst und Werkform* 1958, No. 8, p. 425.

[143] Airport building, seminar project directed by E. Torroja, Instituto Tecnico de la Construccion y del Cemento, Madrid. See publication of the Institute, No. 180, *Formas Resistentes de la Construccion Moderna*, p. 61.

[144] Municipal swimming pool, Wuppertal. Arch: Municipal Building Dept. Wuppertal. Eng: F. Leonhardt, W. Andra. See Leonhardt, Andra: *Entwurf eines Leichtbetonhängedaches*, in *Bauingenieur* 1957, No. 9, p. 344; *Deutsche Bauzeitschrift* 1957, No. 10, p. 1189.

[145] Hall, designed and built by Dyckerhoff u. Widmann.

[146] Exhibition hall Rio Grande do Sul, Brasil. Eng: Borges, Alliana. See Frei Otto: *Neues Bauen in Brasilien*, in *Bauwelt* 1956, No. 39, p. 915.

[147] Livestock judging arena, Raleigh, N.C. Arch: Novicki, Deitrick. Eng: Severud, Elstad and Krueger. In *Architectural Forum* 1952, No. 10, p. 134; 1953, No. 6, p. 170 and 1954, No. 4, p. 133; Frei Otto: *Die Arena in Raleigh, USA*, in *Bauwelt* 1953, No. 5, p. 89; *Bauingenieur* 1953, No. 8, p. 294; Frei Otto: *Das Hängende Dach* (Bauwelt-Verlag), p. 90.

[148] Congress Hall, Berlin. Arch: H. A. Stubbins, with W. Düttmann, F. Mocken, Ass. Archts. Eng: Severud, Elstad and Krueger. Published in *Bauwelt* 1956, No. 42, p. 999 and 1958, No. 1, p. 7; *Baukunst und Werkform* 1958, No. 1, p. 16; *l'architecture d'aujourd'hui*, No. 64, p. 70; *Architectural Forum* 1955, No. 9; 1955, No. 10, p. 155 and 1958, No. 1, p. 117; *Architectural Record* 1957, No. 12, p. 145; see also Lessing: *Suspension Structures*, in *Architectural Forum* 1957, No. 12, p. 135; Curt Siegel: *Ein Beitrag zur Kongresshallen-Debatte*, in *Bauwelt* 1958, No. 23, p. 549.

[149] Gymnase St. Ouen, Paris (proposal). Design and structure: R. Sarger. Unpublished; information supplied by designer.

[150] Swimming pool for Monaco (proposal). Design and structure: R. Sarger. Unpublished; information supplied by designer.

[151] R. Sarger: *Valeur Plastique des Structures à l'Exposition de Bruxelles*, in *l'architecture d'aujourd'hui*, No. 78, p. 6.

[152] French pavilion at the 1958 Brussels exhibition. Arch: G. Gillet. Eng: R. Sarger. In *l'architecture d'aujourd'hui*, No. 76, p. 102 and No. 78, p. 8; R. Sarger: *Conceptions, calculs et essais de la couverture du pavilion de la France à l'exposition de Bruxelles*, in *Études et Réalisations* 1959, No. 59, p. 7; R. Sarger: *La technique des voiles prétendues et leur développements futurs*, in *Études et Réalisations* 1959, No. 67.

[153] U.S. pavilion at the 1958 Brussels exhibition. Arch: E. D. Stone. Steelwork: Köln-Wesselinger Eisenbau. In *Architectural Record* 1957, No. 2, p. 10; *l'architecture d'aujourd'hui*, No. 78, p. 30; see also Cornelius: *Die statische Berechnung eines seilverspannten Daches am Beispiel des US-Pavillons auf der Weltausstellung in Brüssel 1958*, in *Stahlbau* 1958, No. 4, p. 98.

[154] Mast at the 1958 Brussels exhibition. See *l'architecture d'aujourd'hui*, No. 78, title page and p. 3.

[155] Tensegrity mast (designed by R. B. Fuller), displayed at the Museum of Modern Art, New York (R. B. Fuller exhibition). See also Marks: *The Dymaxion World of Buckminster Fuller* (Reinhold, New York), p. 158.

[156] Tents, designed by Frei Otto. See *Bauwelt* 1957, No. 30, p. 754; Frei Otto: *Das Hängende Dach* (Bauwelt-Verlag).

[157] Yale University hockey stadium, New Haven, Conn. Arch: Eero Saarinen. Eng: Severud, Elstad and Krueger. In *Architectural Record* 1957, No. 8, p. 186 and 1958, No. 10, p. 152; *l'architecture d'aujourd'hui*, No. 76, p. 44 and No. 85, p. 20; *Architectural Forum* 1958, No. 12, p. 106; *Bauen und Wohnen* 1959, No. 8, p. 270. See also Lessing: *Suspension Structures*, in *Architectural Forum* 1957, No. 12, p. 135. Bandel: *Betrachtungen über Hängedachkonstruktionen*, in *Bauingenieur* 1958, No. 6, p. 227.

PHOTO CREDITS: Aero-Pix, Raleigh, N.C., USA (p. 285)—Foto Candela, Cubiertas, Ala, Mexico D.F. (p. 265)—Castiglioni, Busto Arsizio, Italy (p. 174, 276)—Christiani & Nielsen, Caracas, Venezuela (p. 131)—film & fotostudio C.A. Stachelscheid, Dusseldorf (p. 185)—Fototecnica Fortunati, Milan (p. 191)—Fuller, Forest Hills 75, N.Y., USA (p. 297)—GM Photography, Detroit, Mich., USA (p. 55)—Foto Haarfeld, Heilbronn (p. 152)—Havas, Helsinki, (p. 220)—Hedrich-Blessing, Chicago, Ill., USA (p. 69)—Foto Heidersberger, Braunschweig (p. 45, 51)—Lucien Hervé, Paris (p. 205)—Kaiser Aluminum & Chemical Corporation, Oakland, California, USA (p. 195)—Laboratorio Fotografico G. Gherardi—A. Fiorelli, Rome (p. 151)—Foto Martinotti, Milan (p. 139)—Dipl.-Ing. Frei Otto, Berlin-Zehlendorf (p. 299)—Stamo Papadaki, New York, USA (p. 115)—Philips, Hamburg (p. 261)—Eero Saarinen, Birmingham, Mich., USA (p. 273, 301)—Foto Oskar Savio, Rome (p. 243)—Dipl.-Ing. R. Schaal, Stuttgart (p. 137, 162, 163, 169, 183, 212, 247, 251)— Foto Scherer, Frammersbach (p. 269)— Foto H. Siegmann, Berlin-Tegel (p. 121, 142)—Ezra Stoller, Kirby Lane, North Rye, New York, USA (p. 47, 171)—Colin Westwood, Weybridge, Surrey, England (p. 65).